PRINCIPLES OF PARTICLE ACCELERATORS

PRINCIPLES

OF

PARTICLE

ACCELERATORS

Enrico Persico

Ezio Ferrari

University of Rome

Sergio E. Segre

CNEN, Frascati, Rome

W. A. BENJAMIN, INC.
New York   Amsterdam
1968

Principles of Particle Accelerators

Copyright © 1968 by W. A. Benjamin, Inc.
All rights reserved

Library of Congress Catalog Card Number 68-18558
Manufactured in the United States of America

W. A. Benjamin, Inc.
New York, New York 10016

PREFACE

This book originated in a course on particle accelerators that the senior author (E.P.) gave for several years at the Graduate School of Physics of the University of Rome. The lecture notes collected by the two junior authors became the starting point for extensive rearrangement and expansion to which all three authors contributed. The chapter on linear accelerators was written by Dr. Mario Puglisi, formerly in charge of the radio frequency section at the Laboratori Nazionali del CNEN (Frascati, Rome), now professor of radio engineering at the University of Palermo, Italy.

The book is intended for physicists and engineers interested in the principles of operation or in the construction of particle accelerators; it can serve as an introduction to the specialized papers. The mathematical and physical notions required to understand the book do not exceed those ordinarily given to physics or engineering students in the first two years of college.

Emphasis has been placed on the mechanics of particle motion in the various types of accelerators, but some essential notions on the construction and technology of these machines have also been included. We have not attempted to include extensive historical data on the development of accelerators.

The mechanics of the different types of accelerators has been treated as far as possible by a uniform method. In order to minimize the mathematical background required, we have avoided the use of Hamiltonian equations. As is briefly shown in Chapter 3, these equations allow a more concise and elegant treatment, but their use would have required a rather lengthy introduction for the benefit of readers unacquainted with relativistic analytical mechanics. The main line of the treatment is based, instead, on a few elementary formulas of relativistic dynamics which are briefly summarized in the first chapter.

Rationalized mks units and standard notation have been used as a rule. An exception in the notation is the use of $\mathbf{P}$ instead of $\mathbf{p}$ for the momentum of a particle. This notation offers the advantage of stressing the conceptual distinction between the components P_r, P_θ, P_z of the momentum (in cylindrical coordinates, as used in the text) and the canonical momenta (p_r, p_θ, p_z) conjugated to the coordinates r, θ, z.

The bibliography has been divided into two parts. The first contains the references which have been specifically quoted in the text. The second part contains general surveys of particle accelerators and advanced treatments of some topics not covered in detail in the book. These can be consulted by the reader wishing to extend his study of the subject. No attempt at completeness has been made, and we apologize if some important contribution may have been inadvertently omitted.

The authors are indebted to Prof. Emilio Segrè for his kind interest in this work and to Prof. D. L. Judd for many valuable criticisms and suggestions.

ENRICO PERSICO
EZIO FERRARI
SERGIO E. SEGRE

Rome
February 1968

CONTENTS

CHAPTER 1

REVIEW OF DIFFERENT TYPES
OF PARTICLE ACCELERATORS

1-1 INTRODUCTION

Particle accelerators are machines built with the aim of accelerating charged particles to kinetic energies sufficiently high that they can be used to produce nuclear reactions. Usually the accelerated particles are electrons or light positive ions (H^+, D^+, He^{++}); heavy ions are also sometimes accelerated (for example, C^+). The kinetic energies one can obtain depend on the type of machine and in some existing accelerators energies of tens of billions of electron volts[1] are reached. The energy is limited not for theoretical reasons but only by the enormous cost of these machines: accelerators for some hundreds of billion electron volts are being planned at the present time (see, for example, Smith, 1965; Livingston, 1966).

In practice the only method for accelerating charged particles is to use an electric field in the proper direction. The different types of accelerators differ essentially in the way this field is produced and how it acts on the particles to be accelerated.

In principle, the operation of an accelerator consists of the following sequence of phases. The particles to be accelerated are injected into the machine from a "source." Then the particles, collimated into a beam, follow

---

[1] We recall that the *electron volt* (abbreviated eV) is the energy gained by an electron (or any particle having the same charge) in passing through a potential drop of one volt. Since the absolute value of the electron charge is $e = 1.6021 \times 10^{-19}$ coulomb, it follows that 1 eV $= 1.6021 \times 10^{-19}$ joule. The following symbols for multiples of this unit are of general use: 1 keV $= 10^3$ eV; 1 MeV $= 10^6$ eV; 1 GeV (also 1 BeV) $= 10^9$ eV.

1

a certain trajectory (in a vacuum) under the action of an accelerating electric field (which can be continuous or pulsed) until they have reached the required energy. At this moment the beam is made to hit a "target," where the desired nuclear reactions occur. The secondary particles produced in the reaction can be selected, collimated, and used to study further reactions. The target may be placed inside the machine; but in some cases it is possible to extract the beam of accelerated particles from the machine and make them hit an external target. The particles must move in a vacuum in order to avoid being slowed down and deflected by collisions with gas molecules. Often a vacuum of the order of 10^{-5} to 10^{-6} mm Hg is sufficient.

In evaluating the performance of a particle accelerator, the following points should be considered:

1. Maximum energy of the particles.
2. Intensity of the beam—that is, the number of particles accelerated per unit time.
3. Energy stability (in some machines the energy fluctuates in time about a mean value).
4. Energy homogeneity (often particles arriving on the target at the same time have slightly different energies).
5. Collimation of the beam (a beam is "collimated" if all the particles have approximately parallel velocities).
6. Type of particles accelerated.
7. Pulsed or continuous operation (some machines produce a continuous flow of particles; others instead produce "bunches" of particles, following each other at radio frequency, or at low frequency, or else in low-frequency pulses, each carrying many rf bunches).
8. Cost of the machine.

Accelerators can be divided into two large classes. The first class consists of *electrostatic accelerators*, in which the particles are accelerated by applying a voltage difference, constant in time, whose value fixes the value of the final energy of the particles. The Van de Graaff and the Cockcroft-Walton accelerators belong to this class (see Section 1-3 and Chapter 2).

The energy that this sort of machine can reach is limited by the discharges that occur between the high-voltage (HV) terminal and the walls of the accelerator chamber when the voltage drop is greater than a certain critical value (of the order of 10^6 V). Thus particles can be accelerated up to a few million electron volts.

In order to overcome this limit one must avoid the use of electrostatic fields. These are conservative and their circulation is always zero. Whatever the trajectory of the particles in these fields, the kinetic energy gained depends only on the point of departure and on the point of arrival and hence cannot be larger than the potential energy corresponding to the maximum voltage drop existing in the machine. If, instead, a variable nonconservative electric field is used (necessarily associated with a variable magnetic field by the equation curl $\mathbf{E} = -\partial \mathbf{B}/\partial t$), it is possible to find some closed paths along which the circulation of $\mathbf{E}$, and hence the kinetic energy gained by a particle, differs from zero. If the particles are made to follow such a path many times, one obtains a process of gradual acceleration which is *not* limited by the maximum voltage drop existing in the machine.

The machines which use this principle constitute the second class of accelerators and are called *cyclic accelerators*. In these machines the accelerating voltage corresponds to a small fraction of the value of the final energy attained by the particles and this is obtained by applying the accelerating voltage to the same particle a large number of times. The trajectories of the particles can be straight or curved. In the first case we have the *linear accelerators* (see Section 1-5 and Chapter 8); in the second case we have machines of various types (differing in the details of the acceleration process): the *betatron*, the *cyclotron*, the *synchrocyclotron*, and the *synchrotron* (see Sections 1-4, 1-6, 1-7, and 1-8, and Chapters 4 to 7).

1-2 ELEMENTS OF RELATIVISTIC DYNAMICS

We shall briefly review the results of the relativistic dynamics of a particle. The use of relativistic mechanics is necessary in the study of particle accelerators, because in these machines the particles reach velocities comparable with the velocity of light ($c = 2.99792 \times 10^8$ m/sec) and sometimes very near to it. Under these conditions classical mechanics is not even approximately applicable.

In relativistic mechanics also, the fundamental equation of motion of a point particle can be written (see, for example, Panofsky and Phillips, 1962, Chapter 17)

$$\frac{d\mathbf{P}}{dt} = \mathbf{F}, \tag{1-1}$$

where $\mathbf{F}$ is the total force acting on the particle and the momentum $\mathbf{P}$ is given by

$$\mathbf{P} = m_v\mathbf{v} = \frac{m\mathbf{v}}{(1 - v^2/c^2)^{1/2}}. \tag{1-2}$$

In this relation m is a constant, characteristic of the particle, called the "rest mass," and coincides with the mass of classical mechanics; $m_v = m/(1 - v^2/c^2)^{1/2}$ is called the "mass at the velocity v." By this definition, implying a variation of mass with velocity, the momentum still has the formal expression of the product of mass and velocity, as in classical mechanics. It should be noted that, for velocities small compared with c (and precisely such that v^2/c^2 is negligible with respect to 1), Equations 1-1 and 1-2 reduce to the law of classical mechanics, $\mathbf{F} = m\, dv/dt$.

By taking the components of Equation 1-1 along the tangent (t), along the normal (n), and along the binormal (b) to the trajectory and denoting by R the radius of curvature, we obtain the following equations:

$$F_t = P, \qquad F_n = \frac{Pv}{R}, \qquad F_b = 0, \tag{1-3}$$

which are formally equal to those of classical mechanics. The second of Equations 1-3 gives the expression of the centrifugal force. It can be shown that the kinetic energy T of a particle is given by the expression

$$T = (m_v - m)c^2 = mc^2\left(\frac{1}{(1-\beta^2)^{1/2}} - 1\right) = mc^2(\gamma - 1), \tag{1-4}$$

where, as usual, we have put

$$v/c = \beta, \qquad 1/(1-\beta^2)^{1/2} = \gamma. \tag{1-5}$$

It is easily verified, by expanding in series of powers of β^2 and neglecting β^4 and higher powers, that for $\beta^2 \ll 1$ Equation 1-4 reduces to the classical expression $T = \frac{1}{2}mv^2$.

Equation 1-4 suggests that one should attribute to a particle having rest mass m, an energy E_0 called "rest energy,"[2]

$$E_0 = mc^2, \tag{1-6}$$

and define a "total energy" E by

$$E = E_0 + T = m_v c^2 = E_0/(1-\beta^2)^{1/2} = \gamma E_0. \tag{1-7}$$

The use of E instead of T simplifies many formulas of relativistic mechanics. From the preceding equations the following important relations are obtained:

$$m_v = m\left(1 + \frac{T}{E_0}\right), \tag{1-8}$$

$$(cP)^2 + E_0{}^2 = E^2, \tag{1-9}$$

$$cP = \beta E, \tag{1-10}$$

and hence

$$\beta = \left(1 - \frac{E_0{}^2}{E^2}\right)^{1/2} = \frac{cP}{(c^2 P^2 + E_0{}^2)^{1/2}}. \tag{1-11}$$

From Equation 1-7 it can be seen that the condition for the validity of the classical approximation, that is, $\beta^2 \ll 1$, can also be written in the form

$$T \ll E_0, \tag{1-12}$$

---

[2] This is also justified by Einstein's principle of equivalence between mass and energy.

which is sometimes more convenient. Therefore it is useful to recall the values of E_0 for the particles most commonly used in accelerators (Table 1-1).

TABLE 1-1. *Rest Energies of the Particles Most Commonly Used in Accelerators*

Particle	E_0 (MeV)
Electron	0.5110
Proton (H+)	938.2
Deuteron (D+)	1875
α Particle (He++)	3727

From this table it can be seen that, for electrons, classical mechanics is completely inapplicable, even in the case of the more modest machines, whereas for ions up to a few hundred million electron volts it is a good first approximation.

For velocities very near the velocity of light ($\beta \simeq 1$, $T \gg E_0$) one can put $\beta = 1$ in all the formulas, except where the expression $(1 - \beta^2)^{-1/2}$ appears, and neglect E_0 compared with T (*ultrarelativistic approximation*). Equations 1-8, 1-9, and 1-10 then become

$$m_v \simeq m \frac{T}{E_0},$$ (1-13)

$$E \simeq T \simeq cP.$$ (1-14)

An important immediate application of the above formulas is the calculation of the motion of a charged particle in a constant uniform magnetic field, directed perpendicular to the initial velocity. The particle is subject only to the Lorentz force, $\mathbf{F}_L = q\mathbf{v} \times \mathbf{B}$, where $\mathbf{v}$ is the velocity of the particle, q its charge, and $\mathbf{B}$ the magnetic induction at the point it occupies.[3] From Equation 1-3 we obtain in this case

$$\dot{P} = 0,$$ (1-15)

$$|q|vB = Pv/R.$$ (1-16)

Hence the scalar momentum P is constant and the particle describes a circle of radius R given by

$$R = \frac{P}{|q|B}.$$ (1-17)

[3] Henceforth mks units will be used, unless otherwise specified. We recall that the mks unit of magnetic induction is the weber per square meter (Wb/m²), equal to 10^4 gauss.

For electrons, protons, or deuterons ($| q | = e$), Equation 1-17 can be written, using Equations 1-10 and 1-11, in the useful form

$$R = 33.356 \times 10^{-4} \beta \frac{E}{B} = 33.356 \times 10^{-4} \frac{E}{B} \left[1 - \left(\frac{E_0}{E} \right)^2 \right]^{1/2} \quad (1\text{-}18)$$

and in the ultrarelativistic limit

$$R \simeq 33.356 \times 10^{-4} \frac{T}{B} . \quad (1\text{-}19)$$

In formulas 1-18 and 1-19, E, T, E_0 are to be expressed in million electron volts, B in webers per square meter, and R in meters.

1-3 ELECTROSTATIC ACCELERATORS

The electrostatic accelerator is the simplest type of accelerator. It can be used both for electrons and for positive ions (generally protons and deuterons). It consists essentially of an evacuated tube, a fraction of a meter or a few meters in length, with two electrodes, one at each end. One electrode, at ground potential, is the target; the other electrode is maintained at a very high voltage and the source of ions or electrons is placed inside it. (In the following we shall refer to this simply as the ion source.)

The kinetic energy with which a particle hits the target is equal to the voltage drop multiplied by the charge of the particle (if the latter is $\pm e$, the energy in electron volts is equal to the voltage drop in volts). The aim therefore is to obtain the highest voltage possible.

This voltage is limited by discharges which may occur (outside the tube) between the two electrodes or between the HV electrode and earth or the walls of the chamber containing the accelerator. Therefore the tube is made as long as possible and it is kept away from the walls. In practice, it is not possible to obtain voltages greater than a few million volts. This limit can be increased if the whole machine is enclosed in a tank containing an inert gas at a pressure of about 10 or 15 atm. In this way it is possible to attain a voltage of about 9 MV. For higher voltages one is confronted with serious technological difficulties.

The devices used for producing the high voltages required are essentially two: the Van de Graaff generator and the Cockcroft-Walton generator. These are described in detail in Chapter 2.

The advantages of electrostatic accelerators are their high beam intensity, dc operation, high energy stability (in some cases, better than 0.1%), and good beam collimation.

1-4 THE BETATRON

Among the accelerators of the second category (cyclic accelerators), we shall first study the betatron, which is used to accelerate electrons. The schematic design of a betatron is shown in Figure 1-1. The machine consists of a magnet (whose poles have the form of truncated cones), fed by alternating current of a frequency usually between 50 and 200 cps. In the magnet gap is placed a toroidal vacuum chamber, sometimes called a "doughnut," in which the electrons are made to circulate.

In this machine the magnetic field (whose lines of force are the dotted lines shown in Figure 1-1) has a double purpose:

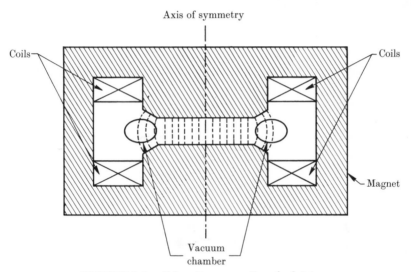

FIGURE 1-1. *Schematic cross section of a betatron.*

1. The magnetic flux linked with the doughnut changes in time, and induces an electric field whose lines of force are concentric circles orthogonal to the axis of symmetry: one of these circles is the "central orbit" of the doughnut.[4] This electric field accelerates the electrons.

2. The magnetic field present in the vacuum chamber exerts a Lorentz force on the electrons, directed toward the center, and so tends to keep them on a circular orbit.

We note that conceptually the betatron can be considered as the analog of a

---

[4] By "central orbit" we shall denote the circumference defined by the centers of the meridian sections of the vacuum chamber (or, more generally, by the centers of gravity of the meridian sections, which can also be noncircular).

transformer, where the primary current is the alternating current which excites the magnet and the secondary current is the electron current circulating in the vacuum chamber.

In order that the magnetic field both guide and accelerate the particles on the central orbit, a certain relation must hold between the field, B, at the central orbit and the average value, $\bar{B}$, within the area enclosed by the central orbit. The relation is known as the "betatron relation." Let us now derive it. If R is the radius of the central orbit, the magnetic flux linked with it is

$$\Phi = \pi R^2 \bar{B}, \tag{1-20}$$

and so the electric field E acting on the electrons has a circulation given by

$$2\pi R E = -\frac{d\Phi}{dt}. \tag{1-21}$$

On the other hand, the first of Equations 1-3 gives (for a charge $-e$)

$$F_t = -eE = \frac{dP}{dt} \tag{1-22}$$

and, by substituting into Equation 1-21 and using Equation 1-20,

$$\frac{dP}{dt} = \frac{e}{2\pi R}\frac{d\Phi}{dt} = \tfrac{1}{2}eR\frac{d\bar{B}}{dt}. \tag{1-23}$$

As R is given by the relation (1-17),

$$P = eRB \tag{1-24}$$

(where B is the field at the central orbit), by differentiation we obtain

$$\frac{dP}{dt} = eR\frac{dB}{dt}. \tag{1-25}$$

By comparing Equations 1-23 and 1-25, we finally obtain

$$\frac{dB}{dt} = \frac{1}{2}\frac{d\bar{B}}{dt}, \tag{1-26}$$

and after integration

$$B(t) = \tfrac{1}{2}\bar{B}(t) + \text{constant}. \tag{1-27}$$

This is the betatron relation.

Because the induced electric field is alternating it can accelerate electrons only in the half-cycles during which it has a given sign and therefore the electrons circulate only for half (or less) of the period of the alternating current. Thus the machine has a pulsed operation with the same frequency as the current. The electrons are injected when the magnetic field is nearly zero.

When the magnetic field has reached its maximum value and would then start to decelerate the electrons, the beam is used (often by sending it onto a target for the production of high-energy x rays).

The betatron is used for energies between 5 and 300 MeV, approximately. For lower energies electrostatic machines are more convenient; for higher energies the great quantity of iron required makes the magnet too costly. For the same reason this machine is not used to accelerate ions: for protons of 30 MeV, for example, the required radius would be 8 times larger than for electrons of the same energy.

The first practical construction of a betatron, due to D. W. Kerst (1940, 1941), was made possible by a detailed theory of orbit stability (Kerst and Serber, 1941) and by accurate calculations of the magnet design.

We note that, beside producing nuclear reactions, betatrons (especially those of energy less than 20 MeV) have important applications in medicine and in industry. In medicine small betatrons are used as sources of high-energy x rays in the treatment of tumors; in some cases the therapy uses the electron beam extracted from the machine directly. The most important industrial applications are connected with the analysis of the structure of metals and alloys by means of x-ray diffraction patterns. The betatrons required for these purposes are also produced commercially by specialized firms.

1-5 THE LINEAR ACCELERATOR

The linear accelerator, also called "linac," accelerates charged particles along approximately straight trajectories by means of alternating electric fields. As we shall see later, the particles move along the axis of a structure with cylindrical symmetry, along which the accelerating fields are also made to propagate. As the alternating electromagnetic fields used have frequencies between about ten and a few thousand megacycles per second, the accelerating structures (which allow a continuous transfer of energy to the particles from the electromagnetic wave) can be obtained either from resonant cavities or from waveguides (of special design) according to requirements that will be discussed later. Consequently, in linear accelerators, the type of structure that supports the accelerating fields determines the nature of the whole machine.

The simplest structure was first proposed by R. Wideröe (1928), and by D. H. Sloan and E. O. Lawrence (1931). The machine of Sloan and Lawrence consists essentially of a series of cylindrical tubes (see Figure 1-2) which are connected to a high-frequency oscillator. The connection between the electrodes and the supply line is arranged in such a way that successive electrodes have alternating polarity. The beam of particles is injected along the axis of this structure (inside a vacuum chamber). The mechanism of operation is the following. Inside the cylinders the electric field is always zero and in the gaps between two consecutive cylinders the electric field alternates with the frequency of the generator. The length of the cylinders is chosen in such a way that a particle which encounters the required accelerating field in the first gap crosses each tube in a time equal to the half-period of the generator. Hence this particle always encounters the field in each gap with the same phase as in the first, and so it is accelerated at each transit, where it receives an energy qV, if V is the voltage drop across the gap at the instant of the transit.

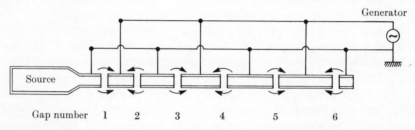

FIGURE 1-2. *Schematic diagram of the drift-tube type of linear accelerator. The arrows at the gaps show the direction of the electric field at a given time.*

Obviously the length l of each cylinder must be equal to $vT/2$, where T is the period of the oscillator and v the velocity of the particles in the cylinder. Since v increases from each cylinder to the next one, the cylinders are of increasing length: however, when v approaches c (strongly relativistic particles) the velocity jumps become smaller and smaller and so the length l tends to a constant value, equal to $cT/2$.

The greatest difficulties with this type of linear accelerator are of technological nature. If the velocity of the particles is to be large, either the total length of the machine must be great, or the frequency used must be high. In order to avoid enormous machine lengths, very high frequencies are used, but then the transmission of energy becomes difficult in practice because of the large energy losses in the conductors. We shall see later how the technical problems of this type of accelerator can be solved by the use of resonant cavities.

The acceleration mechanism we have just described is not the only possible one. Another important method is to have electromagnetic waves propagating inside the structure where the particles are to be accelerated.[5] If the electric field at the point occupied by a moving particle on the average has the direction of the particle motion and if certain phase relations are satisfied, then the

[5] A diagram of the structure generally used is given in Chapter 8, Figure 8-2.

particles can receive energy from the electromagnetic wave. (For an exhaustive discussion of this point, see Section 8-3.)

According to the type of structure used it is possible to divide linear accelerators into two classes, that is, machines with discontinuous acceleration and machines with continuous acceleration. The first class refers to machines using the structure previously described, consisting of a succession of cylindrical electrodes (called "drift tubes"), where the acceleration only occurs in the gaps between tubes. This type of accelerator is used for heavy particles (protons and heavier ions). The second class of machines makes use of waveguides of a special nature (see Chapter 8) to propagate electromagnetic waves together with the particles. Linear accelerators for electrons belong to this class.

Linear accelerators are in common use for energies below 200 MeV and are often used as auxiliary machines (injectors) for large accelerators (synchrotrons, see Section 1-8). There also exist linear accelerators for electrons that reach very high energies (1 BeV or more). The most significant example is the 20-BeV electron accelerator, 10,000 ft in length, in operation at Stanford University.

1-6 THE CYCLOTRON

The principle of the cyclotron was discovered by E. O. Lawrence in 1930, and tested experimentally for the first time by E. O. Lawrence and M. S. Livingston in 1931, at the University of California, at Berkeley (Lawrence and Edlefsen, 1930; Lawrence and Livingston, 1931a, b, 1932). This machine is used for accelerating ions to an energy of a few million electron volts. In it the particles are accelerated by a rf electric field (frequency 10 to 30 Mc/sec) but instead of moving along a straight line as in linear accelerators they follow a spiral trajectory, guided by a constant and almost uniform magnetic field.

The particles move inside a vacuum chamber of the form of a flat cylinder. This encloses two hollow electrodes whose shape can be thought of as obtained by cutting a very flat, hollow cylinder along a meridian plane (see Figure 1-3).

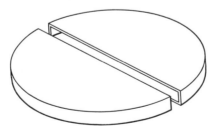

FIGURE 1-3. *Diagram showing the shape of the rf electrodes of a cyclotron (dees).*

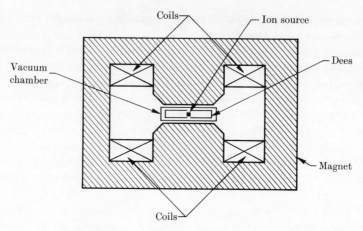

FIGURE 1-4.   *Schematic cross section of a cyclotron.*

Because of its shape, such an electrode is commonly called a "dee." The rf voltage is applied between the electrodes, so that there is an alternating electric field in the gap, but no field inside the dees. The vacuum chamber is placed between the pole pieces of a large magnet (see Figure 1-4) which produces a constant and practically uniform magnetic field perpendicular to the plane of the dees. The ion source is placed at the center of the vacuum chamber so that the ions, leaving the source at low speed, are accelerated in the gap and enter one of the dees. Here the magnetic field makes them follow a semicircular orbit, with constant speed, until they cross the gap again. If in the meantime the electric field has reversed its direction, the particles are again accelerated; then in the other dee they follow a semicircle of larger radius than the former one, and so on. The resulting orbit has the shape shown in Figure 1-5. This operation of the machine is possible if the time required for

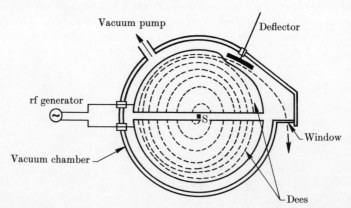

FIGURE 1-5.   *Schematic plan of the cyclotron vacuum chamber.* S = *ion source.*

the particles to describe each semicircle is practically constant and if the angular frequency ω_e of the rf generator is chosen so that the transit time inside one of the dees is equal to the half-period of the field oscillation. Thus the particles always encounter the electric field in the gap with the same phase and they gain the same amount of energy at each transit.

The time τ required to describe a semicircle of radius r with constant velocity v is $\tau = \pi r/v$. By Equation 1-17, r is given by

$$r = \frac{P}{|q|\,B} = \frac{m_v v}{|q|\,B} \tag{1-28}$$

so that

$$\tau = \frac{\pi m_v}{|q|\,B}. \tag{1-29}$$

If we require this time to be equal to the half-period, π/ω_e, of the radio frequency, we obtain

$$\omega_e = \frac{|q|\,B}{m_v}. \tag{1-30}$$

It can be seen from this equation that ω_e depends on the particle energy through m_v; however, as long as particles behave classically $m_v \simeq m$ and $\tau = $ constant. In this case the angular frequency of the radio frequency can be chosen to be

$$\omega_e = \frac{|q|\,B}{m}. \tag{1-31}$$

The frequency given by Equation 1-31 is called the "cyclotron frequency" or "(nonrelativistic) magnetic resonance frequency." The condition, $T \ll E_0$, for the validity of the classical approximation (see Equation 1-12), limits the maximum energy to a few percent of the rest energy of the particles; thus the cyclotron cannot be used to accelerate electrons. If the kinetic energy increases to values not negligible with respect to E_0, as the mass increases, so does the transit time; therefore the particle delays with respect to the electric field until eventually it encounters a negative field and is decelerated. For this reason the practical energy limit of a standard cyclotron is about 20 MeV for protons and a little more for deuterons. Within this limit, however, the cyclotron is one of the most convenient machines. It can produce a high-intensity beam comparable to that of electrostatic accelerators, with the advantage of avoiding difficult insulation problems: with respect to standard linear accelerators of the same energy it has greater energy homogeneity and it is more compact.

In order to obtain an idea of the dimensions of a cyclotron, we note that the radius R of the vacuum chamber, if v_f and T_f are the final velocity and the final kinetic energy of the particles, respectively, is given by

$$R = \frac{mv_f}{|q|\,B} = \frac{(2mT_f)^{1/2}}{|q|\,B}. \tag{1-32}$$

As the fields used in practice are of the order of 1 Wb/m², Equation 1-32, for this value of B, and for 10-MeV protons, gives $R = 0.45$ m; and for 20-MeV deuterons, $R = 0.90$ m.

It should be noted that the cyclotron is conceptually similar to a linear accelerator of the type shown in Figure 1-2, where, however, the trajectory is wound up into a spiral by the magnetic field, and the successive electrodes are replaced by only two, which are crossed repeatedly.

1-7 THE SYNCHROCYCLOTRON

The synchrocyclotron, or frequency-modulated cyclotron, is a variant of the cyclotron which overcomes the energy limit of the latter, which is due to the relativistic change of mass.

On the whole the construction of the synchrocyclotron is similar to that of the cyclotron. The main difference is that the frequency of the rf generator is modulated, that is, made to change periodically, and the machine is used during the times when the frequency is decreasing. In this way relation 1-30 can be made to hold even when the mass is increasing with energy and the time required to describe a semicircle inside the dees is also increasing. It follows that not all the particles leaving the source reach the end of the acceleration, but only those emitted when the frequency has the value fitted to the value of the magnetic field in the source region, so that during the acceleration the resulting variation of m_v and the assigned variation of ω_e are always consistent with Equation 1-30 (at least within certain limits, as is discussed in detail in Sections 1-9 and 1-10). It is obvious that in a synchrocyclotron the particles are not distributed along the whole trajectory as in a cyclotron, but they form a single bunch which starts at the center and moves along a tight spiral, with increasing velocity. The bunches leave the center at a rate equal to the rate of frequency modulation (of the order of 100 per second) and so the beam produced by the machine is pulsed at the same rate, leading to a large reduction of the average beam intensity with respect to the cyclotron.

Another important practical difference between the cyclotron and the synchrocyclotron is that in the latter the particles carry out a much greater number of turns (of the order of 10,000 rather than 100), that is, the spiral is much tighter, and thus it is possible to use a much lower accelerating voltage, of the order of 10 kV rather than 100 kV.

The radius of the magnet poles is given by the following formula, similar to Equation 1-32 (where the relativistic expression of momentum has been used):

$$R = \frac{P_f}{\mid q \mid B} = \frac{1}{c \mid q \mid B} (T_f^2 + 2E_0 T_f)^{1/2}. \qquad (1\text{-}33)$$

In the classical limit ($T_f \ll E_0$) this formula reduces to Equation 1-32.

The limit to the energy which can be obtained is given essentially by the cost of the machine; at high energies, the synchrotron is economically more convenient. A 730-MeV proton synchrocyclotron is in operation at the University of California at Berkeley.

Synchrocyclotrons cannot be used to accelerate electrons because the required range of frequency modulation would be too large.

1-8 THE SYNCHROTRON

In a synchrocyclotron the most expensive part is the magnet. As the radius of the magnet is related to the final energy of the particles through Equation 1-33, the size and the cost of the magnet become prohibitive for energies above some hundred million electron volts. For higher energies, machines have been built, the synchrotrons, in which the particles are again accelerated by a rf electric field, but they are made to follow a circular orbit (of radius R) rather than a spiral. Thus the magnetic field is required only in the region of the orbit and not in the space enclosed by it. The cost of such a ring-shaped magnet is roughly proportional to the radius, whereas for a magnet with circular poles it is roughly proportional to the cube of the radius.

In the synchrotron, as the particles follow a fixed orbit, the vacuum chamber is given the shape of a torus ("doughnut") as in the betatron. The rf electric field for the acceleration of the particles is localized at a certain point of the vacuum chamber and is obtained by exciting stationary electromagnetic waves in a metal box (resonant cavity) through which the particles pass.

The angular frequency ω_e of the radio frequency must be such that the corresponding period, $2\pi/\omega_e$, is equal to (or a submultiple of) the time required for a particle to complete one turn. As this time decreases with increasing energy, the frequency must be modulated (ω_e increasing), but it will tend to the limiting value c/R as the velocity approaches c.

In order to keep the particle on a fixed orbit of radius R while the energy increases, the magnetic field must also change: Equation 1-17 shows that it must increase linearly with the momentum, P, of the particle. On the other hand, if the particle is to encounter always the required accelerating field in the cavity, as mentioned above, we must have

$$\omega_e = k \frac{v}{R}, \qquad (1\text{-}34)$$

where v/R is the angular frequency of the particle motion and k is a fixed positive integer. Using Equations 1-34, 1-17, 1-2, and 1-7, we obtain

$$\omega_e = \frac{k \, | \, q \, | \, B}{m_v} = \frac{k \, | \, q \, | \, BE_0}{mE} \, . \tag{1-35}$$

After expressing E as a function of P, and hence of B through Equations 1-9 and 1-17, we obtain the following relation between ω_e and B:

$$\omega_e = \frac{k \, | \, q \, | \, B}{m[1 \, + \, (cqBR/E_0)^2]^{1/2}} \, . \tag{1-36}$$

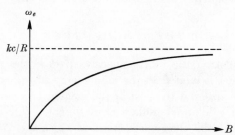

FIGURE 1-6. *Qualitative behavior of the frequency ω_e of the rf cavity as a function of the magnetic field for a synchrotron.*

In practice B varies with time periodically (at low frequency) according to a law determined by the magnet design, and ω_e is made to change so that Equation 1-36 is satisfied. The behavior of the function $\omega_e(B)$ is indicated in Figure 1-6. Even if Equation 1-36 is satisfied, the particles follow the same circular orbit, while they are being accelerated, only if the voltage of the rf cavity has the proper value which will be specified in detail later (see Chapter 5).[6]

Only the particles which find the right value of the electric field in the cavity are accelerated to the maximum energy; therefore the operation of this machine also is pulsed with the period of the magnetic field, and the accelerated particles are bunched.

In order to avoid too wide a range of modulation of the radio frequency, the particles are usually injected into the machine after being accelerated to an energy of a few million electron volts by means of an auxiliary accelerator (usually an electrostatic accelerator or a linear accelerator) called the "injector."

[6] It should be noted that it is not necessary that Equation 1-36 be rigorously satisfied; even in the presence of small deviations from this law, the particles can reach the end of the acceleration phase (see the next section, and Section 5-8).

The magnet consists of two ring-shaped pole pieces; the magnetic circuit is usually closed by a vertical iron wall so that the cross section of the magnet is C-shaped (see Figure 1-7). The magnet coils are fed with low-frequency alternating current or with a saw-tooth current, and, as mentioned above, the particles are accelerated only when B is increasing.

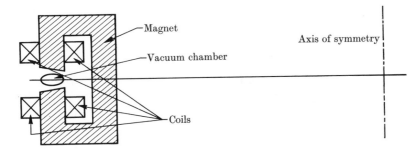

FIGURE 1-7. *Schematic diagram of the cross section of a synchrotron.*

In practice the machine is usually not really circular but is designed so that some parts of the vacuum chamber are straight and do not have any magnetic field. In a typical model, there are four of these field-free straight sections, alternating with four sectors having the length of a quarter of the circumference (see Figure 1-8). This type of synchrotron is sometimes called a "racetrack." The straight sections are very useful for housing the different auxiliary units of the machine. One straight section usually contains the rf cavity; another contains the target. A third straight section contains the inflector for injection of the particles coming from the preliminary accelerator. By passing through the (usually electrostatic) inflector the particles are

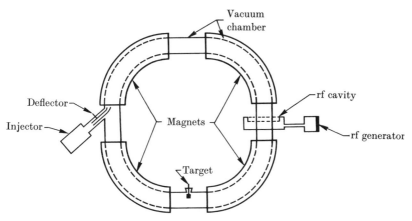

FIGURE 1-8. *Schematic plan of a "racetrack" synchrotron.*

injected tangentially into the vacuum chamber. Also, the vacuum pumps are always connected to the straight sections.

Synchrotrons are the only type of machine economically possible for very high energies (apart from linear accelerators for electrons). For energies above 1 BeV, the problems of construction and operation become very complex: practically each machine is unique, both in its structure and in the particular technical solutions to the different problems which arise. Given the general principles of operation briefly described in this section, some specific features are of great importance and allow us to divide the class of the synchrotrons into different subclasses: "normal" synchrotrons (also called "constant-gradient" or "weak-focusing" synchrotrons), "alternating-gradient" (or "strong-focusing") synchrotrons, and "zero-gradient" synchrotrons. The differences in construction and operation between these types of synchrotrons cannot be described, even schematically, at this point. This subject is treated in detail in Chapters 5 and 6.

1-9   THE PRINCIPLE OF PHASE STABILITY IN SYNCHRONOUS ACCELERATORS: THE LINEAR ACCELERATOR

The mechanism of operation of the accelerators described in Sections 1-5, 1-7, and 1-8 (linear accelerator, synchrocyclotron, synchrotron), which are called *synchronous accelerators*, consists, as we have seen, in supplying a small amount of energy a large number of times successively. The acceleration is provided by an electric field localized at a particular point of the trajectory (the gap between the dees in the synchrocyclotron, the resonant cavity in the synchrotron, and so on). This field changes in time according to a periodic law, and the machine is designed so that a particle which satisfies the proper initial conditions and gains the correct amount of energy at the first transit across the accelerating gap will, on successive transits, find a field always of the same value, directed so as to accelerate it. Any particle satisfying such conditions is called a "synchronous particle" (s.p.); it is accelerated by the desired amount at each transit and reaches the required final energy at the end of the acceleration process.

The synchronism between the particle motion and the accelerating electric field is of essential importance in the design of the machine when the particles must cross the accelerating gap a very large number of times. (When this number is rather small, as in the cyclotron, the problem of synchronism is of an entirely different character.) In practice, however, a negligible number of particles fulfill the conditions for the s.p.; indeed, both because the injection process lasts a certain time, and because all the factors involved in the injection and in the acceleration have finite ranges and are subject to random fluctuations, in crossing the accelerating gap the particles encounter the electric field at phases that are slightly different from that encountered by the s.p. and vary on successive transits, so that their motion is different from that of the s.p. For the practical operation of this type of machine it is necessary that not only the particles in exact synchronism with the accelerating electric field but also those which have slightly different phases be accelerated by the same amount on the average over a large number of turns, so that all these particles reach the desired final energy. This does not imply that, in each single transit, the energy gained by a typical particle should necessarily approximate that gained by the s.p. Indeed, we shall see that in some cases it can be quite different: it can even become negative. However, the machine must operate in such a way that the transits in which a particle gains more energy than the s.p. are compensated by the transits in which it gains less, so that on the average it gains the same energy as the s.p.

The practical construction of the machines described above was made possible through the theoretical discovery, by V. I. Veksler (1944a, b, 1945) and, independently, by E. M. McMillan (1945), of the "principle of phase stability": when certain conditions, easily obtainable, are satisfied, if the phase of the transit of a particle through the accelerating gap is different from the phase of the s.p., the consequent effect is to change the phase on successive turns and make it tend toward that of the s.p. Under the action of this "restoring force," the phase of a typical particle will oscillate about that of the s.p. and the energy gained by both will be the same.

The concept of the "phase" of a particle (relative to the transit through the accelerating gap) is intuitively simple but is not given a quantitative definition of general validity here. In the following chapters, where the different types of machines are treated in detail, the appropriate definition is given in each case.

At this point, for a better understanding of the phenomenon, we shall discuss a specific example and study the motion of particles differing from the s.p. for the case of the linear accelerator with cylindrical electrodes, described in Section 1-6. For this type of accelerator we define the phase relative to the transit through a certain gap by the formula

$$\varphi = \omega_e t - n\pi, \tag{1-37}$$

where n is the number of gaps already traversed; furthermore the origin of time is chosen so that in the first gap ($n = 0$) we have $0 \le \varphi < \pi$. The reason for this choice will appear from the following discussion and, in particular, from the consideration of Figure 1-9. It should be noted that we are only interested in the values of φ corresponding to the instants when the particle crosses the accelerating electric field. For intervals of t during which the particle is traversing the equipotential tubes, Equation 1-37 has no physical meaning.

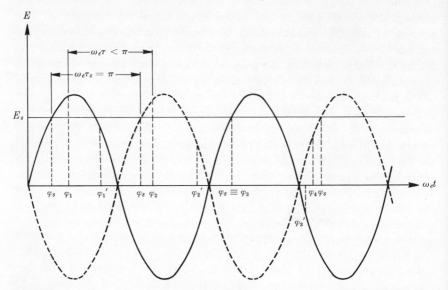

FIGURE 1-9. *Time behavior of the electric field at odd-number gaps (full curve) and at even-number gaps (dotted curve), showing the phases of typical particles and of the s.p. at successive gaps for a linear accelerator. According to Equation 1-37, stable phases are measured on the $\omega_e t$ axis starting from the preceding zero of the sinusoidal curve.*

Figure 1-9 shows the behavior of the accelerating field at the first gap as a function of the quantity $\omega_e t$. It also represents the accelerating field at all the gaps of odd number, while at the gaps of even number the field is inverted and it is indicated by the dotted line. We shall call the "synchronous phase," φ_s, the phase of the s.p. (that is, the phase in which it encounters the accelerating field, in all its transits) and E_s the corresponding value of the electric field. By the definition of the s.p., the synchronous phase is always the same in all the transits. For the other particles which precede or follow the s.p., the phase will be respectively less or greater than the synchronous phase and it will change from transit to transit. Indeed the differences in phase will result in a difference in the energy gained by the particle; this effect will produce a change in the time required to traverse the equipotential tube and hence again a change of phase. Let us qualitatively examine the conditions which must be satisfied for this difference of phase to be limited in magnitude (and zero on the average); that is, the conditions for the phase to be "stable."

Let us suppose that $0 < \varphi_s < \pi/2$, so that the s.p. encounters the electric field as it is increasing in time, and let us see what happens to a particle which on the first transit lags slightly behind the s.p. and has a phase $\varphi_1 > \varphi_s$ (see Figure 1-9). It will encounter an electric field greater than E_s and hence it will be accelerated more than the s.p.; it will need less time than the s.p. to cross the second tube so that in the second gap it will have a phase φ_2 nearer to φ_s.

(The values of $\omega_e \tau_s = \pi$ and $\omega_e \tau < \pi$, where τ_s and τ are the times of transit through the second tube, are indicated in the figure for comparison.) This process will continue until the delay between the particle considered and the s.p. has vanished. Let us suppose that at the third gap φ_3 is already equal to φ_s. At the third gap, therefore, our particle gains the same amount of energy as the s.p.; however, as it had already some excess energy over the s.p. as a result of the previous transits, it continues to advance with respect to the s.p. and crosses the next gap before the s.p. (phase φ_4). This advance, however, decreases in the following transits, because now the particle receives less energy than the s.p.; after some further transits it will again be in phase with the s.p., and so on. Thus the phase of a typical particle oscillates about the phase of the s.p. and along their trajectories the various particles will be bunched around the s.p. It should be noted that this phenomenon occurs if the synchronous phase is less than $\pi/2$, that is, if the s.p. is injected in the quarter-period when the voltage is accelerating and increasing. In the next quarter-period, just the opposite phenomenon occurs, as can be seen by a simple analysis of the type discussed above. The particles which, for instance, lag behind the s.p., such as the one having phase φ_1' at the first transit (see Figure 1-9), increase their delay indefinitely (phases φ_2', φ_3', . . . at successive transits) and on the average do not gain any energy. It can also be seen that, if φ_s is fixed, the range of useful phases (which can oscillate about the synchronous phase) extends to the value $\varphi_{max} = \pi - \varphi_s$ and, on the other side, down to a minimum value φ_{min} generally not symmetric with respect to φ_s (see Figure 1-10).[7] If the phase of a particle is not included within this range,

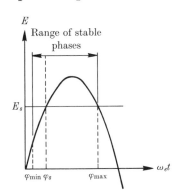

FIGURE 1-10. *Diagram of the time behavior of the electric field at an accelerating gap showing the range of stable phases for a linear accelerator.*

[7] If φ_s is sufficiently small, this minimum value can also be negative. This means that during a phase oscillation the particle can, in some transits, encounter a decelerating electric field. However, this effect is compensated by the greater energy gained by the particle during the oscillation when $\varphi > \varphi_s$.

during the oscillation it falls into the zone of instability and the particle is lost. The value of E_s must not be too near the peak value of the field; otherwise the useful range of phases would be too small (of zero extension in the limiting case $\varphi_s = \pi/2$). On the other hand, E_s should not be too small for the particles to be given a sufficient acceleration. Usually E_s is chosen to be about half of the peak field so that φ_s is of the order of 30°.

1-10   THE PRINCIPLE OF PHASE STABILITY: GENERAL DISCUSSION. MOMENTUM COMPACTION

In the case described in the previous section, the choice $0 < \varphi_s < \pi/2$ is determined by the fact that an increase in the energy given to a particle leads to a decrease in the time between two successive transits through the accelerating field. However, this does not occur in all synchronous machines. For example, in the normal synchrotron, as is mentioned later and proved in Chapter 5, an increase of the energy gained leads to an increase of the transit time. In this case, by following the same argument as in the previous section one finds that phase stability exists for $\pi/2 < \varphi_s < \pi$ (accelerating electric field *decreasing* in time). The situation for a synchrotron with only one cavity is illustrated in Figure 1-11, which is similar to Figure 1-9, apart from the

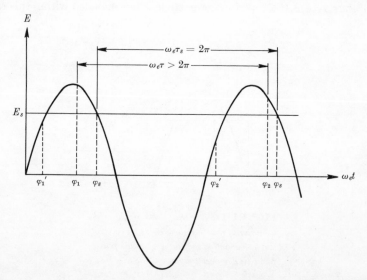

FIGURE 1-11. *Time behavior of the electric field in the rf cavity of a synchrotron showing the phases of typical particles and of the s.p. at successive transits. Stable phases are measured from the preceding zero (with positive derivative) of the sinusoidal curve.*

duplication of the curve.[8] In this case, it is convenient to define the "phase" by a formula which is slightly different from Equation 1-37, but still determined essentially by the quantity $\omega_e t$. We shall not deal with the question now because it is discussed in detail in Chapter 5 (Sections 2 and following). In order to obtain a general description of the mechanism of phase stability for the different synchronous machines, it is useful to introduce a characteristic parameter called "momentum compaction." If S is the length of the path followed by a particle between two successive transits through the accelerating field and P the momentum of the particle along this path, the "momentum compaction," α, is defined by

$$\alpha = \frac{dP/P}{dS/S} . \tag{1-38}$$

If α is large, this means that trajectories very near to each other can correspond to appreciably different momenta (so that in a narrow bundle of trajectories many momenta are "compressed together"). If α is small, a slight change of momentum corresponds to a sharp change in trajectory. In the latter case it may happen that the faster particles delay with respect to the slower ones, owing to the corresponding lengthening of the trajectory. The case of the linear accelerator, described above, corresponds to $\alpha = \infty$, because all particles follow the same path (length of the cylinders) independently of momentum, and $dS = 0$. Equation 1-38 can also be written in the form

$$\alpha = \frac{dP/P}{dR/R} \tag{1-39}$$

by defining an "equivalent radius" $R = S/2\pi$. In circular machines R coincides with the radius of the orbit. The value of α depends on the characteristics of the machine and can be computed for each case: it can be used to obtain the relation between change of momentum and change of transit time τ between two successive accelerations. Precisely, as $\tau = S/v$ and $v = c\beta$, we have

$$\frac{d\tau}{\tau} = \frac{dS}{S} - \frac{dv}{v} = \frac{dS}{S} - \frac{d\beta}{\beta} . \tag{1-40}$$

Recalling the relation between β and P (Equation 1-11) we obtain

$$\frac{d\beta}{\beta} = (1 - \beta^2) \frac{dP}{P} = \frac{1}{\gamma^2} \frac{dP}{P} \tag{1-41}$$

and, from Equations 1-38, 1-40, and 1-41,

$$\frac{d\tau}{\tau} = \left(\frac{1}{\alpha} - \frac{1}{\gamma^2}\right) \frac{dP}{P} . \tag{1-42}$$

---

[8] The variation of the electric field here also is supposed to be periodic, i.e., we neglect the effect of frequency modulation during the time required for one turn. It must be relatively small for phase stability to exist.

This equation describes the influence of the change of momentum on the transit time, if we assume for P and τ the momentum and the transit time of the s.p. and for dP and $d\tau$ the corresponding differences of a typical particle with respect to the s.p. In the linear accelerator, as we have seen, $\alpha = \infty$ and hence $d\tau/\tau$ always has the opposite sign to dP/P. In the machines where α is small (such as the normal synchrotrons where $\alpha < 1$; see Chapter 5), as $1/\gamma^2$ is always less than 1 (and tends to zero for ultrarelativistic particles), we see that $d\tau/\tau$ always has the same sign as dP/P. Finally in some machines there exists a value of the energy (called "transition energy") for which $\alpha = \gamma^2$; at this value $dP/d\tau$ changes sign, phase stability no longer exists, and great care is needed to avoid loss of the particles at this critical energy. (See Chapter 6 for the case of alternating-gradient synchrotrons.) From the preceding discussion it can be seen that phase stability exists for $0 < \varphi_s < \pi/2$ when $\alpha > \gamma^2$, and for $\pi/2 < \varphi_s < \pi$ when $\alpha < \gamma^2$.

1-11 ION SOURCES

All particle accelerators require a source to supply the charged particles to be accelerated. If these are electrons the source is simply a heated filament: The electrons released by thermionic emission are extracted from the region of the filament and focused by one or more electrodes (at a positive potential with respect to the filament), and then injected into the machine. In the case of positive ions, these are produced by ionizing the molecules of a gas which is sent into the source. The gas molecules can be ionized in different ways and one can classify the ion sources accordingly. The ions produced are extracted from a hole in the wall of the source by means of an electrode at the proper potential ("probe electrode") and hence they pass into the accelerator.

We now briefly describe the types of source more commonly used. Frequently the ionization is produced by an electric discharge in the gas to be ionized. The sources which use this mechanism can be divided into *high-voltage* (HV) *sources*, which use a low-current discharge, and *low-voltage sources*, which use an arc discharge. The voltage used in sources of the first type is of the order of 10–20 kV. The simplest and oldest HV source is the canal-ray tube. However, this source has the disadvantage that the energy of the ions obtained depends on the position at which the ions have been produced; furthermore, the intensity is low. A variant due to Oliphant and Rutherford (1933) is shown schematically in Figure 1-12. A and B are two concentric cylindrical electrodes between which there is a voltage drop of 10–20 kV. The discharge does not occur in the gap between the cylinders because the distance is too small to allow the multiplication necessary for breakdown; it occurs instead between B and the base of A, which has a hole, C, drilled through it. Because of the geometry the electric lines of force tend to converge

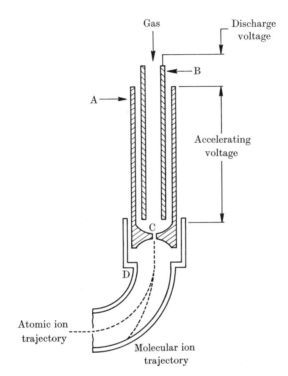

FIGURE 1-12. *Schematic diagram of the high-voltage source by Oliphant and Ruther-ford* (1933).

near C so that the electric field is very high and a strong ionization is produced. The resulting ion energy has a rather uniform distribution because most of the ionization occurs near C. In the region between C and D the ions are accelerated and extracted from the source. Figure 1-12 also illustrates the use of a magnetic field to eliminate the unwanted molecular ions.

Sometimes HV sources are difficult to use, as, for instance, in the case of electrostatic accelerators, where the source must be placed inside the HV terminal electrode. Furthermore, the construction of these sources raises some technological problems connected with the requirement of avoiding wall recombination of the ions formed: to this end, special coatings are used or the walls are kept at high temperature. The efficiency of the source depends critically on the geometry of the probe electrode. In machines with pulsed operation it may be convenient to use a spark discharge source which supplies a high peak pulse current but a low average current.

Low-voltage sources use an arc discharge and voltages of the order of 100 V. In the arc the cathode releases electrons by thermionic emission and the current intensity is much higher than in the HV discharge; the ionization is strong and the ions are extracted by a probe electrode on one side of the arc (see Figure 1-13). The former is kept at a small negative potential and is usually placed near a constriction in the discharge tube where the ion density is high (capillary arc). These sources give a rather high ion intensity and a uniform energy distribution; however, the cathode has a rather short lifetime (some hours) because of ion bombardment.

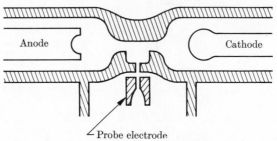

FIGURE 1-13. *Schematic diagram of the capillary-arc source by Tuve, Dahl, and Hafstadt* (1935).

Another way of producing ions consists in accelerating a beam of electrons emitted from a heated filament and making it collide with a jet of gas, whose local density is sufficiently high. In the collision, ionization occurs and the ions produced can be extracted by an electrode at a negative potential. The efficiency can be increased by making the electrons oscillate many times in the gas. Usually a constant magnetic field is applied parallel to the direction of the electron beam, so that the electron trajectories are wound up into spirals and their length is increased for given dimensions of the chamber. The cathode does not suffer ion bombardment and has a longer lifetime than in low-voltage sources. This type of source is called the *electron-oscillation source*: a typical design is illustrated in Figure 1-14. The source consists of two heated filaments, F, which emit electrons, and a metal box, S, kept at a positive potential with respect to them. The walls of the box facing the filaments are open so as to allow the passage of the electrons. The electrons emitted by each filament are accelerated by the voltage drop between the box and the filament. Then as they cross the box they produce some ionization of the gas molecules: in this way they lose energy, and since they are not able to overcome the retarding field between the box and the other filament, they are repelled. Thus they perform a series of damped oscillations inside the box. In stationary conditions, space charge near the filaments keeps the electron beam intensity constant. This type of discharge, first produced by F. M. Penning (1937), is called "electron-oscillation discharge" or "Penning discharge"; an ion source using this mechanism is also called a PIG (Philips Ionization Gauge) source because the same principle has been used in a type of Philips vacuum gauge.

Finally, we describe the *radio-frequency source*, in which the gas is ionized by applying a high-frequency (1–100 Mc/sec) electric field. This is produced by an oscillating circuit in which a coil (supplying the inductance) and a capacitor are always present. The tube containing the gas to be ionized can be placed either inside the coil (Figure 1-15a) or between the plates of the capacitor (Figure 1-15b), where the electromagnetic field is very strong. Sources of this type do not have the problem of cathode lifetime and, as the gas is not contained in a metal vessel, wall recombination of the ions is reduced.

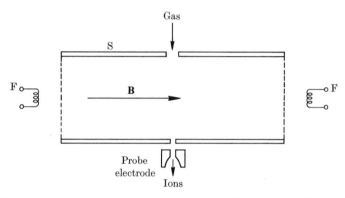

FIGURE 1-14. *Schematic diagram of the electron oscillation source.* F *indicates the filaments,* S *the metal box, and* B *the direction of the magnetic field.*

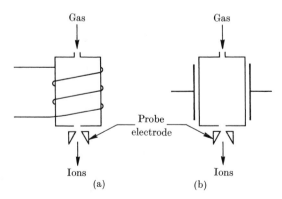

FIGURE 1-15. *Schematic diagram of rf source with* (a) *inductive coupling and* (b) *capacitive coupling.*

In any type of source, the gas pressure is low ($\sim 10^{-2}$ mm Hg) but always much higher than in the rest of the machine ($\lesssim 10^{-5}$ mm Hg). For this reason there is a continuous flow of gas from the source into the accelerator, so that the source must be continuously supplied with gas. In order to avoid too much outflow of gas into the accelerator (and the consequent deterioration of the vacuum) the extraction hole is made rather small and a good vacuum pump is connected near it (see Figure 1-16). This pump preferentially absorbs neutral gas molecules, which only have the random thermal motion, whereas it is inefficient in removing the ions, which because of the acceleration produced by the probe electrode have a strong velocity component along the axis of the exit tube. This mechanism, shown in Figure 1-16, is called "differential pumping."

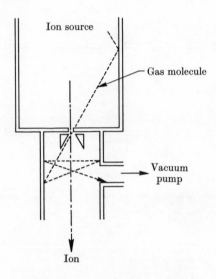

FIGURE 1-16. *Diagram illustrating differential pumping. Typical trajectories for an ion and for a gas molecule are shown.*

Usually, the following features are sought in ion sources:

1. High ion current intensity.
2. High proportion of atomic ions with respect to molecular ions.
3. Uniform energy distribution.
4. Low consumption of gas (it is necessary that the amount of gas flowing into the tube and taken away by the pumps be small, especially in the case of an expensive gas such as deuterium, tritium, or He^3).

5. Low consumption of electric power, especially in the case where the energy must be supplied by generators enclosed, together with the source, inside a limited space (such as the interior of the terminal electrode of electrostatic accelerators).

6. Long lifetime, that is, ability to work for a long time without replacement or repairs.

Finally we note that in cyclotrons the ion source has to be placed at the center of the machine, where strong electric and magnetic fields are present, and then it has some special features. These sources are discussed in greater detail in Section 7-9.

1-12   THE PARAMETERS OF SOME TYPICAL ACCELERATORS

In Tables 1-2 and 1-3 are gathered the most important data for some examples of the different kinds of machines described in the previous sections. The data for "low-energy" and "high-energy" machines are considered separately. Indeed, these two classes are quite different. The number of low-energy machines now existing is large. Furthermore, such machines are not always used for nuclear research: as we have mentioned, some accelerators are used in medicine and in industry. The technical problems presented by low-energy machines in most cases have been solved by standard methods, and indeed some of these machines are now built commercially. In Table 1-2 are given data for a single typical example of each kind of machine. Some cases of special interest (for example, the 300-MeV betatron or the cyclotrons modified according to the FFAG principle: see Chapter 9) are also included. The high-energy accelerators (essentially synchrotrons and linacs) are relatively few in number and they are only used for research in nuclear physics, generally at large and expensive laboratory centers. The technical problems associated with the construction and operation of such machines are usually so complex that specific solutions must be found according to the requirements of each accelerator by the combined effort of a large number of scientists. Table 1-3 gives data for most of the machines of this kind that are in operation or in an advanced state of construction.[9] In comparison with Table 1-2 we have added a few other characteristics, in schematic form. The discussion of the construction details of each machine, although interesting, is beyond the scope of this volume; for literature on this subject, see the General References given at the end of the book.

The transition from high to low energies, of course, is not a sharp one, but

---

[9] Storage-ring projects are not included in the tables; they are described in Chapter 9.

it is reasonable to assume a value of 1 BeV for the energy separating the two classes.

Finally, we give two interesting diagrams which, in a sense, represent a survey of the development of accelerators up to the present time, and which can be used to obtain an estimate of future developments. Figure 1-17 gives the energy reached by each type of machine as a function of the time when it went into operation. On the whole, the energy increase is approximately exponential. Figure 1-18 is a plot of the energy and the average intensity of

TABLE 1-2.   *Characteristics of Some Typical Machines of Energy*
< 1 BeV[a]

Type of machine	Institution	Type of accelerated particle	Final energy (MeV)	Injection energy (MeV)	Average intensity[b] (μA)	Dimension[c] (m)
Van de Graaff	Princeton University	p	3	—	200	2.1
Cockcroft-Walton	Ist. Sup. di Sanità, Rome	p, d, e	1.1	—	500	2.4
Two-stage tandem	Florida State University	p, ions	12(p)	—	0.5	7.2
Proton linac	UCRL, Berkeley	p	32	4	0.2	12
Electron linac	Stanford University (Mark II)	e	75	0.08	0.6	6.1
Betatron	Los Alamos Scientific Laboratory	e	24	0.06	0.15[d]	0.38
Betatron	University of Illinois	e	315	0.1	0.01[e]	1.2
Cyclotron	Columbia University (Pupin Laboratory)	p, d	15(p) 11(d)	—	200	0.9
FFAG Cyclotron	University of Illinois	p, d, ions	15(p)	—	500	1.1
Synchrocyclotron	CERN, Geneva	p	600	—	0.3	5
Synchrocyclotron	UCRL, Berkeley	p	730	—	0.75	4.8
Electron Synchrotron	University of Glasgow	e	340	—[f]	—	2.5

[a] Data taken at the end of 1965.

[b] Representative values.

[c] For electrostatic and linear accelerators: length of the accelerating tube. For betatrons and synchrotrons: diameter of the orbit. For cyclotrons and synchrocyclotrons: diameter of the magnet pole tips.

[d] 5.2×10^9 electrons/pulse; 180 pulses/second.

[e] 10^{10} electrons/pulse; 6 pulses/second.

[f] 70-keV electron gun, then betatron acceleration up to about 4 MeV.

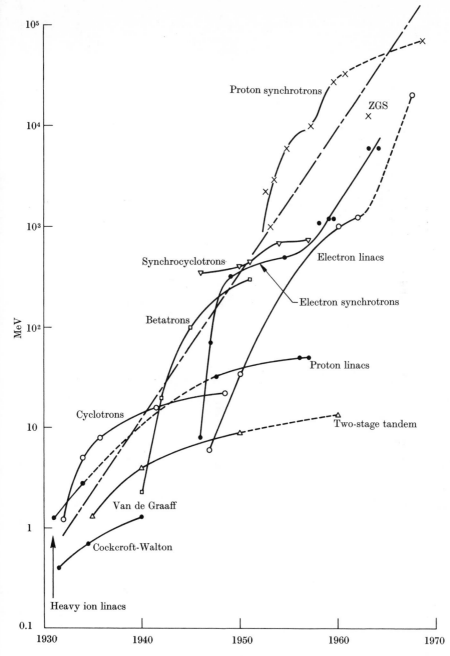

FIGURE 1-17. *Plot of the energy reached by single machines of each kind as a function of time. Points along the various curves represent actual machines, but many existing accelerators are not reported in the figure. Points representing analogous machines and machines under construction are connected by dashed curves. The dot-dashed line is an "average" curve illustrating the exponential growth of accelerator energy.*

31

TABLE 1-3. *Characteristics of Some Machines of Energy* $\geq 1\ BeV$[a]

Type of machine	Institution and name	Type of accelerated particle	Final energy (BeV)	Injection energy (MeV)	Average intensity[b] (μA)	Number of particles per pulse[b]	Repetition rate[b] (pulses per minute)	Diameter of the machine[c] (m)	Harmonic number (k)	Peak field on the orbit (Wb/m²)
Synchrotron	University of Birmingham	p	1	0.46	8×10^{-5}	5×10^{9}	6	9	1	1.26
Synchrotron	Brookhaven National Laboratory (Cosmotron)[d]	p	3	3.6	1.6×10^{-3}	5×10^{10}	12	18	1	1.38
Synchrotron	UCRL, Berkeley (Bevatron)	p	6.2	19.3^{e}	7.3×10^{-2}	2.5×10^{12}	11	30	1	1.54
Synchrotron	Joint Institute for Nuclear Research, Dubna, USSR (Synchrophasotron)	p	10	9	7×10^{-5}	5×10^{10}	5	56	1	1.3
Synchrotron	CEN, Saclay, France (Saturne)	p	3	3.6	1.5×10^{-2}	3×10^{11}	18	22	2	1.49
Synchrotron	Rutherford High Energy Laboratory, Harwell, England (Nimrod)	p	7	15	10^{-1}	1.5×10^{12}	26	46	4	1.4
Synchrotron	Argonne National Laboratory (ZGS)	p	12.5	50	3.2×10^{-2}	8×10^{11}	15	53	8	2.15
AG Synchrotron	CERN, Geneva	p	28	50	5.3×10^{-2}	10^{12}	20	200	20	1.4
AG Synchrotron	Brookhaven National Laboratory (AGS)	p	33	50	5.3×10^{-2}	10^{12}	20	257	12	1.3

TABLE 1-3. *Characteristics of Some Machines of Energy ≥ 1 BeV* [a] *(Continued)*

Type of machine	Institution and name	Type of accelerated particle	Final energy (BeV)	Injection energy (MeV)	Average intensity [b] (μA)	Number of particles per pulse [b]	Repetition rate [b] (pulses per minute)	Diameter of the machine [c] (m)	Harmonic number (k)	Peak field on the orbit (Wb/m²)
AG Synchrotron	Serpukhov, USSR[f]	p	70	100	—	—	5–8	472	30	1.2
Synchrotron	Lab. Naz. di Frascati, Rome	e	1.1	2.5	3.2×10^{-2}	10^{10}	1200	7.2	4	1.02
AG Synchrotron	Cornell University	e	1.5	2	2.4×10^{-2}	5×10^{9}	1800	8.7	8	1.35
AG Synchrotron	Massachusetts Institute of Technology, Cambridge, Massachusetts (CEA)	e	6	28	0.5	5×10^{10}	3600	72	360	0.76
AG Synchrotron	University of Hamburg (DESY)	e	6	40	0.4	5×10^{10}	3000	101	528	0.81
AG Synchrotron	Cornell University[f]	e	10	200	0.8[g]	10^{11}[g]	3600	240	1790	0.33
Linac	Orsay, France	e	1.3	0.025	2.4	3×10^{11}	3000	170	—	—
Linac	Stanford University (SLAC)[f]	e⁻, e⁺	20(e⁻) 13(e⁺)	0.08	30(e⁻)[g]	5×10^{11}(e⁻)[g]	21600	3×10^{3}	—	—

[a] Data taken at the end of 1965.
[b] Representative values. Actual values may generally depend on the energy and the conditions of experiment.
[c] Average values. For linacs: length of the machine.

[d] Operation to be discontinued.
[e] Former value: 9.9 MeV.
[f] Under construction (1965).
[g] Scheduled.

the high-energy accelerators. It is interesting that, although in the operating machines greater energies tend to be associated with lower intensities, it now appears possible to build machines having both very large energy and high intensity.

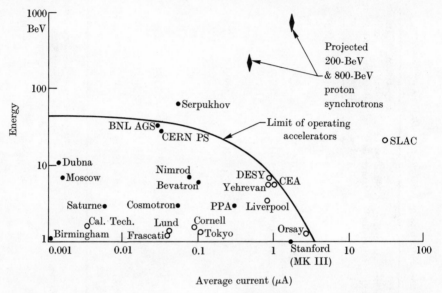

FIGURE 1-18. *Plot of the energy and the average intensity of high-energy accelerators now in operation or under construction. Full circles indicate proton machines; open circles, electron machines. From Laslett (1964).*

CHAPTER 2

THE ELECTROSTATIC

ACCELERATORS

2-1 THE ACCELERATING TUBE

Electrostatic accelerators consist essentially of two parts: the HV generator and the accelerating tube. Different types of electrostatic accelerators have different types of generators, whereas the accelerating tubes are the same. Figure 2-1 is a diagram of the structure of the accelerating tube. It usually consists of a series of glass (or other insulating material) cylinders connected with vacuum-tight seals to metallic electrodes between the sections of insulator. The electrodes are connected to a chain of resistors (with very high resistance) so that a uniform distribution of potential is maintained along the tube. These electrodes also serve other purposes: they protect the walls of the tube from the beam and so reduce the possibility of surface discharges (flashover); and they limit the accumulation of charge on the insulating walls which can produce electrostatic deflection of the beam. Furthermore, as will be shown, these electrodes have a focusing effect on the beam. Their presence also increases the mechanical strength of the accelerating tube.

One of the great problems in the construction of the accelerating tube is presented by the vacuum-tight seals between metal and glass, which usually must operate between a pressure of many atmospheres outside the tube and high vacuum inside. Generally the seal is made with special cements which have low vapor pressure. Direct sealing of metal to glass is difficult, although it has been used in some cases.

The first electrostatic accelerators built followed closely the design indicated in Figure 2-1. In the modern accelerators, where higher voltages are required, a different design has been used (see Figure 2-2): the length of the intermediate electrodes is reduced and their number increased so that they are practically reduced to metallic rings. In this case it is possible to maintain a uniform distribution of potential by means of the corona current, flowing from one ring to the next, rather than by using the current in an external resistive voltage divider. The large inner diameter of the electrodes is required in order to allow high pumping speeds. These are necessary with the modern ion sources which give higher intensities, but also, at the same time, a higher flux of gas into the accelerating tube.

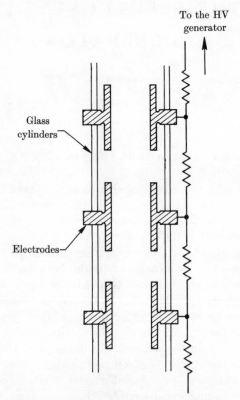

To the HV
generator

Glass
cylinders

Electrodes

FIGURE 2-1. *Schematic diagram of a structure for the accelerating tube.*

In order to understand the focusing effect of the electrodes, consider Figure 2-3, where E_1 and E_2 indicate two cylindrical electrodes at different potentials and the dotted lines are lines of force of the electric field. Let us suppose that a particle with positive charge crosses the gap from E_1 to E_2. The particle is accelerated axially by the component of the electric field parallel to the axis, and it is also accelerated by a small transverse component, directed toward the axis in E_1 and in the opposite sense in E_2. Thus there is a focusing effect at the entrance of the gap and a defocusing one at the exit. However, as the particle is accelerated in crossing from E_1 to E_2, the focusing effect lasts for a longer time and therefore is more effective (as an example a trajectory is also shown in Figure 2-3).

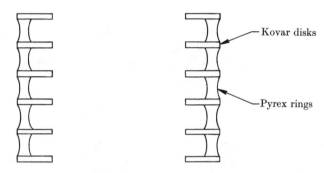

FIGURE 2-2.   *Schematic diagram of a structure for the accelerating tube.*

The study of the trajectories of a charged particle in an electrostatic field has been developed thoroughly and it constitutes the basis of the science called "electron optics." There is a useful analogy between the motion of a particle (of charge q) in an electrostatic field (described by a potential $V(x, y, z)$) and the path of a ray of light in an inhomogeneous medium (of refractive index $n(x, y, z)$). Indeed it can be shown that the trajectory of the particle and the path of the ray coincide if one assumes for n the following form:

$$n(x, y, z) = k\{(C - qV)\,[1 + (C - qV)/(2mc^2)]\}^{1/2}, \qquad (2\text{-}1)$$

where m is the rest mass, C is a constant equal to the sum of the kinetic and the potential energy of the particle, and k is an arbitrary constant which has no

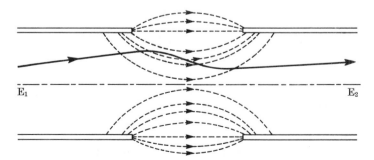

FIGURE 2-3.   *The focusing effect of an electrostatic lens.*

influence on the form of the trajectory. If $(C - qV) \lll mc^2$, that is, if $v^2 \lll c^2$, the relativistic formula 2-1 can be replaced by the classical one

$$n(x, y, z) = k(C - qV)^{1/2} \tag{2-2}$$

(and in this case n is independent of m). In this analogy a device such as that shown in Figure 2-3 is called an *electrostatic lens*. For each such "lens" one can define a focal length: it is found that it increases with the kinetic energy of the particle.

Thus the accelerating tube acts as a system of many lenses which must form on the target an image of the exit hole in the ion source. As the kinetic energy of the particles increases along the tube, only the first few lenses are efficient in focusing. In practice, to obtain on the target the smallest possible image of the exit hole in the ion source, it is sufficient to adjust the potentials and the form of the first two lenses.

Another important factor to be considered is the effect of space charge. If the intensity of the beam is high, electrostatic repulsion between particles tends to broaden the beam and produces some defocusing. This effect is only important in the first stages of the acceleration; indeed, when the velocity is sufficiently high, electrostatic repulsion is partly compensated by an attraction of electromagnetic nature, because the particles in motion can be considered as parallel currents. This effect is important only at relativistic velocities. In order to correct the defocusing due to space charge, the first electrode (probe electrode) is given a slightly concave form so as to introduce a small transverse component of the electric field which tends to bring the particles toward the axis. The proper design for the electrode has been studied by J. R. Pierce (1954, Chapter 10).

2-2 THE HIGH-VOLTAGE TERMINAL

The high-voltage terminal (HV terminal) is essentially a part of the electrostatic generator. However, as many of the problems of its design (especially problems of insulation) are common to all types of generators, it is preferable to treat them separately and in a general way.

The HV terminal consists of a metal shell of spherical or ellipsoidal form with large radius of curvature (order of magnitude of some tens of centimeters or one meter), supported by one or more insulating columns. Inside, the terminal usually contains the ion source and the beginning of the accelerating tube. The shape and dimensions of the terminal are so designed that it can be charged to a high voltage without the occurrence of discharges between it and the walls of the chamber in which it is contained. For the same reason, the insulating columns are surrounded by closely spaced equipotential rings, arranged so that the electric field is constant along the columns. When the machine is working, the HV terminal is continuously supplied with electric charge from the electrostatic generator which feeds it. On the other hand, it is discharged by the beam current and by dissipative currents due to different causes. One of these is the corona current along the accelerating tube (and possibly the current flowing in the voltage divider shown in Figure 2-1); another is the weak conduction current through the insulators supporting the terminal; however, most of the dissipative current (in positive ion accelerators) is due to the so-called "electron loading." This consists in the extraction of secondary electrons by ions hitting the walls toward the end of the accelerating tube: these electrons are focused and accelerated back toward the ion source and constitute a current which reduces the working voltage of the terminal. (It is mainly because of electron loading that some machines must operate at lower voltages than the values for which they were planned.) Furthermore at the end of their path these secondary electrons hit the walls of the tube and produce large quantities of x rays. Therefore adequate shielding is essential for the safety of the persons working on the machine. Usually heavy shielding is built into the walls of the room containing the terminal. Figure 2-4 shows how the different currents flowing from the terminal depend on voltage. The working voltage, V_e, is determined by the value of the maximum charging current, i_m. It can be seen that the beam current remains constant, being determined by the nature of the source rather than by the accelerating voltage; the dissipative currents of resistive nature are proportional to voltage; the dissipative currents due to corona and electron loading are negligible at low potentials, but increase very rapidly

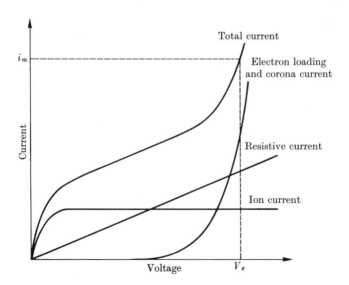

FIGURE 2-4. *Dependence on voltage of the load currents in an electrostatic accelerator.*

above a certain voltage. Figure 2-4 can be considered as the voltage-current characteristic of a particular machine. Figure 2-5 is a graph that has a different meaning. It gives the relationship between the ion current (beam intensity) obtainable in a machine and the corresponding working voltage. If we fix the maximum charging current, i_m, which depends on the generator, and call I the beam current and I' the sum of the dissipative currents, then obviously

$$I + I' = i_m . \qquad (2\text{-}3)$$

The dependence of I' on V_e can easily be obtained from the curves of Figure 2-4 and the dependence of I on V_e shown in Figure 2-5 follows. Each point on the curve of Figure 2-5 represents a possible working condition for a machine. In general the accelerator is designed to operate at the high-voltage end of the curve. Thus one can obtain a voltage V_e^* not much less than the maximum value V_m and a beam current I^* which is not too low, although much smaller than i_m. Both conditions can be satisfied, owing to the steepness of the curve.

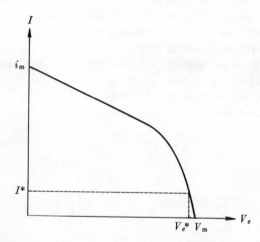

FIGURE 2-5. *Dependence of beam current on the working voltage for a given generator and accelerating tube.*

As mentioned previously, the main limitation to the value of the maximum voltage, V_m, of the terminal is given by the fact that when the electric field at the surface of the electrode is greater than a certain value (dielectric strength of air), discharges occur between the terminal and the walls of the surrounding chamber. The terminal is given a spherical or ellipsoidal form precisely in order to minimize the electric field for a given voltage. For a given form of electrode, of course, the electric field which produces the breakdown of the gas corresponds to a value V_b of the voltage, called "breakdown voltage," which must not be exceeded. In order to increase the dielectric strength of the medium surrounding the HV terminal, the entire machine is usually enclosed in a high-pressure tank filled with an inert gas (freon, CCl_2F_2, for example) at a pressure of 10–15 atm. Indeed, for a given electrode geometry the breakdown voltage only depends on the product, pl, of gas pressure and distance between electrodes (Paschen's law). For two plane-parallel electrodes in air, the dependence of V_b on pl is found experimentally to be that shown in Figure 2-6. The behavior of V_b for very high or very low values of p, for a given l, can be understood by considering the breakdown mechanism. Breakdown occurs through the ionization of the gas molecules by electrons accelerated in the electric field. At high pressures the mean free path of the electrons is shorter and a higher voltage is required in order to transfer to them the energy necessary for ionization in one free path. At low pressures, instead, the ionization rate is low because although the energy an electron gains between collisions is sufficient for producing ionization, the number of ionizing collisions is small, since the length l contains a small number of mean free paths (possibly less than one).

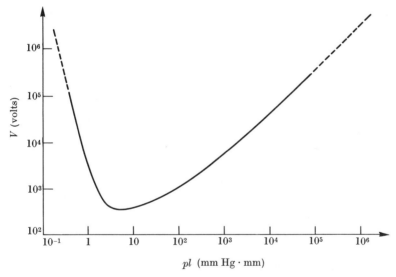

FIGURE 2-6. *Breakdown voltage in air for plane-parallel electrodes (Paschen's curve).*

It can be seen from Figure 2-6 that, for a given value of l, there are two pressure ranges such that $V_b > V_m$. In the existing machines high pressure has been preferred as this is simpler in practice. It is possible that with further progress in vacuum technology the very low pressures may be used.

Again with the aim of reducing the electric field for a given voltage, it is useful to introduce intermediate concentric electrodes, called "equipotential shields," between the HV terminal and the high-pressure tank, which is usually kept at ground potential. It can easily be shown that, if the intermediate electrodes are maintained at intermediate voltages, the maximum electric field occurring in the machine is reduced. In order to show this let us first calculate the maximum electric field between the HV terminal and the tank, considered as concentric spherical electrodes of radii r_0 and R, respectively, with a voltage difference of V_0.

In the space between the electrodes the potential has the form

$$V(r) = V_0 \frac{(1/r) - (1/R)}{(1/r_0) - (1/R)}. \tag{2-4}$$

Calling E_0 the maximum value of the electric field between the electrodes, reached on the surface of the inner one, we have

$$E_0 = -\left(\frac{dV}{dr}\right)_{r=r_0} = \frac{V_0}{r_0(1 - r_0/R)}. \tag{2-5}$$

By changing the ratio of the radii, we change E_0. The optimum value of the ratio is that one for which E_0 is a minimum. This obtains for $R/r_0 = 2$, as can be seen by setting the first derivative of Equation 2-5 with respect to r_0 equal to zero. Calling E^* this minimum value of E_0, we have

$$E^* = 4V_0/R. \tag{2-6}$$

Let us now introduce a third spherical concentric electrode of radius r_1 at a potential V_1. The maximum value of the electric field within the machine can be reached either at the surface of the central (HV) electrode or at the surface of the intermediate one. The corresponding values, according to Equation 2-5, will be given by

$$E_0 = \frac{V_0 - V_1}{r_0(1 - r_0/r_1)}, \qquad E_1 = \frac{V_1}{r_1(1 - r_1/R)}. \tag{2-7}$$

The procedure for minimizing the value of the maximum electric field in the machine now consists in choosing V_1 so that E_0 and E_1 are equal and then minimizing their common value, by setting the partial derivatives with respect to r_0 and r_1 equal to zero. In this way one obtains

$$r_0 = \tfrac{1}{2}r_1, \qquad r_1 = \tfrac{5}{8}R, \qquad V_1 = \tfrac{3}{5}V_0 \tag{2-8}$$

and, under such conditions,

$$E^* = E_0 = E_1 = 2.56 \frac{V_0}{R}, \tag{2-9}$$

which is appreciably less than the value given by Equation 2-6. The usefulness of this reduction is that, for given dimensions of the generator (that is, for a given R), V_0 can be increased until E^* almost reaches the breakdown value E_b.

Thus, with an intermediate electrode, V_0 can almost reach the value $(1/2.56)RE_b$, instead of the value $\frac{1}{4}RE_b$ in absence of the shield, the gain thus being about 56%. It is possible to reduce E^* still further by adding more concentric shields at the proper potentials. However, the gain decreases progressively, so that usually no more than two equipotential shields are used, and these are kept at the desired potentials by means of high-resistance connections to the metal rings of the accelerating tube (see an example in Figure 2-15).

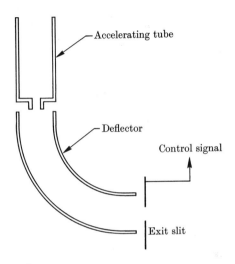

FIGURE 2-7. *Schematic diagram of the deflector and exit slit for an electrostatic accelerator.*

Sometimes an electrostatic or magnetic deflector is placed at the exit of the accelerating tube (Figure 2-7). It has the purpose of ensuring that only particles of the required energy (and mass) reach the target. The deflector can also be used to control the voltage of the generator. The edges of the exit slit are insulated and when a fluctuation in the accelerating voltage produces a deflection of the beam off the desired direction, the particles hit one of the edges of the exit slit and produce an electric signal which can be used to correct the high voltage. This can be done in different ways: (1) by acting on the HV generator; (2) by changing the dissipative current I'; (3) by changing the potential V_1 of the electrostatic shield. The last two methods in general are faster than the first. For ion accelerators control of I' can be obtained by means of a second tube parallel to the accelerating tube, where electrons emitted from a heated filament at ground potential are accelerated toward the HV terminal and produce a current which can be controlled without difficulty by varying the heating current.

In measuring the high voltage, the "generating voltmeter" can be used. It consists essentially of a variable capacitor whose two plates face the HV terminal (see Figure 2-8). The plate nearest the latter is grounded and fixed, whereas the outer plate rotates at a constant speed and is connected to earth through a high resistor. It can be shown that the voltage on the resistor is alternating and its amplitude is rigorously proportional to the voltage V_0 of the terminal. Thus the calibration of the instrument can be carried out at low voltages. The signal from the generating voltmeter can be amplified and used for controlling the stability of V_0. The measurement of the accelerating voltage with the generating voltmeter can be disturbed by different effects, such as corona and the fluctuations of the voltages of the electrostatic shields surrounding the ion source. With accelerators which use the resistive voltage divider for ensuring uniform potential distribution along the tube, the high voltage can be determined by measuring the current in the divider, if the values of the resistances are known with great precision. The energy of the beam can also be measured by means of electrostatic or magnetic deflection.

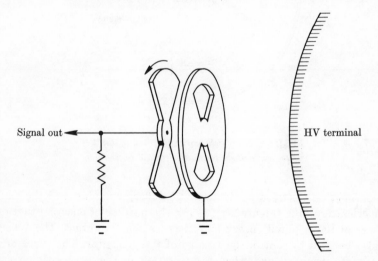

FIGURE 2-8.   *Schematic diagram of the generating voltmeter.*

2-3   THE COCKCROFT-WALTON GENERATOR

In discussing the HV generators used in electrostatic accelerators, we shall first describe the Cockcroft-Walton generator, which was the first used to produce nuclear reactions (Cockcroft and Walton, 1932a,b, 1934). This generator is a development of the idea contained in the so-called voltage multiplier of Greinacher (1921). The Cockcroft-Walton generator consists of two columns of capacitors (see Figure 2-9) connected in series; the two columns are connected by a chain of diodes which conduct only in the direction of the arrows. The generator is fed by a transformer T, capable of producing an ac voltage $U(t)$ with peak value U (order of magnitude of 100 kV). If no current is drawn from the HV terminal it can be seen that, after some initial period of adjustment, a stationary state is reached where all the capacitors (except the first one) are charged to a voltage $2U$; the potentials of the plates of the capacitors on the right are fixed, whereas those of the capacitors on the left oscillate between the limits indicated in Figure 2-9. In these conditions the diodes do not conduct any current. If, for any reason, this state is altered, the diodes (for some fraction of the period) conduct a current which tends to bring the system back to the stationary state. During the operation of the machine a constant current, i, is drawn from the HV terminal. In this case all the potentials are slightly decreased and they fluctuate according to a law that will now be derived.

Let us denote by n the number of capacitors in each column; by C_r, C_r' ($r = 1, 2, \ldots, n$), the capacitances of the capacitors on the right and on the left, respectively, numbered beginning from above; and by $u_r(t)$, the voltage to

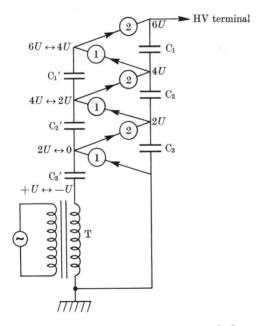

FIGURE 2-9. *Circuit of a three-stage Cock-croft-Walton generator. The numbered circles indicate diodes, and the arrows indicate the direction of conduction.*

which C_r is charged. We shall call the diodes which conduct from the column on the right to that on the left d_1, and the others d_2.

Figure 2-10 shows qualitatively the behavior of $u_r(t)$ in correspondence with $U(t)$. The capacitors, as already mentioned, are all charged to a voltage which is slightly less than in the absence of current. Therefore, when $U(t)$ grows and is near its maximum, it can be seen that the upper plates of capacitors C_r' reach potentials higher than those of the upper plates of capacitors C_r, so that, for a short time around the instant t_2, the diodes d_2 carry a current, which increases u_r as in Figure 2-10. During the next half-period the

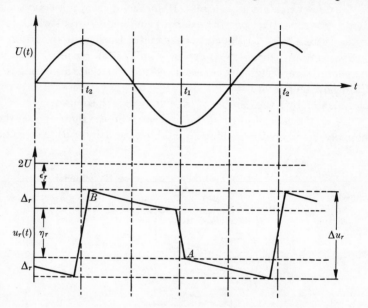

FIGURE 2-10. *Diagram showing the sinusoidal transformer voltage waveform and the corresponding voltage on capacitor* C_r. (*Different scales are used on the ordinates.*)

whole column on the right is discharged, with an extremely high time constant, on the load (accelerating tube) and the voltage $u_r(t)$ decreases exponentially. Near the minimum of $U(t)$ (instant t_1), the upper plate of C_r reaches a potential higher than the upper plate of C_{r-1}'; therefore the diodes d_1 now carry a current and the voltage $u_r(t)$ drops abruptly. In the next half-period the column on the right continues to supply current to the load and the voltage drops further until at the next time of maximum, t_2, it rapidly rises to its initial value.

Thus the voltage $u_r(t)$ is not a constant but it fluctuates with amplitude Δu_r around a value less than $2U$. We shall denote by ϵ_r (see Figure 2-10) the reduction of the maximum of $u_r(t)$ with respect to $2U$; by Δ_r, the decrease of $u_r(t)$ during a half-period; and by η_r, the drop in voltage near the instant t_1. Thus

$$\Delta u_r = \eta_r + 2\Delta_r . \qquad (2\text{-}10)$$

Let us now calculate these quantities.

In a steady state, the charge q supplied by the capacitors in a period T is always $q = iT$. Therefore the change in voltage in a half-period, that is, Δ_r, is given by

$$\Delta_r = \frac{q}{2C_r} = \frac{iT}{2C_r} . \qquad (2\text{-}11)$$

In order to calculate η_r, consider Figure 2-11. The net charge on the electrode consisting of the upper plate of C_{r+1} and the lower plate of C_r is $(C_{r+1}u_{r+1} - C_r u_r)$. The change in this charge at the time t_1 is $(C_{r+1}\eta_{r+1} - C_r\eta_r)$ and is

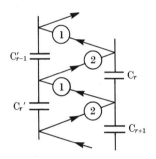

FIGURE 2-11. *Detail of the circuit of a Cockcroft-Walton generator.*

equal to the charge that at this time leaves the electrode and passes through the diode d_1 into the left-hand column. This charge is precisely q. Thus the following recurrence formula holds:

$$C_{r+1}\eta_{r+1} - C_r\eta_r = q \qquad (r = 1, 2, \dots, n). \qquad (2\text{-}12)$$

As $\eta_1 = 0$ (indeed C_1 does not charge any capacitor of the left-hand column), by adding term by term the first s of Equations 2-12 with $r = 1, 2, \dots, s$, we obtain $C_s\eta_s = (s - 1)q$ and hence

$$\eta_s = \frac{(s - 1)q}{C_s} \qquad (s = 1, 2, \dots, n). \qquad (2\text{-}13)$$

Thus by substituting Equations 2-13 and 2-11 into Equation 2-10 we obtain

$$\Delta u_s = \frac{sq}{C_s} \qquad (s = 1, 2, \dots, n). \qquad (2\text{-}14)$$

The fluctuation of the HV terminal will therefore be

$$\Delta u = \sum_{1}^{n}{}_{s} \Delta u_s = q \sum_{1}^{n}{}_{s} \frac{s}{C_s}. \qquad (2\text{-}15)$$

If the capacitances are all equal $(C_s = C)$,

$$\Delta u = \frac{n(n+1)}{2} \frac{q}{C} = \frac{n(n+1)}{2} \frac{i}{C\nu}, \qquad (2\text{-}16)$$

where $\nu = 1/T$. It can be seen that the fluctuation increases roughly as n^2 and is strongly influenced by the capacitors nearest the transformer. It is convenient that these be as large as possible. In practice two values of capacitance are used, the smaller value for the upper capacitors, and the larger one for the lower capacitors.

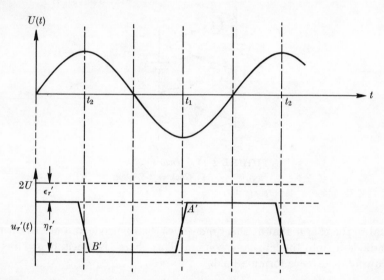

FIGURE 2-12. *Diagram showing the transformer voltage waveform and the corresponding voltage on capacitor $C_r{}'$. (Different scales are used on the ordinates.)*

In order to calculate the reduction ϵ_r of the voltage it is useful to consider Figure 2-12 (analogous to Figure 2-10), which shows the voltage $u_r{}'(t)$ on capacitor $C_r{}'$. The behavior of $u_r{}'(t)$ shown in the figure can be understood by considering that, at times t_2, while the capacitors C_r are discharged (see Figure 2-10), the capacitors $C_r{}'$ are charged, and vice versa, at times t_1. Furthermore, during a half-period the voltage remains constant because no current is drawn from these capacitors. At times t_1, the diodes d_1 carry a current and capacitors C_r and C'_{r-1} are connected in parallel (see Figure 2-11), so that, when the diodes have finished conducting, the voltages on the plates are equal. This means that the ordinates of points A and A' of Figures 2-10 and 2-12 must be equal, that is,

$$2U - \epsilon_r - \Delta_r - \eta_r = 2U - \epsilon'_{r-1}. \tag{2-17}$$

A similar argument for time t_2 (points B and B') gives

$$2U - \epsilon_r = 2U - \epsilon_r' - \eta_r'. \tag{2-18}$$

Furthermore, by following the same argument as that used to derive Equation 2-13 (but taking into account that η_1' is not zero but equals q/C_1', as can easily be seen), the following relation can be obtained:

$$\eta_s' = \frac{sq}{C_{s'}}. \tag{2-19}$$

Hence, by writing Equation 2-18 for the index $(r-1)$ and substituting for Δ_r into Equation 2-17 from Equation 2-11, we obtain the system

$$\epsilon_r = \epsilon'_{r-1} - \eta_r - \frac{q}{2C_r}, \tag{2-20}$$

$$\epsilon_{r-1} = \eta'_{r-1} + \epsilon'_{r-1}.$$

Taking the difference of these two equations and using Equations 2-13 and 2-19 we have

$$\epsilon_r - \epsilon_{r-1} = -\eta_r - \eta'_{r-1} - \frac{q}{2C_r} = -\frac{(r-1)}{C_r}q - \frac{(r-1)}{C'_{r-1}}q - \frac{q}{2C_r}$$

$$= q\left[\frac{1}{2C_r} - \frac{r}{C_r} - \frac{(r-1)}{C'_{r-1}}\right]. \tag{2-21}$$

If we write this relation for all the values of r, from $r=2$ to $r=t$ and if we add up term by term, we obtain

$$\epsilon_t - \epsilon_1 = q\sum_2^t r\left[\frac{1}{2C_r} - \frac{r}{C_r} - \frac{(r-1)}{C'_{r-1}}\right]. \tag{2-22}$$

If we now write Equation 2-22 for $t=n$ and from this subtract Equation 2-22 itself, we obtain

$$\epsilon_n - \epsilon_t = q\sum_{t+1}^n r\left[\frac{1}{2C_r} - \frac{r}{C_r} - \frac{(r-1)}{C'_{r-1}}\right]. \tag{2-23}$$

We now calculate ϵ_n, the reduction of the voltage on the lowest capacitor of the right-hand column. For this purpose consider Figure 2-13. At times t_2, when the diode d_2 has stopped carrying current (points B and B' of Figures

2-10 and 2-12), the voltage on the plates of C_n equals the sum of the voltages on the plates of C_n' and on the transformer T, that is, $u_n = u_n' + U$ and hence

$$2U - \epsilon_n = U - \eta_n' + U, \tag{2-24}$$

where we have taken into account that C_n' is charged to a voltage U rather than $2U$ (see Figure 2-9) and that $\epsilon_n' = 0$, because the capacitor is charged

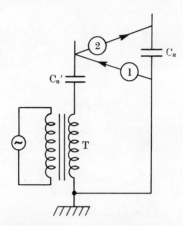

FIGURE 2-13. *Detail of the circuit of a Cockcroft-Walton generator.*

directly by the transformer through the diode d_1 and so has no reduction in voltage. Hence, from Equations 2-19 and 2-24, it follows that

$$\epsilon_n = \eta_n' = \frac{nq}{C_n'}, \tag{2-25}$$

and finally, substituting this into Equation 2-23, we obtain

$$\epsilon_t = q \left[\sum_{t+1}^{n} {}_r \frac{(r - 1/2)}{C_r} + \sum_{t}^{n} {}_r \frac{r}{C_r'} \right]. \tag{2-26}$$

Therefore the reduction of the terminal voltage,

$$\Delta V_0 = \sum_{1}^{n} {}_t \, \epsilon_t \, ,$$

is given by

$$\Delta V_0 = q \sum_{1}^{n} {}_t \left[\sum_{t+1}^{n} {}_r \frac{(r - 1/2)}{C_r} + \sum_{t}^{n} {}_r \frac{r}{C_r'} \right]. \tag{2-27}$$

If all the capacitances are equal ($C_r = C_r' = C$), we obtain

$$\Delta V_0 = \frac{q}{C}\left(\frac{2}{3}n^3 + \frac{1}{4}n^2 + \frac{1}{12}n\right),$$ (2-28)

showing that the reduction increases approximately as the cube of the number of stages.[1] It is therefore convenient to reduce the number of stages and use a transformer with high peak voltage. As ΔV_0, proportional to q, is inversely proportional to the supply frequency, it is also convenient to use high frequencies. In practice frequencies above about 500 cps are not used, because otherwise effects due to stray capacitance become important.

In modern Cockcroft-Walton generators, solid state rectifiers are used instead of diodes. The advantage is that the rectifiers do not require a power supply (whereas each diode requires a separate supply as the working voltages are very different) and they can operate without difficulty inside a pressure chamber.

2-4 THE VAN DE GRAAFF GENERATOR

This type of machine, which uses a convective current to charge the high-voltage terminal, was first proposed by R. J. Van de Graaff (1931). Its principle is shown in the schematic diagram of Figure 2-14. An insulating belt between two pulleys (a and b) is made to move by a motor connected to the pulley b, at ground potential. Near this pulley a row of points extends across the width of the belt and is maintained at a voltage of 20 to 30 kV with respect to the plate P. In the figure the points are supposed to be at a positive voltage. A corona discharge between the points and the belt ionizes the gas, and electric charge (positive in the figure) is deposited on the moving belt. The upper pulley, a, is inside the high-voltage terminal S. Here another corona-point collector, connected to S, removes the charge carried by the belt; this charge accumulates progressively on the outer surface of the terminal and the voltage hence increases. Inside the high-voltage electrode there is also the ion source and the beginning of the accelerating tube (not shown in the figure).

---

[1] Formula (2-2) of the book by Livingston and Blewett (1962) gives an expression for ΔV_0 different from our formula 2-28 and precisely, in our notation,

$$\Delta V_0 = \frac{q}{C}\left(\frac{2}{3}n^3 + \frac{3}{4}n^2 + \frac{1}{12}n\right).$$

This formula is essentially derived from a calculation of A. Bouwers and A. Kuntke (1937), where the voltage drops, which have been called Δ_r in Figure 2-10, are neglected and only the total variation Δu_r expressed by our Equation 2-14 is considered. With this approximation, formula 2-17 contains $-\Delta u_r$ instead of $-\Delta_r - \eta_r$ and this leads to the difference mentioned above. However, the dominant term of ΔV_0, proportional to n^3, is not affected.

In general, in accelerators using high-pressure gas around the terminal, the high-pressure tank (at ground potential) surrounds and protects the whole accelerator, so that the resulting form (see Figure 2-15) is very compact. This type of machine is also produced commercially for specific purposes such as the production of x rays for industrial and medical uses. It should be noted that an apparatus of the type shown in Figure 2-15 can be placed in both a vertical and a horizontal position.

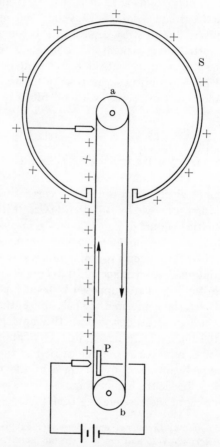

FIGURE 2-14. *Schematic diagram of a Van de Graaff generator.*

The charging current i_m is determined by the characteristics of the belt. If we call the surface charge density ρ, the speed of the belt v, and its width a, we have

$$i_m = \rho v a. \tag{2-29}$$

In general the values of ρ, v, and a are limited by practical reasons. Usually $v < 25$ m/sec and $a < 50$ cm. The value of ρ also is limited by gas breakdown. When the belt is inside a high-pressure tank higher values of ρ can be obtained (of the order of 10^{-4} coulomb/m^2 against 10^{-5} coulomb/m^2 at atmospheric pressure).

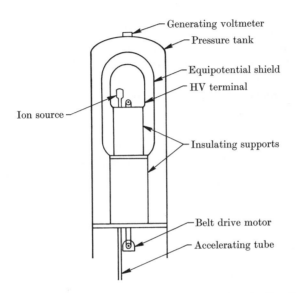

FIGURE 2-15. *Diagram showing the structure of a Van de Graaff accelerator.*

In this way charging currents of some milliamperes can be produced. It is possible to increase the charging current in various ways. For instance, more than one belt can be used, with the belts arranged in parallel in such a way as to limit losses through corona currents. Another method is to charge the belt also in its downward motion with charges of opposite sign to those in the upward motion, so that the charging current is doubled.

In comparing the two types of generator described above it must first be pointed out that the Van de Graaff reaches high voltages more easily than the Cockcroft-Walton and above a certain particle energy (~ 2 MeV) it is the only practical electrostatic generator. In the energy range where both types of generator can be used, the Van de Graaff gives greater stability of particle energy (up to 0.01%); the Cockcroft-Walton can give high beam intensities more easily than the Van de Graaff but its voltage has fluctuations of the order of 1%. Modern, carefully designed Van de Graaff accelerators can reach intensities comparable with those produced by existing Cockcroft-Walton machines (~ 1 mA).

2-5 THE TANDEM ACCELERATOR

Finally, we describe a machine called the "tandem accelerator," which accelerates positive ions to twice the energy corresponding to the voltage of the HV terminal. The main feature of this machine, illustrated in the diagram of Figure 2-16, is that the accelerating tube crosses the HV terminal so that the ion source and the target, at the ends of the tube, are both at ground potential. The positive ion beam from the ion source passes through an "electron adding" canal where a flow of hydrogen produces successive attachment of two electrons to an ion, transforming positive ions into negative ions. These are accelerated down to the (positive) HV terminal. Here the beam passes through a "stripping" canal where neutral gas strips electrons from the negative ions, transforming them to positive ions. These are again accelerated from the terminal down to the target. Thus the energy gained by the particles at the end of the acceleration is twice the value corresponding to the voltage produced in the machine. This type of accelerator gives high energies (12–20 MeV) and has the advantage that both ion source and target are at ground potential, so that problems of construction and control are greatly simplified. On the other hand, the accelerated beam intensity is low (a few microamperes) because of the low efficiency of the electron adding and stripping processes. The energy can be increased by using a tandem accelerator with more than one stage. Three-stage tandem accelerators have already been built (P. H. Rose, 1961).

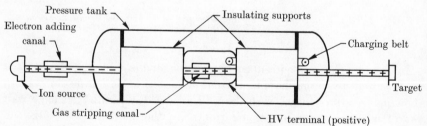

FIGURE 2-16. *Diagram showing the structure of a tandem accelerator.*

CHAPTER 3

THE DYNAMICS OF A
CHARGED PARTICLE IN AN
ELECTROMAGNETIC FIELD

3-1 INTRODUCTION

An arbitrary electromagnetic field can be described either by means of the vectors $\mathbf{E}$, electric field, and $\mathbf{B}$, magnetic induction, or by means of the scalar $V(x, y, z, t)$ and the vector $\mathbf{A}(x, y, z, t)$, called respectively *scalar potential* and *vector potential*. These quantities are related to $\mathbf{E}$ and $\mathbf{B}$ through the following equations:

$$\mathbf{E} = -\operatorname{grad} V - \frac{\partial \mathbf{A}}{\partial t}, \tag{3-1}$$

$$\mathbf{B} = \operatorname{curl} \mathbf{A}. \tag{3-2}$$

It should be noted that the potentials V and $\mathbf{A}$ are not uniquely defined: the same electromagnetic field can be described by different choices of the functions V and $\mathbf{A}$. The passage from one choice of the potentials to another is effected through a so-called "gauge transformation." (See, for example, Panofsky and Phillips, 1962, p. 240.)

We recall that in a purely electrostatic field the vector potential $\mathbf{A}$ can be chosen equal to zero, and so the field is described simply in terms of $V(x, y, z)$ (electrostatic potential). This applies to the case of electrostatic accelerators.

We recall also that the most general electromagnetic field, in those regions where there are no charges producing it, can always be represented by the vector potential $\mathbf{A}$ only, with $V = 0$. This can be applied to the vacuum chamber of all the accelerators, insofar as we neglect (as we shall do) the space-charge effects of the accelerated particles.

The force acting on a particle of charge q and velocity $\mathbf{v}$ is given by

$$\mathbf{F} = q(\mathbf{E} + \mathbf{v} \times \mathbf{B}) = q\left(-\operatorname{grad} V - \frac{\partial \mathbf{A}}{\partial t} + \mathbf{v} \times \operatorname{curl} \mathbf{A}\right). \quad (3\text{-}3)$$

With this expression of the force, the fundamental equation of relativistic dynamics 1-1, $\dot{\mathbf{P}} = \mathbf{F}$, becomes the following:

$$\dot{\mathbf{P}} = q\left(-\operatorname{grad} V - \frac{\partial \mathbf{A}}{\partial t} + \mathbf{v} \times \operatorname{curl} \mathbf{A}\right). \quad (3\text{-}4)$$

3-2 THE ELECTROMAGNETIC FIELD OF CIRCULAR ACCELERATORS

We call those accelerators in which the particle orbits are approximately circular *circular accelerators* (for example, betatron, cyclotron, synchrotron). In most cases, for obvious practical reasons, the electromagnetic field in these machines has a vertical axis of symmetry and a horizontal plane of symmetry, which will be called the "median plane." In defining these elements of symmetry we do not take into account the high-frequency field existing between the "dees" of the cyclotron or in the accelerating cavities of the synchrotron. This is permissible because these fields act only on very short parts of the trajectory of the particles, whereas the formulas of the present chapter can be applied to the remainder of the trajectory, and the high-frequency, localized fields can be taken into account as causing discontinuities in the motion of the particles.

In order to study the dynamics of a charged particle in an electromagnetic field having the symmetry described above, it is convenient to introduce a system of cylindrical coordinates r, θ, z, taking the axis of symmetry as the z axis (directed upward) and the median plane as the plane $z = 0$. The positive direction of the coordinate θ will be defined so as to be right-handed with respect to the positive direction of z.

In all circular accelerators the component B_θ of the magnetic induction is zero, and the remaining components, B_r and B_z, as a consequence of the symmetry with respect to the z axis, are functions of r and z only, and not of θ. Electrostatic fields due to the space charge of the accelerated particles and to charges on the external conductors will be neglected so that any electric fields present are produced only by electromagnetic induction.

As stated in Section 3-1, an electromagnetic field of this sort can be described by a vector potential only. Moreover, because of the symmetry of the field, it is possible to assume the following particular choice of potentials:

$$V = 0,$$

$$A_r = 0, \qquad A_\theta = A(r, z, t), \qquad A_z = 0. \tag{3-5}$$

Of course this choice is not the only possible one, but for our purpose it is the most useful. It is easily verified that it describes a field having just the desired symmetry characteristics. Indeed, putting the expressions 3-5 in formulas 3-1 and 3-2, we obtain the following components of the field:

$$E_r = E_z = 0, \qquad E_\theta = -\frac{\partial A}{\partial t}, \tag{3-6}$$

$$B_r = -\frac{\partial A}{\partial z}, \tag{3-7}$$

$$B_\theta = 0, \tag{3-8}$$

$$B_z = \frac{1}{r}\frac{\partial}{\partial r}(rA) = A' + \frac{A}{r}. \tag{3-9}$$

In the last formula, the prime denotes differentiation with respect to r. This convention will be used henceforth.

Thus, all the components of the electromagnetic field are expressed by means of the scalar function $A(r, z, t)$ only. An interesting physical interpretation of this function can be obtained as follows.

Let us calculate the flux of **B** linking any circle $r = $ const, $z = $ const: it will be a function $\Phi(r, z, t)$. Using Equation 3-9 we obtain

$$\Phi = \int_0^r B_z 2\pi r \, dr = 2\pi \int_0^r \frac{1}{r}\frac{\partial}{\partial r}(rA)r \, dr = 2\pi r A. \tag{3-10}$$

So $A(r, z, t)$ is simply related to the flux of the magnetic induction. Moreover, if we denote by $\bar{B}_z$ the average value of B_z in the circle considered, it will be $\Phi = \pi r^2 \bar{B}_z$. Then Equation 3-10 gives

$$A = \tfrac{1}{2}r\bar{B}_z, \tag{3-11}$$

which is another simple interpretation of $A(r, z, t)$.

3-3   THE DYNAMICS OF A CHARGED PARTICLE IN THE ELECTROMAGNETIC FIELD OF A CIRCULAR ACCELERATOR[1]

For a particle moving in an electromagnetic field of the sort described in the preceding section, the fundamental formula of relativistic dynamics, Equation 3-4, referred to the coordinates r, θ, z, gives the three scalar equations

$$(\dot{\mathbf{P}})_r = qv_\theta \left(A' + \frac{A}{r} \right),$$ (3-12)

$$(\dot{\mathbf{P}})_\theta = q \left[-\frac{\partial A}{\partial t} - v_z \frac{\partial A}{\partial z} - v_r \left(A' + \frac{A}{r} \right) \right],$$ (3-13)

$$(\dot{\mathbf{P}})_z = qv_\theta \frac{\partial A}{\partial z}.$$ (3-14)

Here we have denoted by v_r, v_θ, v_z, the components of the vector $\mathbf{v}$ along the directions of the three coordinate lines, and similarly by $(\dot{\mathbf{P}})_r$, $(\dot{\mathbf{P}})_\theta$, $(\dot{\mathbf{P}})_z$, the components of the vector $\dot{\mathbf{P}}$. It must be recalled that the latter components are not necessarily equal to the time derivatives of the components of $\mathbf{P}$, which will be indicated by $\dot{P}_r$, $\dot{P}_\theta$, $\dot{P}_z$.

In order to find the relations between these two sets of quantities, let us define, at any point of space, the unit vectors in the r, θ, z directions, which will be indicated by $\mathbf{r}$, $\boldsymbol{\theta}$, $\mathbf{z}$. The last one has obviously the same direction everywhere, so that it is independent of r, θ, z; the other two depend on θ, but not on r and z. It can easily be shown (see, for example, Brand, 1947, p. 90) that the relations

$$\frac{\partial \mathbf{r}}{\partial \theta} = \boldsymbol{\theta}, \qquad \frac{\partial \boldsymbol{\theta}}{\partial \theta} = -\mathbf{r},$$ (3-15)

[1] We have deliberately avoided any recourse to analytical relativistic mechanics in favor of more elementary methods. The reader familiar with that theory can get the same results in a much simpler and more elegant way. He should first find out the relativistic Hamiltonian function for a particle in cylindrical coordinates for a field of the sort described in the preceding section, which is

$$H = c \left[p_r{}^2 + \left(\frac{p_\theta}{r} - qA \right)^2 + p_z{}^2 + (mc)^2 \right]^{1/2}$$

where p_r, p_θ, p_z are the canonical momenta conjugated to the coordinates r, θ, z. Then the first set of Hamilton equations gives (if we take into account that $H = m_v c^2$)

$$p_r = m_v \dot{r}, \qquad p_\theta = r \left(m_v v_\theta + qA \right), \qquad p_z = m_v \dot{z},$$

that is, in the notation of this section,

$$p_r = P_r, \qquad p_\theta = p, \qquad p_z = P_z.$$

Finally, the second set of Hamilton equations gives Equations 3-26, 3-32, and 3-28.

hold, while all other derivatives are zero. Now the components of the momentum **P** can be written

$$P_r = \mathbf{P} \cdot \mathbf{r}, \qquad P_\theta = \mathbf{P} \cdot \boldsymbol{\theta}, \qquad P_z = \mathbf{P} \cdot \mathbf{z} \qquad (3\text{-}16)$$

Differentiating them with respect to t and taking into account Equation 3-15 we get the desired relations:

$$\dot{P}_r = \dot{\mathbf{P}} \cdot \mathbf{r} + \mathbf{P} \cdot \dot{\mathbf{r}} = \dot{\mathbf{P}} \cdot \mathbf{r} + \mathbf{P} \cdot \boldsymbol{\theta}\dot{\theta} = (\dot{\mathbf{P}})_r + P_\theta\dot{\theta}, \qquad (3\text{-}17)$$

$$\dot{P}_\theta = \dot{\mathbf{P}} \cdot \boldsymbol{\theta} + \mathbf{P} \cdot \dot{\boldsymbol{\theta}} = \dot{\mathbf{P}} \cdot \boldsymbol{\theta} - \mathbf{P} \cdot \mathbf{r}\dot{\theta} = (\dot{\mathbf{P}})_\theta - P_r\dot{\theta}, \qquad (3\text{-}18)$$

$$\dot{P}_z = (\dot{\mathbf{P}})_z . \qquad (3\text{-}19)$$

Now we can combine these relations with Equations 3-12, 3-13, and 3-14 and obtain

$$\dot{P}_r = qv_\theta \left(A' + \frac{A}{r} \right) + P_\theta\dot{\theta}, \qquad (3\text{-}20)$$

$$\dot{P}_\theta = q \left[-\frac{\partial A}{\partial t} - v_z \frac{\partial A}{\partial z} - v_r \left(A' + \frac{A}{r} \right) \right] - P_r\dot{\theta}, \qquad (3\text{-}21)$$

$$\dot{P}_z = qv_\theta \frac{\partial A}{\partial z} . \qquad (3\text{-}22)$$

These equations can be simplified by noting that

$$v_r = \dot{r}, \qquad v_\theta = r\dot{\theta}, \qquad v_z = \dot{z} \qquad (3\text{-}23)$$

and therefore

$$\frac{\partial A}{\partial t} + v_z \frac{\partial A}{\partial z} + v_r A' = \frac{dA}{dt} . \qquad (3\text{-}24)$$

At this point it is convenient to define a vector

$$\mathbf{P}^* = \mathbf{P} + q\mathbf{A} \qquad (3\text{-}25)$$

(which is, in a way, a generalized momentum),[2] so that, using Equations 3-23 and 3-24, we can write Equations 3-20, 3-21, and 3-22 in the simple form

$$\dot{P}_r = qr\dot{\theta}A' + P_\theta{}^*\dot{\theta}, \qquad (3\text{-}26)$$

$$\dot{P}_\theta{}^* = -q\dot{r} \frac{A}{r} - P_r\dot{\theta}, \qquad (3\text{-}27)$$

$$\dot{P}_z = qr\dot{\theta} \frac{\partial A}{\partial z} . \qquad (3\text{-}28)$$

---

[2] This vector is sometimes called "canonical momentum," because its *Cartesian* components are the canonical momenta conjugated to the *Cartesian* coordinates. But the same interpretation does not hold for the components in a cylindrical system of coordinates.

These can be taken as the fundamental equations of the dynamics of our particle. Of course, $P_r{}^*$ and $P_z{}^*$ could be written in the place of P_r and P_z.

The generalized momentum $\mathbf{P}^*$ has a very important property: its moment p with respect to the z axis is a constant of the motion.[3] Indeed, this moment is defined by the formula

$$p = rP_\theta{}^*, \tag{3-29}$$

which, by differentiation with respect to t and use of Equations 3-25 and 3-27, gives

$$\dot{p} = \dot{r}P_\theta - rP_r\dot{\theta}. \tag{3-30}$$

Now, by definition

$$P_r = m_v\dot{r}, \qquad P_\theta = m_v r\dot{\theta}. \tag{3-31}$$

So Equation 3-30 becomes $\dot{p} = 0$, that is,

$$p = \text{const.} \tag{3-32}$$

This is a generalization of the ordinary theorem of the conservation of angular momentum. Note that in this type of field the ordinary moment of momentum (or angular momentum) rP_θ, in general, is not conserved, because the force may have a nonvanishing moment with respect to the z axis.

The fundamental equations 3-26, 3-27, and 3-28 can be transformed in a useful way if we define a function $\mathscr{F}(r, z, t, p)$ by means of the following equation:

$$\mathscr{F}(r, z, t, p) = \frac{p}{r} - qA. \tag{3-33}$$

The derivatives of this function with respect to r (which we shall denote by $\mathscr{F}'$, as we have done for the function A) and to z are given by

$$\mathscr{F}' = -\frac{p}{r^2} - qA', \qquad \frac{\partial \mathscr{F}}{\partial z} = -q\frac{\partial A}{\partial z}.$$

When these formulas are used, Equations 3-29 and 3-25 immediately give

$$P_\theta = \mathscr{F} \tag{3-34}$$

and Equations 3-26 and 3-28 can be written

$$\dot{P}_r = -\frac{1}{m_v}\mathscr{F}\mathscr{F}', \tag{3-35}$$

$$\dot{P}_z = -\frac{1}{m_v}\mathscr{F}\frac{\partial \mathscr{F}}{\partial z}. \tag{3-36}$$

---

[3] This quantity is often denoted by p_θ, being the canonical momentum conjugated to the coordinate θ. We drop the subscript, since no confusion can arise. (Remember that we call P, not p, the kinetic momentum.)

The formulas of this section, of course, are valid only if no other force besides those deriving from the potential **A** acts on the particle. The possible effect of other forces is considered in Section 5-3.

3-4 ENERGY LOSS BY RADIATION

It is a known consequence of Maxwell's equations that a charged particle whose motion is not rectilinear and uniform radiates energy in the form of electromagnetic waves. This occurs also for particles in accelerators and especially for electrons in circular accelerators. Hence a part of the energy supplied by the machine to the particles is not used to increase their kinetic energy but is lost in radiation. This phenomenon, in the large electron accelerators, is of considerable practical importance.

The general expression for the power radiated by a particle of charge q and velocity $\mathbf{v}(t)$ in mks units is[4]

$$W = \frac{q^2}{6\pi\epsilon_0 c^3} \frac{\dot{\mathbf{v}}^2 - (\mathbf{v} \times \dot{\mathbf{v}})^2/c^2}{(1 - \beta^2)^3}. \tag{3-37}$$

Let us apply this formula to the uniform circular motion which exists approximately in the circular accelerators. In this case, $\mathbf{v}$ and $\dot{\mathbf{v}}$ are orthogonal and, if R is the radius of the orbit, we have

$$|\dot{\mathbf{v}}| = \frac{v^2}{R} = \frac{\beta^2 c^2}{R}, \qquad |\mathbf{v} \times \dot{\mathbf{v}}| = \frac{v^3}{R} = \frac{\beta^3 c^3}{R}. \tag{3-38}$$

Therefore, Equation 3-37 becomes

$$W = \frac{q^2}{6\pi\epsilon_0} \frac{\beta^4 c}{R^2} \frac{1}{(1 - \beta^2)^2}. \tag{3-39}$$

From Equation 1-7 it follows that

$$\frac{1}{1 - \beta^2} = \left(\frac{E}{E_0}\right)^2, \tag{3-40}$$

and hence,

$$W = \frac{q^2}{6\pi\epsilon_0} \frac{\beta^4 c}{R^2} \left(\frac{E}{E_0}\right)^4. \tag{3-41}$$

Now, we want to calculate the energy L_r radiated by the particle during one complete revolution. Since the calculation will be applied only to highly

[4] For the derivation of this formula, see, for example, Panofsky and Phillips (1962, p. 370).

relativistic particles, we may put $\beta^4 = 1$ in Equation 3-41 and assume $2\pi R/c$ as the duration of the revolution. In this approximation we get

$$L_r = W \frac{2\pi R}{c} = \frac{q^2}{3\epsilon_0} \frac{1}{R} \left(\frac{E}{E_0}\right)^4. \tag{3-42}$$

Hence it can be seen that the energy loss per turn is inversely proportional to the radius of the orbit, and very rapidly increasing with the ratio E/E_0.

For particles having a charge q equal in absolute value to the elementary charge e, Equation 3-42 becomes (with L_r expressed in electron volts and R in meters)

$$L_r = \frac{6.05 \cdot 10^{-9}}{R} \left(\frac{E}{E_0}\right)^4, \tag{3-43}$$

and for electrons (L_r in electron volts, E in million electron volts, and R in meters)

$$L_r = 8.85 \cdot 10^{-8} \frac{E^4}{R}. \tag{3-44}$$

It must be pointed out that the total power radiated by the particles accelerated in a machine can be obtained by multiplying the power radiated per particle by the number of particles, only as long as the average distance between them is large compared with the dominant wavelength of the radiation emitted. In the opposite case one must take into account the interference of the radiation emitted by neighboring particles, which in general increases the power radiated: it is evident, indeed, that in the extreme case where n particles form a bunch whose dimensions are small compared with the dominant wavelength of the radiation, they would behave like a single particle of charge nq, and hence the power radiated would be proportional to n^2 instead of n ("coherence effect"). Some accelerators, whose beams are very strong, correspond to an intermediate case, more difficult to calculate. The other machines, whose beams are weaker, do not give rise to any appreciable coherence effect.

The classical electromagnetic theory allows one to calculate (see, for example, Schwinger, 1949; Tomboulian and Hartman, 1956) the distribution in direction and in wavelength of the electromagnetic radiation emitted by a particle in uniform circular motion (sometimes called "synchrotron radiation"). We summarize here the main results.

The distribution in direction is such that most of the energy is emitted in a cone centered on the instantaneous velocity of the particle and having a half-angle $\alpha = E_0/E$. Therefore, in the case of highly relativistic particles, the radiation is practically all concentrated in a very narrow cone in the forward direction (for example, for electrons of energy $E = 1000$ MeV, $\alpha = 1'\ 45''$).

The wavelength distribution is that of a continuous spectrum with a maximum at the wavelength given, in angstroms, by the formula (R in meters)

$$\lambda_m = 1.76 \cdot 10^{10} R \left(\frac{E_0}{E}\right)^3.$$ (3-45)

The density of the spectrum falls off very rapidly on the short-wavelength side and much less rapidly on the opposite side.

The synchrotron radiation was observed for the first time (Elder *et al.*, 1948) in an electron synchrotron of 1 m radius and 80 MeV maximum energy. Under these conditions formula 3-45 gives $\lambda_m = 4600$ Å, which is a wavelength in the blue range of the visible spectrum. Looking through a mirror and a transparent window into the vacuum chamber, in a direction tangential to the beam and opposite to the direction of the rotation, the section of the beam appeared as a bright bluish-white spot. Of course this light was a mixture of the radiation from electrons of all energies up to 80 MeV: the light begins to be visible at 30 MeV. This was the first time that light was produced by artificial acceleration of electric particles.

The synchrotron radiation of electrons has been subsequently observed and analyzed in different machines and in a wide spectral range. The theoretical predictions concerning the spectral and the angular distribution, as well as the total power radiated, have been verified. Moreover, this phenomenon has found an important application in the study of absorption spectra, especially in the far ultraviolet, where it is difficult to find another intense, calibrated radiation source of continuous spectrum.

Since the radiation emitted by an accelerated particle carries momentum besides energy, it exerts on the emitting particle a force, called "radiative reaction," which for rectilinear motion and for uniform circular motion is opposite to the velocity. This force has important practical consequences in the operation of betatrons and electron synchrotrons of very high energy (see, for example, the end of Section 5-6).

CHAPTER 4

THE BETATRON

4-1 INTRODUCTION

The principle of operation of the betatron has already been illustrated in Section 1-4. This machine has been described schematically as a magnet of the proper shape, excited by a coil fed by alternating current. In the practical construction of a betatron, as will be explained in detail further on, there are usually two or more coils, and some of them, called "bias coils," are fed with direct current. In all cases the magnetic field $B_z(t)$ produced at the central orbit of the vacuum chamber and the average field $\bar{B}_z(t)$ produced in the interior area of the central orbit satisfy the betatron condition (Equation 1-27):

$$B_z(t) - \tfrac{1}{2}\bar{B}_z(t) = \text{const.} \tag{4-1}$$

As this condition is satisfied at each instant of time, an electron injected tangentially to the central orbit of the vacuum chamber with the proper velocity would continue to follow this orbit with increasing momentum. However, in practice it is not possible to inject electrons in this way because the injector would intercept the orbit and hence the electrons could not make more than one turn. Therefore the electrons are injected from a position slightly displaced from the central orbit. Furthermore it is unavoidable that most of the electrons do not have exactly the required initial velocity: indeed they constitute a slightly divergent beam which has a small spread in energy. Thus in general they do not follow exactly circular orbits. We must therefore study the orbits of electrons in a betatron in general, using the formulas of Chapter 3. Many of the conclusions we shall reach are also valid for the synchrotron.

For reasons that will be understood further on (Section 4-4), in the region occupied by the vacuum chamber (or "doughnut") the magnetic field is not uniform but slightly decreasing in the radial direction. It is convenient to introduce a number n, called the *field index*, defined by the following formula (where the prime denotes differentiation with respect to r):

$$n = -r \left(\frac{B_z'}{B_z} \right)_{z=0} \tag{4-2}$$

It may be of course a function of r, but it is usually nearly constant in the vicinity of the central orbit (if it is exactly a constant, B_z is proportional to r^{-n}).

During the acceleration of the particles, the magnetic field increases in time by the same factor at all points (except possibly for small perturbations, which we neglect, due to eddy currents and to the fact that the iron of the magnet approaches saturation at certain points). This condition is fulfilled if we assume the vector potential A to be of the form (on the median plane, $z = 0$)

$$A(r, t) = f(r)h(t) + C/r, \tag{4-3}$$

where h is an increasing function of time and C a constant (which may be zero). Hence (see Equation 3-9) the field on the median plane $z = 0$ will be given by

$$B_z(r, t) = \left(f' + \frac{f}{r} \right) h(t) \tag{4-4}$$

and the field index will be independent of t. The case of a uniform field index is obtained if $f(r)$ is of the form $f = ar^{1-n} + br^{-1}$, with a and b constants. These conditions are approximately satisfied in the vicinity of the central orbit, but we need not restrict our calculations to this case.

The last term in Equation 4-3, which does not contribute to the field in the vacuum chamber, represents a constant flux $2\pi C$ ("bias flux") passing through the core of the machine and linked with any orbit in the vacuum chamber (see Equation 3-10).

4-2 EQUILIBRIUM ORBIT

First, let us find the condition for which the orbit is perfectly circular and, precisely,

$$z = \text{const}, \qquad r = \text{const.} \tag{4-5}$$

For this we must have

$$P_z = P_r = \dot{P}_z = \dot{P}_r = 0, \tag{4-6}$$

and so, from Equations 3-36 and 3-35,

$$\mathscr{F}\,\frac{\partial \mathscr{F}}{\partial z} = 0, \tag{4-7}$$

$$\mathscr{F}\mathscr{F}' = 0. \tag{4-8}$$

As we must exclude $\mathscr{F} = 0$ (otherwise Equation 3-34 would give $P_\theta = 0$), we obtain the following two results.

1. $\partial \mathscr{F}/\partial z = 0$, that is,

$$\frac{\partial A}{\partial z} = 0, \tag{4-9}$$

and this, with Equation 3-7, gives $B_r = 0$ (as could be anticipated, considering that the Lorentz force must have no z component). This condition is satisfied in the plane of symmetry (or median plane) $z = 0$; indeed, as A by symmetry is an even function of z, its derivative $-B_r$ is an odd function of z and consequently is zero for $z = 0$. In practical cases there are no other points where $B_r = 0$; hence a circular orbit must lie in the median plane.

2. $\mathscr{F}' = 0$. We can write this condition, using the definition 3-33 of $\mathscr{F}$, as

$$r^2 A'(r, 0, t) = -\frac{p}{q}. \tag{4-10}$$

The meaning of this equation is also very simple: By substituting for p the expression 3-29 and using Equation 3-9 we arrive at

$$P_\theta = -qrB_z(r, 0, t). \tag{4-11}$$

This is nothing but the relation 1-17 between momentum, magnetic field, and radius of curvature (the minus sign depends on the convention used for the positive directions of θ and z, related by the right-hand rule). We find therefore (as was to be expected) that the momentum $P = P_\theta$ must be such that the field B_z gives rise to a radius of curvature equal to the distance r of the particle from the axis.

But to enable this condition to persist during the motion, the value of r must be chosen in a particular way. Indeed, putting into Equation 4-10 the expression for A' obtained by differentiating Equation 4-3, and denoting by r_0 the radius of this particular orbit (called the *equilibrium orbit*) we obtain

$$r_0^2 f'(r_0)h(t) - C = -\frac{p}{q}. \tag{4-12}$$

Since $h(t)$ varies in time, while the second and third term are constant, this relation cannot be satisfied at all times unless

$$f'(r_0) = 0 \tag{4-13}$$

and

$$p = qC. \tag{4-14}$$

Equation 4-13 determines the value of r_0: it has usually only one root in the region of interest, and the machine is so built that this root coincides approximately with the radius of the central orbit of the vacuum chamber. Combining this equation with Equations 4-4 and 3-11, we find Equation 4-1 with the value $-C/r_0^2$ for the constant. So the betatron condition is proved again.

Equation 4-14 determines the value that the constant p must have in order for the particle to follow the equilibrium orbit (this value is zero if there is no flux bias). This equation is equivalent to Equation 4-11 written with $r = r_0$. Thus, in order that a particle describe a truly circular path, it should be injected at a point of the equilibrium orbit, in a tangential direction, and with a momentum $P = P_\theta$ such that Equation 4-11 is initially satisfied. In practice these conditions are never fulfilled at the injection.

It is of interest, of course, to determine experimentally the location of the equilibrium orbit in a given magnet. This can be achieved in the following way. The tangential electric field produced by induction at any point is given, according to Equation 3-6, by

$$E_\theta = -\frac{\partial A}{\partial t} = -f(r)\frac{\partial h}{\partial t}. \qquad (4\text{-}15)$$

If we consider E_θ as a function of r, we see, by Equation 4-13, that its first derivative vanishes for $r = r_0$: It will be shown later (end of Section 4-4) that $f''(r_0)/f(r_0) > 0$ so that the modulus of E_θ has a *minimum* at $r = r_0$. To find experimentally the position of this minimum we place in the median plane of the magnet a set of thin circular coils, concentric with the axis of the machine, of different radii but with the same total length of wire (so that smaller coils have a larger number of turns). In each coil, the varying flux will induce an electromotive force $\int E_\theta\, dl = E_\theta l$. We measure the emf in each coil, and the coil for which it is minimum will be the nearest to the equilibrium orbit.

4-3   SPIRAL MOTION. THE INSTANTANEOUS CIRCLE

We now study the motion under a less restrictive condition than in the preceding section. We consider a motion still in the median plane (hence with $P_z = 0$), but with $P_r = $ const, not zero as in the preceding section. Of course, instead of $r = $ const (circular motion) we now have $r = r_i(t)$, where r_i is a function for which we want to find a differential equation.

Since $\dot P_r = 0$, Equation 4-10 is still valid, and will be written

$$r_i^2(t)A'(r_i(t), 0, t) = -p/q. \qquad (4\text{-}16)$$

By taking the *total* derivative with respect to time, we obtain (marking, as we shall always do, by a suffix i the functions in which r has been replaced by $r_i(t)$)

$$2r_i\dot{r}_iA_i' + r_i^2A_i''\dot{r}_i + r_i^2\frac{\partial A_i'}{\partial t} = 0,$$

whence

$$\dot{r}_i = \frac{-\partial A_i'/\partial t}{A_i'' + (2/r_i)A_i'}. \tag{4-17}$$

This is the required differential equation. It becomes particularly expressive in the case in which A has the form of Equation 4-3 and the trajectory is very near to the equilibrium orbit. Indeed, if we substitute Equation 4-3 into Equation 4-17, the terms containing C cancel out and we have

$$\dot{r}_i = \frac{-f_i'}{f_i'' + (2/r_i)f_i'}\frac{\dot{h}}{h}. \tag{4-18}$$

Now, let us put $r_i = r_0 + \rho$, with $\rho \ll r_0$, and expand numerator and denominator of Equation 4-18 as series of powers of ρ. Remembering that $f'(r_0) = 0$, and denoting by $O(\rho^k)$ terms of order ρ^k or higher, we obtain

$$f_i' = f_0''\rho + O(\rho^2), \tag{4-19}$$

$$f_i'' + \frac{2}{r_i}f_i' = f_0'' + O(\rho). \tag{4-20}$$

Substituting into Equation 4-18, and neglecting $O(\rho^2)$, we find

$$\frac{\dot{\rho}}{\rho} = -\frac{\dot{h}}{h}, \tag{4-21}$$

or, remembering Equation 4-4,

$$\frac{\dot{\rho}}{\rho} = -\frac{\dot{B}_z}{B_z}, \tag{4-22}$$

whence, by integration,

$$\rho B_z = \text{const.} \tag{4-23}$$

From this equation we can infer, since $|B_z|$ increases steadily during the acceleration, that $|\rho|$ will decrease steadily, and therefore r_i will vary monotonously approaching to r_0. The trajectory will be a spiral, and the motion will be inward if the particle starts with $r > r_0$, outward if it starts with $r < r_0$.

It can easily be seen that in all practical cases the spiral is very tight. Indeed, if we call $\Delta\rho$ the pitch of the spiral and ΔB_z the variation of B_z during one turn, Equation 4-22 gives, approximately,

$$\left|\frac{\Delta\rho}{\rho}\right| = \left|\frac{\Delta B_z}{B_z}\right|. \qquad (4\text{-}24)$$

Now, in all betatrons the particles perform very many thousands of turns during one cycle of B_z, so that the relative variation of B_z during one turn is a very small number, and therefore $\Delta\rho \ll \rho \ll r_0$. This would fail, of course, at $B_z \simeq 0$, but in modern betatrons the particles are injected when B_z already has an appreciable value; thus even at the injection $\Delta\rho/\rho$ is very small.

This allows us to consider the spiral motion approximately (as far as a few turns are concerned) as a circular motion of radius r_i, slowly varying in time. Each turn of the spiral is called, in this approximation, the "*instantaneous circle*" of the particle. The radius r_i of the instantaneous circle at time t, for a particle of given P_θ, can be determined by solving Equation 4-11, which in this case can be written

$$P_\theta = -qr_iB_z(r_i, 0, t). \qquad (4\text{-}25)$$

In order for a particle, injected in the median plane at any distance r_i from the axis, to perform the spiral motion just described, it must be injected with a tangential momentum P_θ given by Equation 4-25, and a (small) radial momentum $P_r = m_v\dot{r}_i$, with $\dot{r}_i$ given by Equation 4-18. So, for any given instant and position of injection, there will be a unique value of the initial momentum and a unique direction of injection (almost tangential) leading to a spiral motion.

It must be noted that for the spiral motion the betatron condition 4-1 is not exactly fulfilled (although it is, of course, in the circular motion on the equilibrium orbit). Indeed, the field at the particle is $B_i = A_i' + A_i/r_i$, and the average field inside the instantaneous circle is (by Equation 3-11) $\bar{B}_z(r_i) = 2A_i/r_i$; therefore, using Equation 4-16, we obtain

$$B_i - \tfrac{1}{2}\bar{B}_z(r_i) = A_i' = -\frac{p}{qr_i^2}. \qquad (4\text{-}26)$$

So, the difference is not a constant, except for $r_i = r_0$ (see the preceding section).

4-4   GENERAL MOTION AND CONDITIONS FOR STABILITY

Let us finally consider the motion of a particle injected in conditions slightly different from those required for the spiral motion, and not necessarily in the median plane: such will be, in general, the conditions for most of the injected particles.

We shall associate with the particle, at each time t, an "instantaneous circle" in the median plane, defined as the instantaneous circle which would belong to a fictitious reference particle performing, at the time t, a spiral motion with the same P_θ as the real particle. Its radius r_i is therefore defined by Equation 4-25. We put

$$r - r_i = x \tag{4-27}$$

where r is the radial coordinate of the real particle, and assume x, as well as the z coordinate of the particle, to be a small quantity, whose square will be neglected in comparison with r^2. Our aim is to find equations for $x(t)$ and $z(t)$.

To this effect, we must apply the dynamical equations 3-35 and 3-36, and therefore we need expressions for $\mathscr{F}$ and its first derivatives. We shall obtain them by adding small perturbation terms to the corresponding quantities for the reference motion, which will be marked with a suffix i.

First, we note that P_θ is the same in both motions, so Equation 3-34 will give

$$\mathscr{F} = \mathscr{F}_i = P_\theta = m_v r \omega, \tag{4-28}$$

where ω is the angular velocity of the reference motion (which is very close to $\dot\theta$) and the difference in mass is neglected.

For the derivatives of $\mathscr{F}$ we can use in our approximation the following Taylor expansions, limited to first-order terms:

$$\mathscr{F}' = \mathscr{F}_i' + \mathscr{F}_i''x + \frac{\partial \mathscr{F}_i'}{\partial z} z, \tag{4-29}$$

$$\frac{\partial \mathscr{F}}{\partial z} = \frac{\partial \mathscr{F}_i}{\partial z} + \frac{\partial \mathscr{F}_i'}{\partial z} x + \frac{\partial^2 \mathscr{F}_i}{\partial z^2} z. \tag{4-30}$$

Now, $\mathscr{F}_i' = 0$ because of Equation 4-10. Moreover, since $\mathscr{F}$ and $\mathscr{F}'$ are even functions of z, their first derivatives vanish for $z = 0$. Thus, the preceding formulas reduce to

$$\mathscr{F}' = \mathscr{F}_i''x, \tag{4-31}$$

$$\frac{\partial \mathscr{F}}{\partial z} = \frac{\partial^2 \mathscr{F}_i}{\partial z^2} z. \tag{4-32}$$

In order to calculate the second derivatives entering these equations, it is convenient to start from formula 3-33 multiplied by r, and to differentiate it by using Equations 3-7 and 3-9. So we obtain

$$(r\mathscr{F})'' = -q(rB_z)', \tag{4-33}$$

$$\frac{\partial^2 \mathscr{F}}{\partial z^2} = q \frac{\partial B_r}{\partial z}. \tag{4-34}$$

In these expressions we must put $r = r_i$. The first one, if we write B_i for $B_z(r_i, 0, t)$ and remember that $\mathscr{F}_i' = 0$, gives

$$r_i \mathscr{F}_i'' = -q(B_i + r_i B_i'). \tag{4-35}$$

If we introduce the field index n defined by Equation 4-2 the latter formula gives

$$\mathscr{F}_i'' = -q B_i \frac{1 - n_i}{r_i}. \tag{4-36}$$

The magnetic field can be eliminated by using Equations 4-25 and 4-28, which give

$$-q B_i = m_v \omega. \tag{4-37}$$

Hence

$$\mathscr{F}_i'' = m_v \frac{1 - n_i}{r_i} \omega. \tag{4-38}$$

Turning now to Equation 4-34 we note that, inside the vacuum chamber, the magnetic field is very nearly irrotational (because in that region there are no currents except the space charge current and the displacement current, both of which we neglect). Therefore

$$\frac{\partial B_r}{\partial z} = B_z' = -n \frac{B_z}{r}.$$

So from Equation 4-34, again using Equation 4-37, we obtain

$$\frac{\partial^2 \mathscr{F}_i}{\partial z^2} = m_v \frac{n_i}{r_i} \omega. \tag{4-39}$$

Thus we have calculated both coefficients of Equations 4-31 and 4-32, which become

$$\mathscr{F}' = m_v \frac{1 - n_i}{r_i} \omega x, \tag{4-40}$$

$$\frac{\partial \mathscr{F}}{\partial z} = m_v \frac{n_i}{r_i} \omega z. \tag{4-41}$$

Now substituting these expressions together with Equation 4-28 into the dynamical equations 3-35 and 3-36, we get

$$\dot{P}_r = -m_v(1 - n_i)\omega^2 x, \tag{4-42}$$

$$\dot{P}_z = -m_v n_i \omega^2 z. \tag{4-43}$$

Let us now discuss, briefly and qualitatively, the meaning of these equations. Taking, for instance, the first one, we can interpret its right-hand side as a force, directed along the radius and proportional to the horizontal displacement x of the particle from the instantaneous circle. If the coefficient of x is negative, that is, if $n_i < 1$, the force is a "restoring" (or "focusing") force, which "attracts" the projection of the particle on the median plane toward the instantaneous circle. In this case, obviously, this projection oscillates along the r direction about the instantaneous circle, but always remains in its vicinity: one says that there is "radial stability." In the opposite case ($n_i > 1$) the particle is repelled from the instantaneous circle and x increases exponentially: there is "radial instability."

We can discuss Equation 4-43 similarly, reaching the conclusion that if $n_i > 0$ the particle oscillates up and down around the median plane and there is "vertical stability"; if $n_i < 0$ the particle is repelled away from the median plane and there is "vertical instability."

Evidently, for the operation of the betatron as described in this chapter[1] both radial and vertical stability are required; hence the field must be such that, in a region as wide as possible around the central orbit,

$$0 < n < 1. \tag{4-44}$$

Usually, values of n between 0.6 and 0.75 are chosen; it is preferable to have a stronger restoring force in the vertical than in the horizontal direction (that is, $n > 1 - n$) because usually there is more room in the vacuum chamber for horizontal than for vertical oscillations.

We are now in a position to prove what we have anticipated in Section 4-2, namely that the equilibrium orbit corresponds to a *minimum* and not a maximum of $| E_\theta |$. In fact, the expression 4-2 for n, for a field of the form 4-4, becomes

$$n = \frac{f - rf' - r^2 f''}{f + rf'} , \tag{4-45}$$

and since $f'(r_0) = 0$, on the equilibrium orbit

$$n(r_0) = 1 - r_0^2 f_0'' / f_0 . \tag{4-46}$$

Since horizontal stability requires $1 - n > 0$, this gives $f_0'' / f_0 > 0$, which is the condition for r_0 to be a minimum point of $| f |$ and hence of $| E_\theta |$.

4-5 BETATRON OSCILLATIONS AND THEIR DAMPING

In this section we study in more detail the transverse (radial and vertical) oscillations introduced in the preceding section, assuming the condition 4-44. They are called *"betatron oscillations"* because they were first studied in this machine (Kerst and Serber, 1941); however, the same theory also applies to the synchrotron.

[1] In the case of other machines (alternating-gradient accelerators) values of n outside the interval 4-44, but not constant along the orbit, are used (see Chapter 6).

If we put

$$(1 - n_i)^{1/2}\omega = \omega_r, \qquad (n_i)^{1/2}\omega = \omega_z, \qquad (4\text{-}47)$$

and remember that

$$P_r = m_v \dot{r} = m_v(\dot{r}_i + \dot{x}), \qquad P_z = m_v \dot{z}, \qquad (4\text{-}48)$$

Equations 4-42 and 4-43 can be written

$$\ddot{x} + \frac{\dot{m}_v}{m_v}\dot{x} + \omega_r{}^2 x = -\ddot{r}_i - \frac{\dot{m}_v}{m_v}\dot{r}_i, \qquad (4\text{-}49)$$

$$\ddot{z} + \frac{\dot{m}_v}{m_v}\dot{z} + \omega_z{}^2 z = 0. \qquad (4\text{-}50)$$

In a first approximation we can neglect the terms in $\dot{m}_v$, $\dot{r}_i$, $\ddot{r}_i$, and consider ω_r, ω_z as constants. This is justified, when only a few oscillations are being considered, because the variations of v and r_i are very slow compared with those of x and z. Then the equations become

$$\ddot{x} + \omega_r{}^2 x = 0, \qquad (4\text{-}51)$$

$$\ddot{z} + \omega_z{}^2 z = 0 \qquad (4\text{-}52)$$

and their solutions are, as is well known,

$$x = a_r \sin(\omega_r t + \gamma_r), \qquad (4\text{-}53)$$

$$z = a_z \sin(\omega_z t + \gamma_z), \qquad (4\text{-}54)$$

where a_r, a_z, γ_r, γ_z are constants determined by the initial conditions. Using Equation 4-47 and writing θ for ωt, we can also write them as

$$x = a_r \sin[(1 - n_i)^{1/2}\theta + \gamma_r], \qquad (4\text{-}55)$$

$$z = a_z \sin[n_i{}^{1/2}\theta + \gamma_z]. \qquad (4\text{-}56)$$

It is seen that each radial oscillation takes an arc of instantaneous circle of $2\pi/(1 - n_i)^{1/2}$ radians, and each vertical oscillation, $2\pi/n_i{}^{1/2}$, so both take more than one turn. Figure 4-1 gives an idea of a radial oscillation (greatly exaggerated in amplitude), showing the projection of the trajectory on the median plane.

Now we turn to a better approximation, taking into account the terms in $\dot{m}_v$ in Equations 4-49 and 4-50 and the slow variation in time of ω_r and ω_z associated with the change in B_z and in particle energy, but we will still neglect the right-hand side of Equation 4-49. In this case both equations 4-49 and 4-50 have the same form.

A well-known procedure[2] for solving such linear equations with slowly

---

[2] The same procedure, applied to the Schrödinger equation in wave mechanics, is known as the Wentzel-Kramers-Brillouin (or WKB) method.

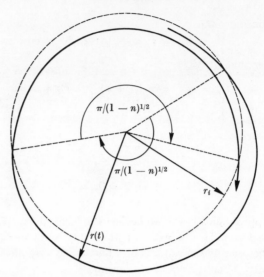

FIGURE 4-1. *Schematic diagram of the projection of the trajectory on the median plane during one complete horizontal betatron oscillation. The amplitude of the oscillation shown is greatly exaggerated.*

varying coefficients is to write the solution (for example for z) in the form

$$z = a_z(t) \sin \Phi_z(t), \tag{4-57}$$

assuming that the amplitude a_z and the angular frequency $\dot{\Phi}_z$ change very slowly in time, so that, when this expression is substituted into Equation 4-50, $\dot{a}_z$, $\dot{m}_v$, and $\ddot{\Phi}_z$ will be considered as small quantities of the first order, $\ddot{a}_z$ and $\dot{a}_z \dot{m}_v$ as second-order quantities, and of course a_z and $\dot{\Phi}_z$ as zero-order quantities. By substituting Equation 4-57 into Equation 4-50 we obtain

$$(\omega_z{}^2 - \dot{\Phi}_z{}^2)a_z \sin \Phi_z + \left[a_z\ddot{\Phi}_z + 2\dot{a}_z\dot{\Phi}_z + \frac{\dot{m}_v}{m_v} a_z\dot{\Phi}_z \right] \cos \Phi_z$$

$$+ \left[\ddot{a}_z + \frac{\dot{m}_v}{m_v} \dot{a}_z \right] \sin \Phi_z = 0, \tag{4-58}$$

where the first term is of order zero, the second term first order, and the last term second order. Thus, up to first-order terms, we have

$$\omega_z{}^2 - \dot{\Phi}_z{}^2 = 0 \tag{4-59}$$

and

$$a_z\ddot{\Phi}_z + 2\dot{a}_z\dot{\Phi}_z + \frac{\dot{m}_v}{m_v} a_z\dot{\Phi}_z = 0. \tag{4-60}$$

Thus from Equation 4-59

$$\Phi_z(t) = \int_0^t \omega_z(t') \, dt' + \gamma_z \,, \tag{4-61}$$

where γ_z is a constant, and Equation 4-60 can be integrated to give

$$a_z{}^2 m_v \omega_z = \text{const.} \tag{4-62}$$

Using Equations 4-47 and 4-37 and calling C_z a constant, we can write (neglecting a possible variation of n with r)

$$a_z{}^2 B_i = C_z{}^2 \,. \tag{4-63}$$

Summing up, the approximate solution for vertical oscillations is

$$z = \frac{C_z}{B^{1/2}} \sin\!\left(\int_0^t \omega_z(t') \, dt' + \gamma_z \right), \tag{4-64}$$

where the two constants are determined by the initial conditions for z and $\dot{z}$. A similar expression, with different constants and ω_r in the place of ω_z, is obtained for x by the same procedure. Figure 4-2 shows schematically the behavior of the vertical and the radial oscillations, as well as the contraction of the instantaneous circle.

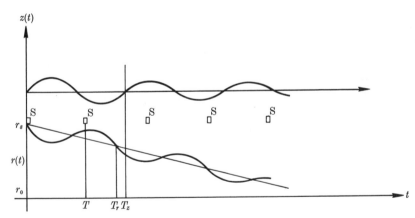

FIGURE 4-2. *Qualitative behavior of $z(t)$ and $r(t)$ immediately after injection. The amplitudes of the oscillations are greatly exaggerated. The rectangles* S *indicate the position of the source.*

Since B is increasing during the acceleration, the amplitudes of the radial and vertical betatron oscillations are both damped proportionally to $B^{-1/2}$. This is a very important fact, which is used in the injection (see Section 4-6) and which assures (together with the convergence of r_i toward r_0 proved in Section 4-3) that all particles will ultimately form a very narrow beam along the equilibrium orbit. A few particles may start to oscillate again after collision with a molecule of the residual gas, but at high energies the amplitude o these oscillations is very small.

For the radial oscillations, we should still consider the effect of the (very small) terms on the right-hand side of Equation 4-49, depending on $\dot{r}_i$ and $\ddot{r}_i$. These terms induce forced oscillations (superimposed on those just studied) owing to the fact that, if r_i changes too rapidly, the particle tends to lag behind the displacement of its instantaneous circle. However, in all practical cases these oscillations are of negligible amplitude, so we omit their calculation.

4-6   THE INJECTION AND UTILIZATION OF ELECTRONS

The source of the electrons in a betatron is a special electron gun called the "injector." It consists (see Figure 4-3) of a heated filament F surrounded by a focusing electrode G at a slightly negative potential with respect to the filament; F and G are contained in a grounded box S with a hole for the emission

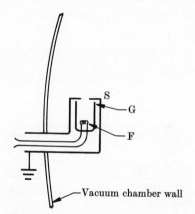

FIGURE 4-3.   *Schematic diagram of the electron gun.*

of the electrons. The filament is kept at a negative potential $-V$ with respect to S, so the electrons come out of the hole with a kinetic energy of V electron volts. In the earlier small betatrons V was very low (less than 1 kV); in the modern ones it goes from a few kilovolts to more than 100 kV, depending on the final energy to be attained. The outgoing electrons form a pulsed, rather divergent beam (5° to 10° aperture) whose intensity can attain several hundreds of milliamperes.

The injector protrudes inside the vacuum chamber, usually through its outer wall, sometimes through the inner wall: its tip arrives just at the border of the region where $0 < n < 1$, thus leaving as much room as possible for stable orbits between the injector and the central orbit. Some of the injected electrons, after one or a few turns, hit the back of the injector and are lost; others are lost by hitting the walls of the vacuum chamber. The fundamental problem of the injection is to reduce these losses as far as possible and so achieve a high "injection efficiency."

Each injected electron oscillates around its own instantaneous circle, which contracts (supposing the injection takes place from the outside of the equilibrium orbit), so that after the first turn it will find itself shifted inward by the algebraic sum of the instantaneous circle contraction and the displacement from the latter due to the first radial oscillation. If the phase and amplitude of this oscillation are favorable, the inward shift will be sufficient to prevent the particles from hitting the back of the injector; moreover, some of the particles can avoid the injector by passing above or below it by virtue of the vertical oscillations (and for this reason the vertical thickness of the injector must be kept as small as possible). Thus a fraction of the injected particles will perform a second turn, at the end of which some of them will again avoid the injector (and since by this time the instantaneous circle will be smaller, the conditions required for the phase of the radial oscillation will be less stringent). And so on for successive turns, until the instantaneous circle is contracted beyond the tip of the injector, and the oscillations are so damped that all of the surviving particles continue to accelerate up to the end, except for a small fraction scattered to the walls by collisions with the molecules of the residual gas.

Although this theory can explain qualitatively the survival of a fraction of the injected electrons, it is not sufficient to predict the injection efficiency quantitatively. This turns out to be much higher in practice then predicted by the theory. Moreover, it increases with the injection potential V (roughly as $V^{3/2}$) while the theory would predict the reverse. These discrepancies are due to several effects not taken into account by the theory, including the following:

1. the further contraction of the instantaneous circle due to the loss in kinetic energy of the injected particles, necessary to build up the electromagnetic field of the circulating beam (Kerst, 1948);

2. the reciprocal electromagnetic action between the particles in the beam (space-charge and space-current effects);

3. the electrostatic repulsion by the charges accumulated on the walls of the vacuum chamber.

A complete theory is still lacking. The best injection conditions are usually found largely by semiempirical methods. Different artifices can be used in order to increase the injection efficiency. All of these essentially consist in altering the betatron relation during injection in such a way as to enhance the inward spiraling of the particles. A simple method consists in carrying on the injection for a while after the correct time. The electrons injected late are eventually lost, but while they circulate they produce a variable magnetic field which delays the rise of the central flux and so increases the inward spiraling of the electrons. This mechanism can be obtained more effectively by means of circular coils (on each pole face above and below the position of the orbit) which carry a pulse of current during the injection time. This device is called an "orbit contractor."

Now, a few words on the use which is made of the electrons of a betatron at the end of their acceleration. In most machines, when the electrons have reached the required energy, the betatron relation is altered so that the particles spiral outward (or inward) and hit a metal target, put inside the vacuum chamber near its outer (or inner) wall. The collision of the high-energy electrons with the target produces high-energy x rays which pass through the chamber wall and are utilized outside.

In some other betatrons it is desired to extract the electron beam out of the vacuum chamber. This is obtained by means of a device called a "peeler." It consists essentially of an iron channel which screens out the magnetic field from the outer part of the vacuum chamber. At the end of the acceleration the particles are made to spiral outward as described above. When the beam passes through the peeler it is no longer deflected and it can be brought out of the machine through a window in the vacuum chamber wall, closed by a thin foil.

4-7 THE MAGNET OF THE BETATRON

In Section 1-4 we have given a schematic description of the betatron magnet (see Figure 1-1) but this is actually used only in the simplest betatrons. In these there is only one magnetic circuit, which produces both the guiding field in the vacuum chamber and the flux in the central region needed for particle acceleration. The magnetic circuit is excited by one or more coils fed by alternating current.

However, as we have briefly mentioned in Section 4-1, the betatron magnet is usually excited by two separate groups of coils, one carrying alternating current, the other (called "bias coils") carrying direct current. We shall now explain the reason for the latter.

In the absence of the bias, the ac coils produce the magnetic field both in the vacuum chamber and in the central region. These two fields therefore vary in the same phase and when[3] $\bar{B} = 0$, also $B = 0$; hence the constant in the betatron relation 4-1 is zero and this reduces to

$$B = \tfrac{1}{2}\bar{B}. \qquad (4\text{-}65)$$

[3] In this Section B and $\bar{B}$ are used to indicate B_z and $\bar{B}_z$.

Now, $\bar{B}$ can never exceed the value B_s corresponding to the saturation of the iron; hence B can never exceed half this value. However, it is convenient that B should also reach the saturation value B_s, because in this case, for a given final electron energy, the radius of the machine can be made smaller. In order to obtain this the constant in the betatron relation must be different from zero, and precisely such that when $\bar{B} = B_s$, also $B = B_s$: then Equation 4-1 becomes

$$B - \tfrac{1}{2}\bar{B} = \tfrac{1}{2}B_s . \tag{4-66}$$

This can be obtained by means of a bias, in two different ways.

In the first method ("flux bias") the dc coils act in the central region only, producing in this region a constant magnetic field $-B_s$ superimposed on the alternating field of amplitude $2B_s$ (see Figure 4-4a). In the vacuum chamber

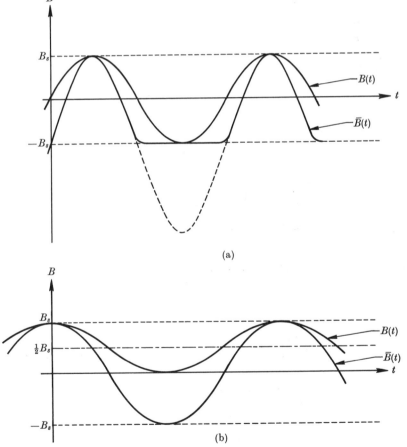

(a)

(b)

FIGURE 4-4.   *Combinations of guiding field and accelerating field for bias flux applied* (a) *only in the central region and* (b) *only in the region of the vacuum chamber.*

the field oscillates sinusoidally between B_s and $-B_s$. In the positive half-periods the betatron condition is satisfied but not in the negative ones because the central field $\bar{B}$ saturates, as is shown in Figure 4-4a. This, however, is of no harm because the electrons are accelerated only during the quarter-periods in which B is positive and increasing.

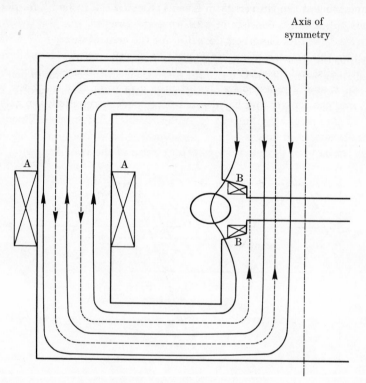

FIGURE 4-5. *Diagram illustrating a method for applying the bias field only to the region of the vacuum chamber. Full lines indicate flux produced by coils* A; *dotted lines, flux produced by coils* B.

In the second method ("field bias," see Figure 4-4b) a constant[4] magnetic field $\frac{1}{2}B_s$ is applied in the region occupied by the vacuum chamber, super-imposed on the alternating field of amplitude $\frac{1}{2}B_s$. So, in this region, B oscillates between 0 and B_s; there is no inversion of the field and the entire half-period in which B is increasing can be used for acceleration; the central region has no bias and $\bar{B}$ oscillates between $-B_s$ and B_s. In practice this type of bias is usually obtained (see Figure 4-5) by applying a dc excitation

---

[4] This field is also uniform, apart from a slight variation in the r direction, necessary to maintain the desired value for the field index.

to the whole magnetic circuit (coils A) and another dc excitation (coils B) acting only in the central region, where it compensates exactly the magnetic flux produced by coils A. Thus the net bias field, resulting from the combined action of coils A and B, is only applied in the region of the vacuum chamber.

In the largest betatrons, such as the 300-MeV betatron designed by Kerst and operating at the University of Illinois (Kerst *et al.*, 1950a,b), for practical reasons the magnet consists of two separate circuits, one for the guiding field in the vacuum chamber, the other for the central flux (see Figure 4-6). Naturally the ac excitation of the two magnetic circuits is produced by separate coils, and these are fed in parallel in order to ensure the synchronism between B and $\bar{B}$ required by the betatron condition. The magnetic circuit producing the central flux has no air gap, as this is superfluous in this case.

In all betatrons, the ac coils have a very high inductance. They would require a very high power supply if a capacitor bank were not connected in parallel so as to constitute an oscillating circuit of the same frequency as the

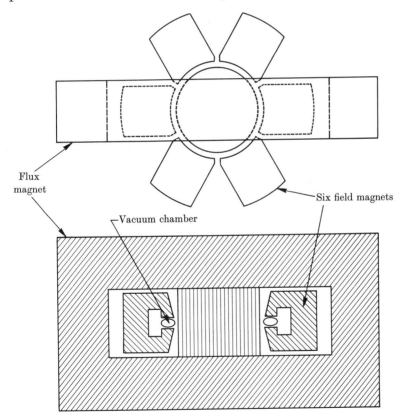

FIGURE 4-6.   *Schematic diagram of the construction of a betatron with two independent magnetic circuits, one for the accelerating flux and the other for the guiding field.*

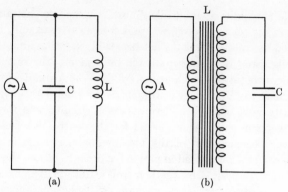

FIGURE 4-7. *Oscillating circuits for exciting the betatron magnet. A = ac generator, L = magnet coils, C = capacitor bank.*

generator. The connection with the latter can be either direct (Figure 4-7a) or inductive (Figure 4-7b). In the second case the coils of the magnet, in addition to the turns of the oscillating circuit, also contain a small number of turns connected to the generator. In order to reduce the capacitance required it is convenient to use higher frequencies, because for an oscillating circuit $LC = (2\pi\nu)^{-2}$.

The ac generator in resonance with the oscillating circuit must supply it with the energy it loses because of

1. ohmic resistance of the coils;
2. hysteresis of the iron;
3. eddy currents in the iron of the magnet and in other conductors;
4. dielectric hysteresis in the capacitors.

In comparison with these losses, the energy supplied to the electron beam is negligible. In the larger machines the energy losses (especially those due to hysteresis and to eddy currents) are so large that, in order to avoid over-

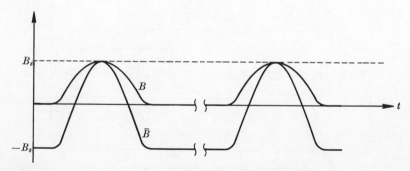

FIGURE 4-8. *Guiding field and accelerating field as functions of time for pulsed operation.*

heating of the magnet, it is preferable to substitute for the alternating current a sequence of pulses separated by a sufficiently long dead time (for instance 20 times the pulse length). The time dependence of B and $\bar{B}$ in this type of operation is shown in Figure 4-8, where a bias $-B_s$ is added to $\bar{B}$.

Finally it must be mentioned that in the largest betatrons, to compensate for the energy loss by radiation (see Section 3-4), a slight perturbation of the betatron relation may be required toward the end of the acceleration, so that the central flux will increase more rapidly than is required by Equation 4-1.

CHAPTER 5

THE SYNCHROTRON

5-1 INTRODUCTION

Some of the results we have obtained for the betatron can be applied to the synchrotron. In this machine too, the particles follow a circular orbit of constant radius R (except for small oscillations, which will be considered later) inside a vacuum chamber. The latter has the form of a doughnut and is placed in a magnetic field that changes in time. In the synchrotron, however, the magnetic field exists only in the region of the vacuum chamber, where it has essentially the same radial dependence as in the betatron. Thus a field index n can again be defined through Equation (4-2), which in the case $n = $ const gives:

$$B_z(r, t) = B_0(t) \left(\frac{r}{R} \right)^{-n}. \tag{5-1}$$

The synchrotron magnet, as has been mentioned in Section 1-8, usually has a C-shaped cross section (Figure 1-7). Besides the arrangement shown in Figure 1-7 and in Figure 5-1a, where the C faces the outside of the machine, it is also possible to have the C facing the inside (see Figure 5-1b). In some large proton synchrotrons the magnet has the shape of a double C (also called "picture-frame shape" or "H shape"), as shown in Figure 5-2. In this case the magnet is more expensive and access to the vacuum chamber is difficult, but it is possible to obtain stronger magnetic fields and then reduce the radius of the machine for a given final energy of the particles.

In all cases, a part of the magnetic flux links the orbit. It can be seen that if the vacuum chamber is at the center of the magnet poles the amount of flux linking the orbit is approximately equal and opposite in the two cases of

Figures 5-1a and 5-1b. During the operation of the machine, the magnetic field changes and so an induced electric field appears in the doughnut; this field decelerates the particles in case a, and accelerates them in case b. This is similar to the phenomenon that occurs in the betatron, but in this case $\bar{B} \ll B$, rather than $\bar{B} = 2B$ as in the betatron (because B is practically zero except in the region of the magnet). Hence the energy L_β (positive or negative in

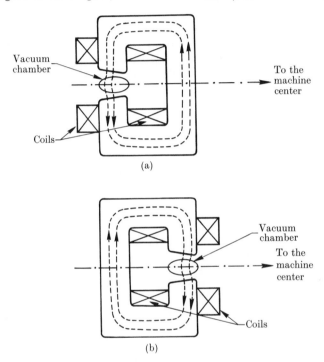

(a)

(b)

FIGURE 5-1. *Schematic diagram of the cross section of a C-shaped synchrotron magnet: (a) the C facing outward; (b) the C facing inward. The dotted lines indicate typical lines of force which link the particle orbit.*

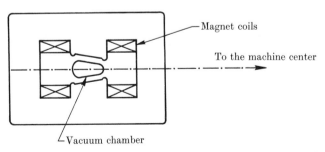

FIGURE 5-2. *Schematic diagram of the cross section of an H-shaped synchrotron magnet.*

cases a and b, respectively) given to a particle in one turn by this effect ("betatron effect") is usually small compared with the energy L_e gained by a particle in one turn by crossing the accelerating system (that is, one or sometimes more rf cavities). If we call L_r the energy lost by radiation per turn (see Section 3-4), the net gain of energy per turn, W, is given by

$$W = L_e + L_\beta - L_r. \tag{5-2}$$

At this point it must be noted that the considerations of Chapter 4 which led us to the discussion of betatron oscillations and of their dependence on the configuration of the magnetic field (essentially on the field index n) are valid also for the synchrotron. Again we have the condition for stability 4-44,

$$0 < n < 1, \tag{5-3}$$

and the expressions 4-47 for the angular frequencies ω_r and ω_z of the radial and vertical oscillations (with, of course, n_i replaced by n).

The voltage $V(t)$ in the cavity will be alternating at radio frequency with an amplitude U and an angular frequency ω_e which in general may be slowly varying functions of t. So we write

$$V(t) = U(t) \sin \int_0^t \omega_e(t') \, dt', \tag{5-4}$$

where we will consider U to be always positive and V positive if directed in such a way as to accelerate the particles. (This is equivalent to a convenient choice of the origin of t.) Thus if a particle crosses the cavity at the time t, the energy gained, L_e, in one turn is

$$L_e = |q| U \sin \int_0^t \omega_e(t') \, dt'. \tag{5-5}$$

It has already been mentioned in Section 1-8 that the angular frequency of the rf cavity must be equal to or a multiple of the angular velocity of the particles, that is,

$$\omega_e = k\omega \qquad (k = 1, 2, \ldots), \tag{5-6}$$

in order to preserve synchronism and have them accelerated by the same amount of energy at each transit. It is preferable to choose $k > 1$ and so have a greater ω_e; this reduces the dimensions of the rf cavity.[1] Since ω is proportional to the velocity of the particles it increases during the acceleration and so ω_e must also increase; only in those electron synchrotrons in which the electrons are injected with ultrarelativistic velocities may the radio frequency be kept constant. The relation between ω_e and $B_z(R, 0, t)$ is expressed by Equation 1-36 as

$$\omega_e = \frac{k |qB_z|}{m[1 + (cqB_zR/E_0)^2]^{1/2}}. \tag{5-7}$$

---

[1] See Table 1-3 for values of k used in some of the existing machines.

As has been mentioned in Section 1-8, the magnetic field is made to change according to a prescribed law and the frequency is modulated according to Equation 5-7. A wide range of modulation gives rise to difficult technical problems. These can be avoided by injecting the particles at high energy, or, in electron synchrotrons, by using "betatron injection" (see Section 5-9), or by turning on two rf cavities successively. The requirement for a wide range of modulation contrasts with that for a high power supply, necessary in the final stage of the acceleration of electrons in order to balance radiation losses. For this reason, in some high-energy electron synchrotrons there are two rf cavities which are switched on successively: the first cavity, of relatively small power, is frequency modulated and accelerates the electrons from the injection velocity up to a velocity very close to c; the second, more powerful, cavity has a fixed frequency $\omega_e = kc/(2\pi R)$ and brings the electrons to the final energy with a very small increase in velocity.

Concerning the energies for which synchrotrons can be used, it must be noted that the situation is quite different for electron synchrotrons from that for proton synchrotrons. For the former, radiation losses place a practical limit on the use of circular machines. This limit is at a few billion electron volts for synchrotrons of the structure described in this chapter; at higher energies it becomes preferable to use alternating-gradient synchrotrons (Chapter 6), or linear accelerators. On the other hand, in the region of low energies, the electron synchrotron competes favorably with the betatron, even at energies of 20 or 50 MeV, and small electron synchrotrons can be used for medical or industrial purposes as sources of x rays.

The proton synchrotron, instead, can be said to be essentially a high-energy machine. At low energies, indeed, the cyclotron and the synchrocyclotron are more convenient as they are less expensive and they give greater intensities. All the proton synchrotrons built to date have energies of at least 1 BeV. However, in this case also, the alternating-gradient version of the machine, described in the next chapter, is by far the most convenient for very high energies, and above a certain energy, the only one practically feasible. In the range of energies accessible to present technology, there is no limit to the value this type of machine can reach; indeed, the energy limit set by radiation losses is, for protons, extremely high (of the order of 10^4 BeV), and still very far from the energies reached at present. Table 1-3 gives the parameters of the principal synchrotrons existing in 1966.

5-2 THE PHASE OF A PARTICLE IN THE SYNCHROTRON

Let us call the angular distance of the particle measured from the position of the cavity $\theta(t)$. Without loss of generality, we can consider the particles as circulating in the positive θ direction, and so identify θ with the positive quantity ω. We define the phase φ of a particle at the time t by the following relation:

$$\varphi = \int_0^t \omega_e(t') \, dt' - k\theta. \tag{5-8}$$

In this way we have defined the phase at each point of the trajectory. However, we are mainly interested in its value at the instants of time when the particle crosses the resonant cavity ($\theta = 2\pi n, \ n = 0, 1, 2 \dots$). In this case we have[2]

$$\varphi = \int_0^t \omega_e(t') \, dt' - 2\pi k n. \tag{5-9}$$

By differentiating Equation 5-8 we obtain

$$\dot{\varphi} = \omega_e - k\omega. \tag{5-10}$$

For the synchronous particle[3] (s.p.; see Section 1-9), φ must be a constant (by definition), and then from Equation 5-10 we obtain that its angular velocity is

$$\omega_s = \omega_e/k, \tag{5-11}$$

that is, precisely the value which satisfies Equation 5-6. For the other particles, instead, having a different angular velocity, the phase will change a little from one transit in the cavity to the next. There is a simple relation between the phase of a particle and the energy L_e which the particle gains in crossing the cavity. If we eliminate the integral between Equations 5-5 and 5-9 we obtain

$$L_e = |q| \, U \sin(2kn\pi + \varphi) = |q| \, U \sin \varphi. \tag{5-12}$$

Let us now derive the expressions for some quantities which refer to the s.p.; they will be denoted by the subscript s. The relation 4-11 between the magnetic field B_z on the central orbit, the momentum, and the radius of curvature, together with Equations 4-28 and 1-7, becomes

$$\omega = - \frac{qB_z}{m_v} = - \frac{qc^2 B_z}{E}. \tag{5-13}$$

For the s.p., Equation 5-11 holds and Equation 5-13 becomes

$$E_s = - \frac{qc^2 B_z}{\omega_s} = - \frac{kqc^2 B_z}{\omega_e}. \tag{5-14}$$

[2] Note the similarity between Equation 5-9 and Equation 1-37 defined for the linear accelerator (where, however, ω_e is constant). In this case too n represents the number of times the particle has crossed an accelerating gap.

[3] At each instant of time there exist along the orbit k positions corresponding to as many synchronous particles whose phases differ by multiples of 2π. We shall refer, as a rule, to the one with $0 < \varphi_s < 2\pi$.

Furthermore from the definition $\omega = c\beta/r$, using Equation 1-11 for the s.p., we have

$$r_s = \frac{kc}{\omega_e}\left[1 - \left(\frac{E_0}{E_s}\right)^2\right]^{1/2}. \tag{5-15}$$

The machine is designed so that $r_s = R$, and then, by substituting Equation 5-14 into Equation 5-15, we again find the relation 5-7 between ω_e and B_z. For an arbitrary particle the energy gain per turn, W, can be written in the form $(dE/dt)T$ (where T is the period of rotation), because W is small with respect to the total energy E of the particle and so can be treated as a differential. Thus Equation 5-2, if we use Equation 5-12, becomes

$$W = \frac{dE}{dt}\,T = |\,q\,|\,U\sin\varphi + L_\beta - L_r \tag{5-16}$$

and this, for the s.p., gives (see Equation 5-14)

$$W_s = \frac{dE_s}{dt}\frac{2\pi}{\omega_s} = -\frac{2\pi k^2 qc^2}{\omega_e}\frac{d}{dt}\left(\frac{B_z}{\omega_e}\right) = |\,q\,|\,U\sin\varphi_s + L_{\beta s} - L_{rs}\,. \tag{5-17}$$

If we define a quantity $u(t)$ (of the dimensions of a potential) by putting

$$-\frac{2\pi k^2 qc^2}{\omega_e}\frac{d}{dt}\left(\frac{B_z}{\omega_e}\right) - L_{\beta s} + L_{rs} = |\,q\,|\,u, \tag{5-18}$$

we have

$$U\sin\varphi_s = u. \tag{5-19}$$

By comparing this result with Equation 5-12 we see that $|\,q\,|\,u$ is the energy which the rf cavity must supply to the s.p. for each turn in order to keep it in synchronism. The quantity u is determined in principle by the characteristics of the machine (time behavior of ω_e and B_z, radiation losses, and so on); it is a slowly varying function of time and we shall consider it as practically constant, as far as a few turns are concerned. The choice of the peak voltage U determines $\sin\varphi_s$ through Equation 5-19. As we have seen in Sections 1-9 and 1-10, $\sin\varphi_s$ must be less than 1; hence we must have $U > u$.[4]

5-3   THE PHASE EQUATION

In the case of the betatron, we have seen that the quantity

$$p = r(P_\theta + qA) \tag{5-20}$$

is a constant of the motion, but for the synchrotron it is not. Indeed, the proof of the constancy of p given in Section 3-3 was based on the assumption that

---

[4] This is the condition regarding the choice of U referred to in Section 1-8. The choice of U is discussed further in Section 5-5.

the total force **F** acting on the particle (see formula 3-3) was that produced by the electromagnetic field described by the vector potential **A**, namely the guiding magnetic field **B** and the induction electric field E_θ. But in the synchrotron, there is also the force produced by the electric field of the rf cavity; moreover, in electron synchrotrons of very high energy there is also the reaction force due to the emission of radiation (see Section 3-4). Neither of these forces is taken into account by the potential **A**. We now show that they give rise to a variation of p with time.

Let us denote by **F** (as in Chapter 3) the force due to the fields described by the potential **A**, and by **F*** any supplementary force, so that

$$\dot{\mathbf{P}} = \mathbf{F} + \mathbf{F^*}. \tag{5-21}$$

Now, let us differentiate Equation 5-20 with respect to time:

$$\dot{p} = \dot{r}(P_\theta + qA) + r(\dot{P}_\theta + q\dot{A}). \tag{5-22}$$

Using Equation 5-21, we have

$$\dot{p} = \dot{r}(P_\theta + qA) + r(F_\theta + q\dot{A}) + rF_\theta{}^*. \tag{5-23}$$

We have shown in Section 3-3 that, if $\mathbf{F^*} = 0$, then $\dot{p} = 0$; therefore all terms in the right-hand side of this equation must cancel out except the last one (as can easily be verified). So we obtain

$$\dot{p} = rF_\theta{}^*; \tag{5-24}$$

that is, the time derivative of p is equal to the torque of all the forces not deriving from the potential **A**.

In the case of the synchrotron, $F_\theta{}^*$ is the sum of two terms: that of the radiation reaction, which acts continuously along the orbit, and that due to the rf field, which acts only during the very short crossings of the cavity and so can be considered as a discontinuous pulse at each turn. Therefore p will vary in time as shown by Figure 5-3. As the relative variation of p in one turn is small

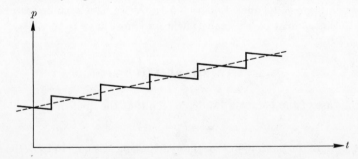

FIGURE 5-3. *Qualitative behavior of the canonical momentum p (see footnote 3 in Section 3-3) of a particle in a synchrotron as a function of time (solid line). The dotted line shows the approximating continuous curve.*

and we are interested only in the long-term behavior of p, it is convenient to smooth out the curve of Figure 5-3, approximating it by the dotted line. To this effect, we replace $\dot{p}$ with its average value $\langle \dot{p} \rangle$ in one turn. If we multiply Equation 5-24 by $d\theta$ and integrate from 0 to 2π, we get

$$2\pi \langle \dot{p} \rangle = \int_0^{2\pi} F_\theta{}^* r \, d\theta, \qquad (5\text{-}25)$$

where the right-hand side represents the total work of the force $F_\theta{}^*$ in one turn. This is the sum of a contribution L_e due to the rf field (see Equation 5-12) and a contribution $-L_r$ (always negative) due to the radiation loss (Equation 3-42). Hence we have (replacing $\langle \dot{p} \rangle$ with $\dot{p}$)

$$2\pi\dot{p} = L_e - L_r = |q| \, U \sin \varphi - L_r. \qquad (5\text{-}26)$$

Let us now indicate with δX the difference between any quantity, X, referring to an arbitrary particle (not performing betatron oscillations) and the same quantity referring to the s.p. (for example, $\delta E = E - E_s$, and so on). We shall suppose these differences to be small and treat them as differentials.[5] If we specify Equation 5-26 for the s.p. and subtract the resulting equation from Equation 5-26 itself, we obtain

$$2\pi\delta\dot{p} = |q| \, (U \sin \varphi - u) - \delta L_r. \qquad (5\text{-}27)$$

We shall see that δp can be expressed by means of the phase φ. Thus Equation 5-27 will become a differential equation for φ.

First of all, let us determine the quantity δp in terms of the variation of momentum δP. From the definition of p we have

$$\delta p = \delta(rP_\theta) + q\delta(rA) = r\delta P_\theta + P_\theta\delta r + q \frac{\partial}{\partial r} (rA) \, \delta r. \qquad (5\text{-}28)$$

From Equations 3-9 and 4-11 it follows that the last two terms of the right-hand side of Equation 5-28 cancel out, so that

$$\delta p = r\delta P_\theta. \qquad (5\text{-}29)$$

For the particles we are considering, as the displacement from the conditions of circular orbit is small (and we are ignoring betatron oscillations), $P_\theta \simeq P$ and we can also write.

$$\delta p \simeq r\delta P. \qquad (5\text{-}30)$$

We shall now use the general relationship 1-42 between the variation of the period of rotation τ and the variation of the momentum, which we rewrite with the notation used in Chapter 1:

$$\frac{\delta\tau}{\tau} = \left(\frac{1}{\alpha} - \frac{1}{\gamma^2} \right) \frac{\delta P}{P}, \qquad (5\text{-}31)$$

[5] We shall not, however, use $\delta\varphi$ because generally $(\varphi - \varphi_s)$ is not a small angle.

or, as $\tau = \text{const}/\omega$ and $P = \beta E/c$ (see Equation 1-10),

$$-\frac{\delta\omega}{\omega} = \left(\frac{1}{\alpha} - \frac{1}{\gamma^2}\right)\frac{c\delta P}{\beta E}. \qquad (5\text{-}32)$$

Let us use Equation 5-30 and recall that $r = c\beta/\omega$; we have then

$$-\frac{\delta\omega}{\omega} = \left(\frac{1}{\alpha} - \frac{1}{\gamma^2}\right)\frac{\omega\delta p}{\beta^2 E}. \qquad (5\text{-}33)$$

If we put

$$\left(\frac{1}{\alpha} - \frac{1}{\gamma^2}\right)\frac{1}{\beta^2} = K \qquad (5\text{-}34)$$

and solve with respect to δp, we finally obtain

$$\delta p = -\frac{E}{K\omega^2}\delta\omega. \qquad (5\text{-}35)$$

Before using this formula, it is convenient to consider the quantity K introduced by Equation 5-34. Recalling (Section 1-2) the meaning of γ^2, we can write Equation 5-34 as

$$K = \left[\frac{1}{\alpha} - 1 + \beta^2\right]\frac{1}{\beta^2} = 1 + \frac{(1-\alpha)}{\beta^2\alpha}, \qquad (5\text{-}36)$$

which shows (as α is a constant of the machine) that, as β tends to 1, K tends to the value $1/\alpha$, which is practically reached in the ultrarelativistic approximation. In order to render these formulas explicit we must calculate for the synchrotron the quantity α, that is, the "momentum compaction" defined by Equation 1-39. If we differentiate the logarithms of both sides of the relation $P = -qrB_z$, we have

$$\frac{\delta P}{P} = \frac{\delta r}{r} + \frac{\delta B_z}{B_z} \qquad (5\text{-}37)$$

or, recalling the definition 4-2 of the field index n,

$$\frac{\delta P}{P} = \frac{\delta r}{r}(1-n). \qquad (5\text{-}38)$$

The momentum compaction of the synchrotron is thus

$$\alpha = \frac{\delta P/P}{\delta r/r} = 1 - n. \qquad (5\text{-}39)$$

Thus Equation 5-36 becomes

$$K = 1 + \frac{n}{1-n}\frac{1}{\beta^2} \qquad (5\text{-}40)$$

and, for $\beta \simeq 1$,

$$K \simeq \frac{1}{1-n}. \qquad (5\text{-}41)$$

Let us now return to Equation 5-35. From Equations 5-11 and 5-10 we have

$$\delta\omega = \omega - \omega_s = \omega - \frac{\omega_e}{k} = -\frac{\dot{\varphi}}{k}, \qquad (5\text{-}42)$$

so that Equation 5-35 becomes

$$\delta p = \frac{E}{Kk\omega^2}\dot{\varphi}. \qquad (5\text{-}43)$$

If we differentiate with respect to time and note that the operations δ and d/dt are independent and thus can be inverted, we have

$$\frac{d}{dt}\delta p = \delta\dot{p} = \frac{d}{dt}\left(\frac{E}{Kk\omega^2}\dot{\varphi}\right). \qquad (5\text{-}44)$$

This is the expression for $\delta\dot{p}$ to be substituted into Equation 5-27 in order to obtain the differential equation for φ,

$$2\pi \frac{d}{dt}\left(\frac{E}{Kk\omega^2}\dot{\varphi}\right) = |\,q\,|\,(U\sin\varphi - u) - \delta L_r. \qquad (5\text{-}45)$$

In the approximation where the differences indicated by δ are considered as differentials, E can be substituted by E_s and ω by $\omega_s = \omega_e/k$. We thus obtain the *phase equation*:

$$2\pi k \frac{d}{dt}\left(\frac{E_s\dot{\varphi}}{K\omega_e^2}\right) = |\,q\,|\,(U\sin\varphi - u) - \delta L_r. \qquad (5\text{-}46)$$

5-4 DISCUSSION OF THE PHASE EQUATION

The phase equation 5-46 is greatly simplified by the following approximations, which in normal conditions are justified and in all cases allow a qualitative discussion of the behavior of the phase. Later (Section 5-6) we shall consider the corrections to be applied to this first approximation.

Let us suppose that the variation of the radiation per turn δL_r is negligible, and that E_s, K, ω_e change adiabatically (that is, slowly with respect to changes in φ) so that they can be considered as constants in Equation 5-46. With these assumptions, if we put

$$\frac{|\,q\,|\,K\omega_e^2 u}{2\pi k E_s} = C, \qquad (5\text{-}47)$$

Equation 5-46 becomes

$$\ddot{\varphi} = C \left(\frac{\sin \varphi}{\sin \varphi_s} - 1 \right). \tag{5-48}$$

This equation can be interpreted by means of a simple mechanical model introduced by Bohm and Foldy (1946), who first discussed the problem of synchrotron oscillations. Consider (see Figure 5-4) a "biased pendulum," that is, a rigid pendulum, subject, apart from the force of gravity, to a force of constant torque M, such as could be obtained by a string of negligible mass at a constant tension wound around a pulley attached to the pendulum. (The constant tension can be thought of as due to a weight P as in the figure.) If an arbitrary position of the pendulum is identified by the angle φ defined as in the figure (supplementary to the angle normally used in the study of the motion of the pendulum), and the moment of inertia (taking into account the inertia of P) is indicated by I, the mass by m, and the distance of the center of gravity from the axis by l, the differential equation for the motion of the biased pendulum is

$$I\ddot{\varphi} = mgl \sin \varphi - M, \tag{5-49}$$

and is identical with Equation 5-48 if the constants of the pendulum are chosen so that

$$\frac{mgl}{I} = \frac{C}{\sin \varphi_s}, \tag{5-50}$$

$$\frac{M}{I} = C. \tag{5-51}$$

The pendulum is in equilibrium for $\sin \varphi = \sin \varphi_s$ and thus in the two positions

$$\varphi = \varphi_s , $$
$$\varphi = \pi - \varphi_s . \tag{5-52}$$

It is easy to see that, of these two equilibrium positions, only one is stable, the one included between $\pi/2$ and π (that is, position A of the figure). By definition, the synchronous particle must be in the *stable* equilibrium phase (see Sections 1-9 and 1-10), so that position A must correspond to the first of Equations 5-52 and so

$$\frac{\pi}{2} < \varphi_s < \pi. \tag{5-53}$$

This means (see the definition 5-9 of the phase) that the s.p. must cross the rf cavity while the accelerating field is *decreasing*. A particle with phase $\pi - \varphi_s$ (corresponding to the position B of the pendulum in Figure 5-4), which crosses the cavity with increasing field, would have phase equilibrium but it would be unstable (in agreement with the conclusions of Section 1-10). It should be noted that in the synchrotron the stability condition is opposite to that of the linear accelerator. This is essentially due to the fact that $K > 0$ for the synchrotron, whereas the analogous quantity for the linear accelerator (defined again by Equation 5-34) would be negative, because $\alpha = \infty$.

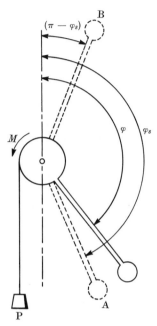

FIGURE 5-4.   *Diagram of a mechanical model for phase oscillations (biased pendulum).*

The model of the pendulum allows us to describe the behavior of the phase oscillations intuitively. Let us, indeed, consider a particle which at the time t_0 has the energy of the s.p. but a phase φ_0 different from φ_s. It will be represented by the pendulum starting from position φ_0 with zero initial velocity. It is clear from Figure 5-4 that, if $\varphi_0 > \pi - \varphi_s$, the pendulum will oscillate (not harmonically, except in the case of small amplitudes) about the equilibrium position A; this means that the phase of the particle will oscillate about the synchronous phase (and we shall see in Section 5-6 that these oscillations are damped so that actually the particle gradually approaches the s.p.). If, instead, $\varphi_0 < \pi - \varphi_s$, the pendulum will rotate anticlockwise and the phase will move indefinitely away from φ_s (we shall see later that these particles eventually hit the walls of the vacuum chamber and are lost). It is simple to extend the argument to a particle that at the time t_0 has neither the energy of the s.p. nor its phase; it will be represented by the pendulum starting from a position φ_0 with a certain initial angular velocity $\dot{\varphi}_0$.

In order to investigate what happens for large values of φ, we can obtain a first integral of Equation 5-48 by multiplying it by $\dot{\varphi}\,dt$ and integrating: we obtain

$$\tfrac{1}{2}\dot{\varphi}^2 = -C\left(\varphi + \frac{\cos\varphi}{\sin\varphi_s}\right) + \text{const.} \tag{5-54}$$

If we put

$$f(\varphi) = \varphi + \frac{\cos\varphi}{\sin\varphi_s}, \tag{5-55}$$

Equation 5-54 becomes

$$\tfrac{1}{2}\dot{\varphi}^2 = C[f_0 - f(\varphi)], \tag{5-56}$$

where f_0 is a constant of integration. Equation 5-56 is a first integral of Equation 5-48: in the model of the pendulum it represents the equation of energy conservation.

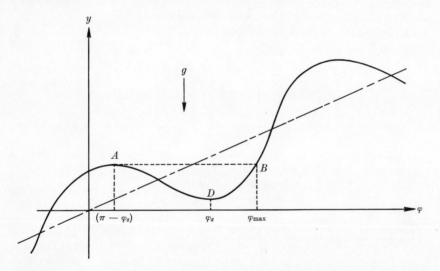

FIGURE 5-5. *Diagram of the function $y(\varphi)$, illustrating the region of phase stability, for $(\pi - \varphi_s) < \varphi < \varphi_{\max}$. See text and Equation 5-55 for the definition of y.*

In order to follow intuitively the variations of φ described by Equation 5-56, it is convenient to use the following approximate model. Consider a heavy ball constrained to move without friction along the profile represented by the function $y(\varphi) = Cf(\varphi)/g$ (see Figure 5-5), where g is the acceleration of gravity in the negative y direction. The equation of energy conservation for the ball is

$$\dot{y}^2 + \dot{\varphi}^2 + 2gy = \text{const.} \tag{5-57}$$

If we suppose the slope to be everywhere sufficiently small (so that $\dot{y}^2$ can be neglected with respect to $\dot{\varphi}^2$),[6] then the motion of the ball (by the definition of y) is described precisely by Equation 5-56. In Figure 5-5 the points where y has a minimum, such as D, and a maximum, such as A, represent positions of stable and unstable equilibrium, respectively. If its kinetic energy is sufficiently low, the ball can remain between A and B (where B and the corresponding value of φ, φ_{max}, are determined by $f(\varphi_{max}) = f(\pi - \varphi_s)$), and then it will oscillate asymmetrically about D. This corresponds to a particle whose phase oscillates about φ_s within the interval from $\varphi = \pi - \varphi_s$ to $\varphi = \varphi_{max}$.

It must be noted that, as from Equation 5-8 we have

$$\varphi - \varphi_s = -k(\theta - \theta_s), \tag{5-58}$$

these phase oscillations correspond to azimuthal oscillations of position with respect to the s.p. If the ball ever gets out of the interval AB, it will eventually move away indefinitely in the negative direction of φ. This corresponds to a particle whose difference of phase with respect to the s.p. increases indefinitely. As we shall see in the next section, such a particle is lost against the walls of the vacuum chamber.

5-5 SYNCHROTRON OSCILLATIONS

The phase oscillations, which are associated with the azimuthal oscillations of an arbitrary particle with respect to the s.p., are necessarily connected with radial oscillations. This fact can be explained easily if we note that the magnetic field satisfies the condition of circular orbit for the s.p., but it cannot satisfy it for the other particles whose difference in phase gives rise to a difference in momentum with respect to the s.p. The radial oscillations caused by the phase oscillations are called "synchrotron oscillations" because they are a characteristic feature of this machine.

In order to make this argument more quantitative and show how the phase oscillations produce radial oscillations, let us find the relation between δr and δp. By eliminating δP between Equations 5-38 and 5-30 we obtain

$$\delta r = \frac{1}{1 - n} \frac{\delta p}{P}. \tag{5-59}$$

The left-hand side is the radial displacement and in order to relate the right-hand side to the phase oscillations it is sufficient to express δp in terms of $\dot{\varphi}$ by means of Equation 5-43. We thus obtain

$$\delta r = \frac{E}{(1 - n)Kk\omega^2 P} \dot{\varphi}. \tag{5-60}$$

---

[6] This condition can be approached as closely as one likes by supposing the value of g to be sufficiently large, in the model.

The quantities E, ω, and P can be replaced by E_s, ω_s, and P_s because the differences are small quantities of the first order. Thus, with $\omega_s = \omega_e/k$, we obtain

$$\delta r = \frac{kE_s}{(1-n)K\omega_e^2 P_s}\,\dot\varphi. \tag{5-61}$$

This shows that for nonsynchronous particles (i.e., with $\dot\varphi \neq 0$) there is a radial displacement with respect to the s.p., and this displacement is proportional to $\dot\varphi$ (of course, this displacement has to be added to that due to the betatron oscillations, which have been ignored in this treatment).

Equation 5-61 can be further transformed by using the relation 1-10 between E_s and P_s and recalling that, for the s.p., $\beta_s = R\omega_e/kc$. We obtain the expression

$$\delta r = \frac{R}{(1-n)K\omega_e\beta_s^2}\,\dot\varphi. \tag{5-62}$$

In the ultrarelativistic approximation, when Equation 5-41 holds, Equation 5-62 reduces simply to

$$\delta r \simeq \frac{R}{\omega_e}\,\dot\varphi. \tag{5-63}$$

For particles whose phase oscillates, $|\dot\varphi|$ is limited and so also $|\delta r|$ will not exceed a certain value. Thus, if the vacuum chamber is sufficiently wide, these particles will not hit against the wall. Instead, for particles whose phase decreases indefinitely, $|\dot\varphi|$ increases indefinitely (see Equation 5-56 and Figure 5-5); hence $|\delta r|$ increases until, whatever the size of the vacuum chamber, they hit against the wall.

By substituting Equation 5-56 into Equation 5-62, we obtain

$$\delta r = \pm R^*[f_0 - f(\varphi)]^{1/2}, \tag{5-64}$$

where

$$R^* = \frac{R}{(1-n)\beta_s^2}\left(\frac{|q|u}{\pi kKE_s}\right)^{1/2} \simeq R\left(\frac{|q|u}{\pi k(1-n)E_s}\right)^{1/2} \tag{5-65}$$

and the approximate form of Equation 5-65 is valid in the ultrarelativistic limit (where Equation 5-63 can be used instead of Equation 5-62).

If (for a given value of φ_s) we plot the function $\pm[f_0 - f(\varphi)]^{1/2}$, for different values of f_0, we obtain a family of curves of the type shown in Figure 5-6. It should be noted that, for a given φ_s, the diagram of Figure 5-6 has a universal nature, that is, it does not depend on the parameters of the machine: these, indeed, only appear in the constant factor R^* of Equation 5-64. The dotted curve (separating closed curves from open ones) corresponds to $f_0 = f(\pi - \varphi_s)$ $= \pi - \varphi_s - \cot\varphi_s$. As $(\varphi - \varphi_s)$, from Equation 5-58, is proportional to $(\theta - \theta_s)$, that is, to the azimuthal displacement of the particle with respect to the s.p., the curves of Figure 5-6 can be interpreted as effective trajectories of nonsynchronous particles in the reference frame of the s.p. (except for a change of scale in the vertical direction and one in the horizontal direction). The various trajectories correspond to different initial conditions. It can be seen that the particles which are inside the dotted curve remain in the neighborhood of the s.p., and form a bunch with the shape of the dotted curve. The other particles are lost. We recall that betatron oscillations are superimposed on the synchrotron oscillations and are much faster, as we shall see. During the acceleration also, as will be shown later, the synchrotron oscillations are damped and the size of the bunch decreases.

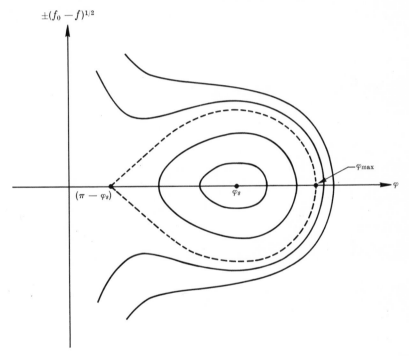

FIGURE 5-6.   *Plot of the function* $\pm\left(f_0 - f(\varphi)\right)^{1/2}$ *for different values of* f_0. *The dotted curve, corresponding to* $f_0 = f(\pi - \varphi_s)$, *separates closed curves from open ones. The function* $f(\varphi)$ *is defined by Equation 5-55.*

We have seen that the synchronous phase φ_s must lie between $\pi/2$ and π. Let us now consider the factors which influence the choice of its value within this range. We recall that, as u is determined by the parameters of the machine, Equation 5-19 shows that the choice of φ_s essentially means the choice of U. Figure 5-7 shows the boundaries of the stability zone (that is, the shapes of the bunch) in the plane $(\delta r, \varphi)$, for different values of φ_s (from Bohm and Foldy,

1946; these curves correspond to the dotted curve of Figure 5-6). It can be seen that if φ_s is too close to 90° the stability zone is small. On the other hand, if φ_s is chosen too close to 180°, this implies a greater amplitude of the radial oscillations and a high value of U, which can raise difficult technical problems. In practice φ_s is chosen around 135°–150° and this condition determines for U a value between $\sqrt{2}u$ and $2u$. As an example, let us find the amplitude of the radial oscillations for an electron of 450 MeV, when $n = 0.6$, $k = 1$, the accelerating voltage u is 1.5 kV, and $\varphi_s = 135°$. From Equation 5-65, $R^* = R/600$ and, from Figure 5-7 (for $\varphi_s = 135°$), the maximum of δr is about 0.6 R^*, so that $\delta r/R \simeq 10^{-3}$.

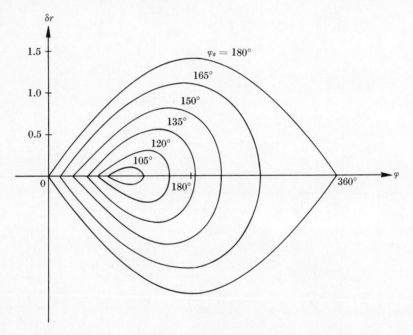

FIGURE 5-7. *Plot of the frontiers of the stability zone for various values of the synchronous phase φ_s. These curves correspond to the dotted curve of Figure 5-6. In the ordinates δr is measured in units of the constant R^* defined by Equation 5-65.*

5-6   THE CASE OF SMALL-AMPLITUDE OSCILLATIONS AND THE DAMPING OF PHASE OSCILLATIONS

Let us now consider the particular case where φ does not differ greatly from φ_s, so that if we put

$$\varphi = \varphi_s + \psi \tag{5-66}$$

we can consider ψ as a small first-order quantity and write

$$\sin \varphi = \sin \varphi_s \cos \psi + \sin \psi \cos \varphi_s \simeq \sin \varphi_s + \psi \cos \varphi_s . \qquad (5\text{-}67)$$

In this case Equation 5-48 becomes

$$\ddot{\psi} = (C \cotan \varphi_s)\psi. \qquad (5\text{-}68)$$

As $C > 0$ and $\cotan \varphi_s < 0$, this equation has oscillatory solutions of the form

$$\psi = \psi_0 \sin(\Omega t + \text{const}), \qquad (5\text{-}69)$$

where the angular frequency Ω is defined by

$$\Omega^2 = -C \cotan \varphi_s = \frac{\mid q \mid K \omega_e^2 u}{2\pi k E_s} \mid \cotan \varphi_s \mid . \qquad (5\text{-}70)$$

In order to get an idea of the magnitude of Ω, let us compare it with $\omega_s = \omega_e/k$. We have

$$\frac{\Omega}{\omega_s} = \left(\frac{\mid q \mid ukK}{2\pi E_s} \mid \cotan \varphi_s \mid \right)^{1/2} . \qquad (5\text{-}71)$$

The quantity $kK \mid \cotan \varphi_s \mid/2\pi$ is usually of the order of unity. Thus

$$\frac{\Omega}{\omega_s} \simeq \left(\frac{\mid q \mid u}{E_s} \right)^{1/2} , \qquad (5\text{-}72)$$

which shows that, as $\mid q \mid u$ (the energy gained per turn by the s.p.) is much smaller than E_s, the phase oscillations are very slow and during one of these oscillations several hundreds of rotations occur. In other words, the motion (in the absence of betatron oscillations) can be described as a circular one, on a circle of slowly pulsating radius. Betatron oscillations are generally super-imposed on this motion, and we have seen (Section 4-5) that their frequencies are of the same order as the frequency of rotation, so we conclude that betatron oscillations are much faster than synchrotron oscillations. This is a justification for the procedure we have used; that is, to consider the two oscillations as uncoupled and to treat them independently.

In the ultrarelativistic limit, as δr is given by Equation 5-63, it follows from Equations 5-66 and 5-69 that, for small-amplitude oscillations,

$$\mid \delta r \mid \leq R\psi_0\Omega/\omega_e \qquad (5\text{-}73)$$

In order to treat the damping of synchrotron oscillations, let us consider the same approximations as we have used in Section 4-5 to discuss the damp-ing of betatron oscillations. In Equation 5-46 we again consider ω_e and K as constants (as is certainly true for $\beta \simeq 1$), and neglect δL_r,[7] but we take into

---

[7] If the effect of radiation losses is taken into account, it can be seen that they give a contribution to the damping term that is nonnegligible only for electron synchrotrons at high energies and is generally positive.

account the variation of E_s with time. In this way we obtain the following equation:

$$\ddot{\varphi} + \frac{\dot{E}_s}{E_s}\dot{\varphi} = C\left(\frac{\sin\varphi}{\sin\varphi_s} - 1\right), \qquad (5\text{-}74)$$

which, for $\dot{E}_s = 0$, reduces to Equation 5-48. It is easy to see that the term in $\dot{E}_s$ gives rise to a damping of the phase oscillations. In the case of small-amplitude oscillations, with the usual definition of ψ (Equation 5-66) we have

$$\ddot{\psi} + \frac{\dot{E}_s}{E_s}\dot{\psi} + \Omega^2\psi = 0. \qquad (5\text{-}75)$$

From the definition 5-70 of Ω, we obtain, in the present approximation,

$$\frac{\dot{E}_s}{E_s} = -2\frac{\dot{\Omega}}{\Omega}, \qquad (5\text{-}76)$$

and so Equation 5-75 becomes

$$\ddot{\psi} - 2\frac{\dot{\Omega}}{\Omega}\dot{\psi} + \Omega^2\psi = 0. \qquad (5\text{-}77)$$

Following the procedure used in Section 4-5 for the betatron oscillations, let us look for a solution of the form

$$\psi = \psi_0(t)\sin\left(\int_0^t \Omega(\tau)\,d\tau + \text{const}\right) = \psi_0(t)\sin\Phi(t), \qquad (5\text{-}78)$$

where ψ_0 and $\dot{\Omega}$ will be considered as small first-order quantities. If we substitute Equation 5-78 into Equation 5-77 and neglect small terms of second order, we obtain

$$(2\dot{\psi}_0\Omega - \psi_0\dot{\Omega})\cos\Phi(t) = 0, \qquad (5\text{-}79)$$

and thus

$$2\frac{\dot{\psi}_0}{\psi_0} - \frac{\dot{\Omega}}{\Omega} = 0. \qquad (5\text{-}80)$$

We see therefore, by integrating, that the amplitude of the phase oscillation is proportional to $\Omega^{1/2}$ and hence, by Equation 5-70, to

$$\omega_e^{1/2}\,|\,KU\cos\varphi_s\,|^{1/4}E_s^{-1/4}.$$

In electron synchrotrons the most important variation is ordinarily that of the last factor, and therefore it can be said that the amplitude of the phase oscillations decreases roughly as $E^{-1/4}$ and that of the synchrotron oscillations, which can be deduced from Equation 5-73, as $E^{-3/4}$. A further damping of the oscillations is produced at high energies (if $n < 0.75$) by the radiation term δL_r in Equation 5-46, which we have neglected in the preceding calculation.

At very high energies, however, the emission of radiation has also an oppo-site effect, namely that of exciting new synchrotron oscillations (Sands, 1955). This effect is due to the energy jumps produced by the quantum nature of the emitted radiation, which is not taken into account by the classical theory of radiation summarized in Section 3-4 but must be considered when the energy of the emitted quanta becomes comparable with the energy of the electron. For a typical electron synchrotron of 1.5 BeV maximum energy, with $R = 3.55$ m and $k = 4$, this effect may become significant above 380 MeV and dominant above 700 MeV. Its consequence is that the size of the electron bunches does not decrease below a certain minimum, and this fact reduces the "coherence effect" mentioned in Section 3-4 and therefore the radiation loss.

5-7 RESONANCE EFFECTS

As we have seen (Equation 5-3) the field index n can have any value between 0 and 1. However, there are some values (theoretically an infinite number) in this interval which must be avoided, because they give rise to resonances between the radial and vertical betatron oscillations, and, possibly, the orbital motion, so that the stability of the beam can be lost.

A *resonance* occurs if there is a relation between the frequencies of the orbital motion, those of the vertical, and those of the horizontal betatron oscillations that has the form

$$p\omega + q\omega_z + r\omega_r = 0, \qquad (5\text{-}81)$$

where p, q, and r are integers (which can be positive, negative, or zero). Using the expressions 4-47 for ω_r and ω_z (with n_i replaced by n), Equation 5-81 gives

$$p + qn^{1/2} + r(1 - n)^{1/2} = 0. \qquad (5\text{-}82)$$

In practice the important cases are those for which these integers are small (between -3 and 3, say) and principally the cases in which one of them is zero. Thus, one must avoid values of n for which at least one of the ratios

$$\frac{\omega_z}{\omega} = \sqrt{n}, \qquad \frac{\omega_r}{\omega} = \sqrt{1 - n}, \qquad \frac{\omega_r}{\omega_z} = \sqrt{\frac{1 - n}{n}} \qquad (5\text{-}83)$$

is a simple rational number.

The resonance would not be dangerous if the vertical oscillations, the horizontal oscillations, and the orbital motion were rigorously independent, such as they have been considered in the discussion up to now. However, horizontal and vertical oscillations are coupled by the nonlinear terms of the equation of motion, which we have neglected in the previous treatment. Furthermore, the horizontal and vertical oscillations are both coupled to the orbital motion by the small inevitable irregularities of the magnetic field.

TABLE 5-1. *Some Values of n Which Give Resonance between Radial and Vertical Betatron Oscillations*[a]

	n		
q	r = 1	r = 2	r = 3
1	0.5	0.8	0.9
2	0.2	0.5	0.692
3	0.1	0.308	0.5

[a] Obtained from Equation 5-84.

In order to understand the effect of these couplings, consider the model consisting of two pendulums attached to a common support which is not perfectly rigid so that oscillation energy can pass from one pendulum to the other. If one of the pendulums is initially at rest while the other oscillates, the first starts to oscillate with increasing amplitude while the other gradually slows down and stops (after which the parts are inverted) and this process is the faster, the smaller the terms of the resonance ratio. Similar phenomena occur for the betatron oscillations: one of them can gradually increase its amplitude and take energy from the other or from the orbital motion. As an example, Table 5-1 gives some values of n which give resonance between radial and vertical oscillations. These values (see Equation 5-83) are given by $[(1 - n)/n]^{1/2} = q/r$, that is

$$\frac{1}{n} = 1 + \frac{q^2}{r^2}. \tag{5-84}$$

From this formula, the forbidden values of n given in Table 5-1 are calculated. As in the betatron, in the synchrotron it is preferable to have a stronger focusing for the vertical oscillations than for the radial ones, because there is less space available in the vertical direction. Usually values of n around 0.6 are chosen so as to avoid the more dangerous conditions for resonance. Finally it should be noted that the problem of avoiding resonances exists also for the betatron. However, in this machine it is less important in practice because in the betatron the ratio between the width and the radius of the doughnut is much greater than in the synchrotron and so larger oscillations are tolerated. It is for this reason that we have elected to treat this subject in the present chapter.

5-8 SOME TECHNICAL PROBLEMS OF THE SYNCHROTRON

Many of the technical problems occurring in synchrotrons have a different stress for electron synchrotrons and for proton synchrotrons. In the first case, indeed, as the mass of the particles is so small that they are practically ultra-

relativistic even at the beginning of the acceleration process, the importance
of some problems (radiation losses, for example) is enhanced and the importance of others (such as the modulation of the rf cavity) is reduced with respect
to the second case. However, in a general discussion such as the one presented
in this section, it is still possible to treat the two types of synchrotrons
together by specifying whether we refer to one of them in particular wherever
it is necessary.

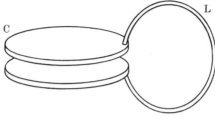

FIGURE 5-8.   *A simple oscillating circuit.*

We first make some remarks on the general structure of the synchrotron.
The model with completely circular orbit, to which we have referred, is used
only in the smaller electron synchrotrons (with energies of some tens of million
electron volts) and in one proton synchrotron, the 1-BeV machine of the
University of Birmingham, which was also the first one to be designed
(Oliphant *et al.*, 1947). For all the other high-energy synchrotrons it has been
found convenient to break up the circular orbit into a certain number of
circular arcs, connected by straight sections without magnetic field. This is
very useful for the disposition of the other components of the machine (such
as the rf cavity, the targets, the vacuum pumps, the systems for injection,
extraction, and control), and access to the vacuum chamber is easier. It
should be noted that, should the ring-shaped magnet have an H cross section
(see Figure 5-2), without straight sections the vacuum chamber would be
completely inaccessible. There can be four straight sections, as shown in
Figure 1-8, but in the larger accelerators there are usually many more of them,
which can have different lengths (as long as the symmetry of the system is
preserved). The presence of straight sections modifies quantitatively some of
the results obtained in the previous sections with respect to betatron oscillations (which have a larger amplitude) and phase stability (which is slightly
reduced). However, these modifications generally are not important, and the
conclusions reached in this chapter still hold qualitatively. A detailed calculation of these effects will be carried out in the next chapter (Section 6-6),
where the mathematical formalism developed will make such a discussion
simpler.

We now discuss the rf cavity. The operation of this device can be understood
intuitively in the following way.

Let us consider (Figure 5-8) a capacitor C made with two parallel circular plates and let us short-circuit it with a loop L. This is an oscillating circuit consisting of a capacitor and an inductance (L) in series. Thus, if the capacitor, initially charged, is discharged through the loop, alternating current will flow and there will be an oscillatory electric field between the plates of C. The same phenomenon will happen if, instead of a single loop, there are many loops in parallel. In the limit this will still be true when all the loops are connected together so as to form a single conductor of toroidal shape. We therefore obtain the structure indicated in Figure 5-9a, which shows a cross section of the cavity through its axis of symmetry. The lines of force of the electric and magnetic field are also indicated. Of course it is not necessary that the shape of the cavity be exactly that of Figure 5-9a: for purposes of construction, indeed, other forms may be preferable, such as the one shown in Figure 5-9b. However, the principle of operation remains the same. Sometimes, especially in small synchrotrons, for reasons of space it is preferable to adapt a part of the vacuum chamber as a cavity. This is done by metallizing the inner and outer surfaces of the wall and connecting them electrically at one end as is shown in Figure 5-10, which represents the cross section of the (quarter-wave) cavity so obtained.

Frequency modulation of the cavity is absolutely necessary for proton synchrotrons; for electron synchrotrons it is required only at the beginning of

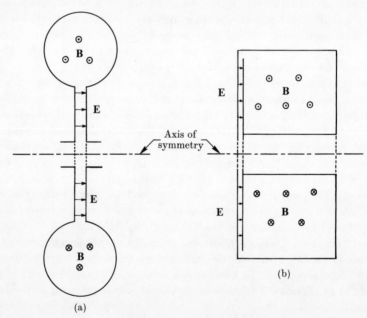

(a)

(b)

FIGURE 5-9. *Diagram of a cross section through the axis of symmetry of a resonant cavity showing how* **E** *and* **B** *are distributed:* (a) *a design illustrating the principle;* (b) *a design used in practice.*

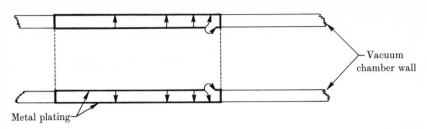

FIGURE 5-10. *Diagram of a quarter-wave cavity obtained from a vacuum-chamber section. Electric lines of force are indicated.*

the acceleration (at 2 MeV the velocity of an electron is already 0.98c) and it can be avoided by the use of betatron injection (see the next section). As we have mentioned in Section 1-8, more than one cavity can be used and in some cases they are turned on successively. For very high energies many cavities excited simultaneously may be necessary in order to increase the energy gain per turn. The frequency modulation can be obtained by the use of a capacitor with rotating plates of the proper form. The angular velocity of the plates is controlled by electric devices which follow the variation of the magnetic field. The most critical phase of the frequency modulation is always the one following the injection, when the magnetic field is increasing rapidly, and the oscillation amplitude of the particles is large. After the first few turns, when the particles captured into stable orbits are bunched, the transit of the bunches in front of an electrode placed in the vacuum chamber can produce a signal by induction for the control of the frequency.

Finally, let us consider the problem of radiation losses, which is of great importance in electron synchrotrons because, according to Equation 3-42, these losses are proportional to $(E/E_0)^4$. For electron energies of a few billion electron volts, radiation losses can be as high as a few million electron volts per turn. This energy must be supplied by the rf cavity, which therefore ought to operate at a very high voltage. But the voltage is limited by electric breakdown, so it is necessary to use more cavities, driven in phase. However, both the power available for the cavities and the dimensions and weight of the magnet are subject to practical and economic limits, so that today it does not seem convenient to build a circular machine for electrons, of the type described in this chapter, for energies much larger than 1 BeV. Higher energies can be obtained with an alternating-gradient synchrotron (see Chapter 6); or, better, with a linear accelerator (of great length; see Chapter 8), where radiation losses are negligible. It should also be noted that, in high-energy electron synchrotrons, the radiation raises some technical problems for the protection of nonmetallic parts, such as the walls of the vacuum chamber, which can suffer radiation damage.

5-9   THE INJECTION AND EXTRACTION OF THE SYNCHROTRON BEAM

Let us first consider the injection of the particles to be accelerated into the synchrotron. There are essentially two types of injection into a synchrotron. The most common method today consists in the injection of the particles at a sufficiently high velocity by means of an electrostatic generator (or, in the larger machines, a linear accelerator), so that it is not necessary to modulate the frequency over too wide a range. The second method, used only in electron synchrotrons (especially the smaller ones), consists in the injection of the electrons at low energy with the machine operating as a betatron until the particles have reached a high speed. At this point the rf cavity is turned on and normal synchrotron operation starts.

Let us now consider the first type of injection, that is, *high-energy injection*. The high-intensity beam from the injector passes through an inflector (usually an electrostatic one, for reasons of space) which sends it into the vacuum chamber in a tangential direction. As we have also seen for the betatron, the injection cannot occur along the equilibrium orbit; otherwise the particle would hit against the edge of the inflector after one turn. Instead the inflector is placed at the outer wall of the vacuum chamber and the particles are injected at a time when the magnetic field is increasing, but the rf cavity has not yet been turned on. The increasing magnetic field causes the particles to spiral inward and thus to miss the back of the inflector. The betatron oscillations of the particles about the instantaneous circle further decrease the probability of hitting the inflector. The instant at which the injection starts is chosen so that the radial distance r_d of the exit of the inflector, the corresponding magnetic field, and the momentum P_0 of the particles injected satisfy the relation

$$P_0 = r_d |\, qB_z(r_d)\,|\,, \tag{5-85}$$

which ensures that the particles are injected on their instantaneous circle.[8] However, in order to obtain a sufficiently high intensity, the injection phase is extended for some time. The particles injected in this later phase, as P_0 remains the same while $B_z(r_d)$ increases, find an instantaneous radius r_i which is less than r_d; that is, they are injected outside their contracting instantaneous circle and therefore start betatron oscillations about it with an amplitude approximately equal to $(r_d - r_i)$. When this quantity is equal to the half-width of the vacuum chamber, the injection is stopped. Indeed, any particle injected later would hit against the inner wall of the vacuum chamber during the first oscillation. When the injection stops the cavity is turned on abruptly

---

[8] As in all this chapter, we refer to the case of a completely circular orbit. If there are straight sections, the particles are injected into one of these, but the considerations of this section are still valid.

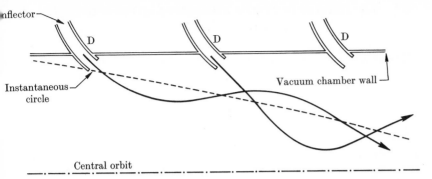

FIGURE 5-11. *Schematic diagram of the vacuum chamber, unrolled and repeated periodically, showing the inflector D and typical orbits of two particles injected one period apart. The transverse and longitudinal dimensions are drawn on completely different scales.*

and the instantaneous circle no longer changes. In order to illustrate the injection mechanism, we present a diagram of the vacuum chamber unrolled and repeated periodically with typical orbits of two particles injected one period apart (Figure 5-11). As we have seen, the instantaneous radius must decrease so rapidly that the particles do not hit the back of the inflector after one turn. On the other hand, it must decrease as slowly as possible in order to have a longer useful time for injection and so, for a given source intensity, a larger number of particles accepted. The rate of variation of r_i depends on $\dot{B}_z$. If, indeed, we differentiate the condition for a circular orbit, Equation 4-11, with respect to time and recall Equation 5-1 together with the fact that P_θ remains constant during the injection, we obtain

$$\dot{r}_i = - \frac{r_i}{1 - n} \frac{\dot{B}_0}{B_0} \simeq - \frac{R}{1 - n} \frac{\dot{B}_0}{B_0}. \tag{5-86}$$

The time required for one turn is $T \simeq 2\pi R/v$, so that the decrease of r_i in one turn, σ, is given by

$$\sigma = - T\dot{r}_i \simeq \frac{2\pi R^2}{(1 - n)v} \frac{\dot{B}_0}{B_0}. \tag{5-87}$$

The first condition that $\dot{B}_0$ must satisfy during the injection is that σ be greater than the effective dimension, d, of the inflector.[9] We therefore obtain

$$\frac{\dot{B}_0}{B_0} > \frac{vd(1 - n)}{2\pi R^2}. \tag{5-88}$$

[9] This dimension is determined by the thickness of the edge of the inflector, by the cross section of the outgoing beam, and by its position with respect to this edge.

On the other hand, $\dot{B}_0$ must not be too large if we want the total number of particles injected, N, to be as large as possible. If we call Q the intensity of the source (the number of particles injected per unit time), and $a/2$ the half-width of the vacuum chamber, then the useful time for injection (as we have seen above) is $\Delta t = \tfrac{1}{2}a/\,|\,\dot{r}_i\,|$ and hence (see Equation 5-86) we have

$$N = Q\Delta t = \frac{Qa}{2R}\,(1 - n)\,\frac{B_0}{\dot{B}_0},\qquad(5\text{-}89)$$

which shows that N increases as $\dot{B}_0$ decreases. In practice the value of $\dot{B}_0$ at the time of injection is chosen as small as possible compatibly with Equation 5-88. If the magnetic field follows a sinusoidal law, a decrease of $\dot{B}_0$ at injection can be obtained by means of a constant bias field, so that the time behavior of the field is of the kind shown in Figure 5-12. In order to increase the injection

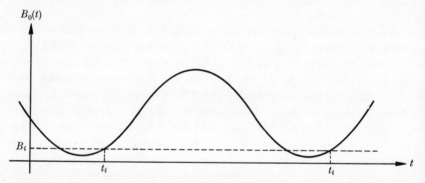

FIGURE 5-12. *Diagram illustrating the use of a bias field in order to increase the injection efficiency by decreasing $\dot{B}$ at injection. The time of injection is indicated by t_i and the magnetic field at injection by B_i.*

efficiency, certain devices can be used that operate only when the particles are sent into the vacuum chamber. For example, the radial and vertical betatron oscillations can be coupled, during the injection phase, in such a way as to increase the amplitude of the latter at the expense of the former. The inflector is thus avoided because the particles pass either above or below it. In order to make this more effective the particles can be injected slightly off the median plane. In this way the particle capture efficiency in the vacuum chamber before the rf cavity is turned on can be very high, from 30% to 90% depending on the small adjustments. When the radio frequency is turned on, as mentioned previously, the contraction of the instantaneous circle stops and this remains at the central orbit. At this time, the particles are distributed uniformly along the entire vacuum chamber, have all the possible phases, and also are carrying out betatron oscillations with all possible amplitudes. The value of the peak voltage, U, on the cavity determines the synchronous phase, φ_s, (see Equation 5-19), and hence the family of curves of Figure 5-6. The particles which, at the time when the radio frequency is turned on, are inside the dotted curve of Figure 5-6 start synchrotron oscillations about the s.p. The others are lost against the walls. However, a portion of the former particles also is lost, namely all those whose synchrotron oscillation amplitude added to that of the radial betatron oscillations exceeds the half-width of the vacuum chamber. These will be mainly the particles which are injected late and thus have betatron oscillations of larger amplitude. Other particles will be lost by collisions with the molecules of the residual gas, but this effect is important only during the early stages of the acceleration. Eventually only a fraction (of the order of 20%) of the particles which fill the doughnut is captured into stable orbits; however, almost all the particles captured reach the end of the acceleration phase, because the fast damping of the oscillations greatly reduces the losses. Of course, if $\omega = \omega_e/k$, there are simultaneously k synchronous particles and around each one of these a bunch of particles is formed. A theory of the capture efficiency and of its dependence on the parameters of the machine has been given by Persico (1955).

Let us now discuss the second type of injection, that is, the *betatron injection*. It can only be used with electron synchrotrons, where the "C" of the magnet faces the inside of the machine. The magnetic circuit is closed by ferromagnetic bars of the proper quality and size, placed as in Figure 5-13 and called "flux bars." These are designed in such a way that the average magnetic field inside the machine satisfies the betatron condition (Equation 1-27) during the early stage of the acceleration, but it saturates when the particles have reached a certain energy. While the magnetic field in the flux bars saturates, the rf cavity is excited gradually, so that a transition from betatron to synchrotron operation is produced.

As the magnetic field in the vacuum chamber at the beginning of the acceleration has rather low values (of the order of a few hundred gauss) it is possible to use flux bars of rather small cross section. The gap between the flux bars and the magnet poles (whose width can be adjusted) is required in order to avoid short-circuiting the magnetic field in the vacuum chamber, but it is much smaller than the gap between the poles of the magnet. Owing to the fast rise of the magnetic field in the flux bars, the required behavior of B can be strongly disturbed by rapidly varying eddy currents in the bars themselves. In order to correct this effect, besides using finely laminated metal, a small negative bias field (whose coils are shown schematically in Figure 5-13) can be added to the main field. Thus the value of magnetic field required for injection is reached a little later, when the eddy currents in the flux bars have reached equilibrium. A bias can also be applied to the flux bars.

When the flux bars approach saturation, the rf cavity is excited. The amplitude U of the cavity voltage is increased rather slowly so that, as the betatron accelerating force decreases, similarly the cavity force increases. Thus a large part of the electrons, initially distributed uniformly, are captured and are gradually bunched. A theory of the betatron injection in synchrotrons has been given by Kaiser (1950).

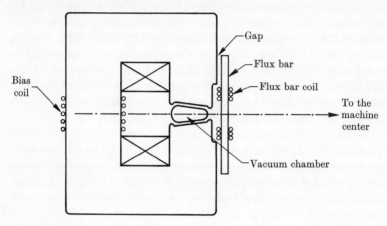

FIGURE 5-13. *Diagram of the cross section of a synchrotron magnet showing the position of the flux bars.*

The source of electrons used is of the same type as the one described for the betatron (Section 4-6, Figure 4-3).

With respect to high-energy injection, betatron injection has the advantage that it reduces or even eliminates the rf modulation required and it gives a greater intensity (because the intermediate preaccelerator stage is absent). On the other hand there are technical difficulties associated with the transition from betatron to synchrotron operation. In general, betatron injection is preferred in small synchrotrons. In the large machines high-energy injection is preferred, with the injection energy as high as possible, in order to reduce the range of frequency modulation.

Finally, we discuss the use of the accelerated beam. As in the other machines described so far, the most direct use consists of sending the accelerated beam against an internal target (especially in electron synchrotrons, with the purpose of producing a beam of high-energy x rays). The particles are sent onto this target by perturbing the trajectory on the last few turns, either through a local alteration of the magnetic field or by turning off the rf cavity so that the particles spiral inward. In the latter case the beam pulse on the target has a long duration ($\sim 10\ \mu\text{sec}$) because the rate of contraction of the orbit is rather slow. Shorter beam pulses ($\sim 0.2\ \mu\text{sec}$) can be obtained by fast local alterations of the magnetic field produced by special coils. On the other hand, the duration of the beam pulse can be extended (up to 2.5 msec!) by turning off the cavity gradually.

As in the betatron, there can be different systems of extracting the beam from the machine. It is possible to exploit the radial betatron oscillations, by properly exciting a resonance through magnetic perturbation of the orbit (Turrin, 1958; Bizzarri and Turrin, 1965). This is usually accomplished by means of two coupled magnetic devices, one called a "peeler" (see Section 4-6), which reduces the curvature of the trajectory, the other called a "regenerator," which enhances the curvature of the trajectory. By successive transits through the peeler and the regenerator, a resonance is excited between the radial betatron oscillations and the orbital motion; the amplitude of the radial oscillations increases rapidly, and the particles are led toward the edge of the doughnut, where a fast magnet ejects them out of the machine through a window in the vacuum chamber wall, closed by a thin foil.

Another method, used in proton synchrotrons, is the following. The beam (see Figure 5-14) is made to pass through a "jump target" which has a lip extending about 0.5 cm toward the central orbit. The beam first passes through the lip where a very small fraction of the energy is lost but the beta-tron oscillations are damped out. The energy loss causes the orbit to contract and finally to pass through the main target, where a larger energy loss occurs so that the orbit radius decreases by a few inches. Then on the next turn the beam passes through a small deflecting magnet (called a "Piccioni magnet," after Piccioni *et al.* (1955)), placed in a straight section and excited with a current pulse at the proper time. This magnet gives the particles such a direction that they can leave the vacuum chamber through a window closed by a thin foil.

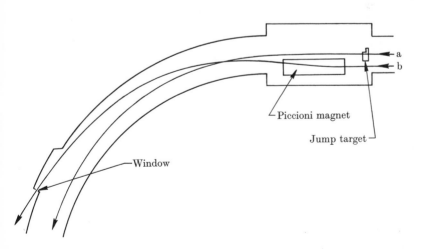

FIGURE 5-14. *Diagram illustrating the use of a jump target for beam extraction. Orbit a precedes orbit b by just one turn.*

5-10   THE MAGNETIC FIELD OF THE SYNCHROTRON

One of the major difficulties in the construction of a synchrotron is that of producing a magnetic field with the required behavior and the required field index n in the entire region where the particles move and for the complete duration of the acceleration. This is obtained to a first approximation by giving the pole pieces the proper shape (see Figure 5-15): the angle between the two pole surfaces determines the value of n, while the small humps A, A, A', A' serve to correct partially for the edge effects. The precise profile is determined by trial and error, first with an electrolytic tank and then on a model of reduced scale, fed by direct current. Thus the required field is obtained inside the region where the particles move (the shaded area of Figure 5-15). The field, however, is modified, during ac operation, for three reasons:

1. residual magnetization from the preceding cycles;
2. eddy current effects;
3. partial saturation of the iron.

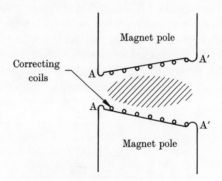

FIGURE 5-15. *Schematic diagram showing the placement of the correcting coils.*

Effects 1 and 2 appear at low values of the field (and in particular, during or just after injection, when the oscillations have the largest amplitude); effect 3, instead, appears at the end of the acceleration, when the beam has narrowed down, and so it is sufficient to correct for it in a small central region. The eddy current effects (especially in the region of the magnet poles) are the most important. In order to limit the eddy currents the magnet is made up of thin laminations cemented together, as in transformer cores. Care must be taken that the dimensions and the arrangement of the laminations be the same for all the elements of the magnet: an azimuthal asymmetry in the eddy currents, indeed, can seriously perturb the particle orbits, especially when the magnetic

ield is low. The eddy currents cannot be eliminated completely even by
amination. In order to compensate all the residual effects, *correcting coils* are
used. These are many tens of wires which run parallel to the doughnut, along
the pole surfaces (see Figure 5-15). Each wire is fed, independently of the
others, with a small current of specified time behavior. These currents are
adjusted by trial and error so as to complete the correction of the magnetic
field, particularly at the beginning of the acceleration. The beam intensity
which a synchrotron can produce is largely determined by the precision with
which the magnetic field is obtained.

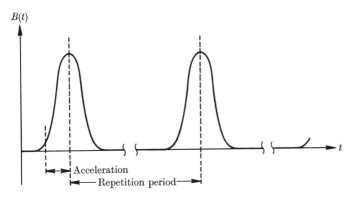

FIGURE 5-16.   *Diagram of the time dependence of the magnetic field used in a synchrotron with pulsed operation.*

As far as the power supply for the magnet is concerned, the problem for the
smaller synchrotrons (usually for electrons) is solved in the same way as for
the betatron: a condenser bank is used, in parallel with the magnet coils, and
fed by an ac or a dc generator (see Section 4-7 and Figure 4-7). When the
amount of energy involved is very large (as in electron synchrotrons of a few
hundred million electron volts), it may be necessary to use pulsed operation for
the synchrotron magnet, with a delay time (repetition period) between successive current pulses that is much larger (of the order of 10 times) than the pulse
length (see Figure 5-16). In the larger synchrotrons, and particularly in those
for protons, it is practically impossible to build a condenser bank large enough
to store the enormous amount of energy required by the magnet. Instead the
required energy is stored in a large flywheel, connected to an ac generator,
which supplies energy to the magnet during the phase when the field increases
and, acting as a motor, returns it to the flywheel when the field decreases.
Between two successive current pulses, an auxiliary low-power motor supplies
the flywheel with the energy lost by Joule effect and other causes. As an
example of an apparatus of this sort, the Brookhaven Cosmotron (a 3-BeV
machine) uses a flywheel 2.7 m in diameter and 42 tons in weight which rotates

at 950 rpm. The kinetic energy which can be stored in such a flywheel is many times larger (15 to 20 times) than the energy required for a pulse of the magnetic field. Of course, a rectifying circuit must be inserted between the ac generator and the field coils, in order that the magnetic field have a time behavior of the type shown in Figure 5-16.

Further difficulties arise in the large synchrotrons from the strong mechanical forces of magnetic origin acting on the current conductors and on the poles of the magnet. Usually the stacks of conductors are sealed in compact blocks of resinous material, which ensure mechanical stability.

CHAPTER 6

THE ALTERNATING-GRADIENT
SYNCHROTRON AND THE
ZERO-GRADIENT SYNCHROTRON

6-1   THE PRINCIPLE OF OPERATION OF THE
ALTERNATING-GRADIENT SYNCHROTRON

The "alternating-gradient" (AG) synchrotron, also called the "strong-focusing" synchrotron, was proposed in 1950 by N. Christofilos in an unpublished report. Independently of this, the principle of strong focusing was discovered by E. D. Courant, M. S. Livingston, and H. S. Snyder (1952), who wrote the first paper on the subject. This principle allows a considerable reduction of the amplitude of the betatron and synchrotron oscillations. Hence the vacuum chamber can have a much smaller cross section, so that the size and cost of the machine are greatly reduced. Indeed, a reduction of the height, or (to a smaller extent) of the width of the magnet gap gives rise to a reduction of the quantity of iron constituting the magnetic circuit, of the quantity of copper of the exciting coils, and of the electromagnetic energy to be stored in the capacitors at each cycle (see Section 5-10). Therefore the overall cost of the machine is extremely sensitive to the gap dimensions, and especially to its height.

The gap height is determined by the amplitude of the vertical betatron oscillations, and the gap width by that of the radial betratron oscillations and of the synchrotron oscillations. Let us first consider the vertical betatron oscillations (see Figure 6-1), and discuss how their amplitude can be reduced. They are caused by the initial slope of the trajectory due to the unavoidable

angular spread at the injection, and also to the scattering of some particl
due to collisions with the residual gas. In both cases, the vertical displaceme
z, as a function of the distance s along the unperturbed orbit from the poi
($s = 0$) where the oscillation has been excited, is given by[1]

$$z(s) = Z \sin ks.$$ (6-

where the "wave number" $k = 2\pi/\lambda$ is connected to the parameters of th
machine by the relation (see Equation 4-47)

$$k = \frac{\omega_z}{v} = \frac{\sqrt{n}}{R}.$$ (6-

The amplitude Z is obviously determined by the initial slope $z'(0)$ (where th
prime means differentiation with respect to s) through the formula

$$Z = \frac{z'(0)}{k} = \frac{z'(0)R}{\sqrt{n}}.$$ (6-3

This formula shows that, in order to reduce Z for a given $z'(0)$, it is necessar
to increase the field index n. This can also be expressed (see Section 4-4) b
saying that a greater value of n gives rise to a stronger "vertical focusin
force",[2] which attracts the particle toward the median plane, and so tends t
decrease the amplitude of the vertical oscillations for a given initial slope.

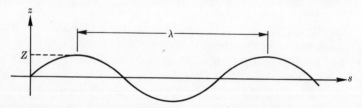

FIGURE 6-1.   *The behavior of the vertical betatron oscillations as a function of the*
distance s along the unperturbed orbit, for an ordinary synchrotron.

[1] We neglect the effect of damping (which is important only over a large number of
oscillations) because we are now interested only in the maximum amplitude of oscillation.

[2] Strictly speaking, the magnetic field is said to be "focusing" for vertical displacements when it produces a restoring force on the particles in the vertical direction. In
this case the curve $z(s)$ is concave toward the s axis, i.e., $z''/z < 0$. In the opposite case
(repulsive force, $z''/z > 0$), the magnetic field is said to be "defocusing." Similar definitions are used for the radial direction where the curve $x(s)$ is referred to the path of the
particles, unrolled and extended along the s axis. However, in this chapter we shall
sometimes use the term "focusing" (or "defocusing") in a wider sense, when the *average*
force over many magnet sectors is restoring (or repulsive), independently of its nature
in the single sectors.

The same argument, applied to the radial betatron oscillations $x(s)$ produced by an initial angular deviation $x'(0)$, similarly gives for their amplitude

$$X = x'(0)R/(1 - n)^{1/2}. \tag{6-4}$$

Therefore, in order to reduce X for a given $x'(0)$, it is necessary to make n negative and large in magnitude. A large negative n gives rise to a strong "radial focusing force" and so reduces the amplitude of the radial oscillations for a given initial deviation.

It is obvious that both requirements cannot be satisfied at the same time. If, indeed, $n \gg 1$, the amplitude of the vertical oscillations is strongly reduced, but (as has been shown in Section 4-4) radial stability is lost. If $n \ll -1$, the amplitude of the radial oscillations is reduced but vertical stability is lost.

The fundamental idea in AG synchrotrons is to satisfy the two requirements alternately rather than simultaneously. In the simplest case, this is obtained by using a magnet consisting of many consecutive sectors, where n is given alternately a value $n_1 \gg 1$ and a value $n_2 \ll -1$ (for example $n_1 = 20$, $n_2 = -20$). In this way there is alternately a focusing and a defocusing action on the particle in the vertical direction, and respectively a defocusing and a focusing action in the radial direction. It is a very remarkable fact that, under easily obtainable conditions which will be discussed later, the overall effect on the particle trajectory is equivalent to a strong focusing action in both directions.[3]

The proof of the above statement will be given in the following sections. However, at this point we shall make some intuitive considerations in order to show the plausibility of the principle of operation of the AG synchrotrons.

Consider Figure 6-2, where we have plotted the qualitative behavior of the vertical displacement $z(s)$ as a function of the distance s along the equilibrium orbit in an AG synchrotron. Within the focusing sectors (with index $n_1 > 1$), the particle is "attracted" toward the median plane (represented by the s axis) by a force proportional to its distance from it, while within the defocusing sectors (index $n_2 < -1$) the particle is repelled away from the median plane by a force again proportional to the distance. But the distance from the median plane (as the figure shows) is *on the average* larger in the focusing sectors than in the defocusing ones, because the particle enters a focusing sector after having been repelled away from the median plane in the preceding defocusing one. Therefore, also the force is on the average stronger in the

---

[3] It is now easy to understand the terms *constant-gradient* (CG) and *weak-focusing* applied to the synchrotrons described in Chapter 5, and the terms *alternating-gradient* (AG) and *strong-focusing* applied to the type of synchrotron described in this chapter. The word "gradient" refers to the gradient of B_z, i.e., essentially to the field index n.

focusing sectors than in the defocusing ones, and hence the focusing action is overall prevailing.[4]

The portions of the trajectory within the focusing sectors ($n = n_1$) are arcs of sinusoids, whereas those within defocusing sectors ($n = n_2$) are arcs of catenaries, in agreement with Equation 6-1. Since the sectors are short in comparison with the radius of curvature of the arcs of trajectory, and these are smoothly joined, the sequence of these arcs forms a smooth curve, whose overall shape is that of a sinusoid with small irregularities (full line in Figure 6-2). This curve represents the betatron oscillations of the particle.

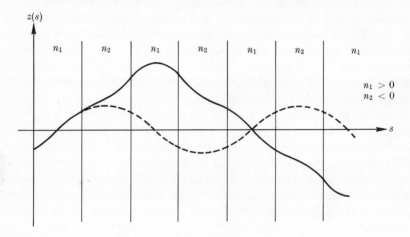

FIGURE 6-2. *Qualitative diagram of the vertical displacement $z(s)$ as a function of the distance s along the unperturbed orbit for an AG synchrotron. The dotted line shows the oscillation there would be if the field index were equal to n_1 in the whole machine.*

The wavelength of these oscillations is of course longer than that which would be produced by focusing sectors only (see the dashed curve in Figure 6-2, representing the extrapolation of the arc of sinusoid of the first focusing sector), but it is nevertheless much shorter than that obtainable in a constant-gradient (CG) synchrotron, where n must lie between 0 and 1. Indeed, in the latter case a betatron oscillation takes more than one revolution (see Section 4-5) whereas in an AG synchrotron many betatron oscillations are performed in one revolution. This shorter wavelength gives rise (as has been explained above) to a smaller amplitude of oscillation for a given initial slope.

[4] An interesting analogy of this principle can be found in optics: Indeed, an optical system consisting of a converging and a diverging lens, of equal and opposite strengths, placed at any (nonzero) distance, is always converging. This analogy will be examined in detail in Appendix 1, in connection with linear quadrupole lenses, which have many similarities with the elements of an AG synchrotron.

A similar argument could be developed for the radial betatron oscillations, for which the n_1 sectors are defocusing and the n_2 ones are focusing: The overall effect is a trajectory oscillating around the instantaneous circle with much shorter wavelength (and therefore smaller amplitude for a given initial deviation) than in a CG synchrotron. It must be added that also the amplitude of synchrotron oscillations is much reduced in AG synchrotrons, because of the higher value of the momentum compaction α (see Sections 5-3 and 5-5).

The enormous reduction in cost for a given final energy of the particles, allowed by the principle of AG synchrotrons, has permitted the construction of synchrotrons, both for electrons and for protons, of very high energy, whose cost would have been prohibitive without the AG principle. The largest AG synchrotrons operating in 1966 were (see Table 1-3) the 6-BeV electron synchrotrons of Massachusetts Institute of Technology at Cambridge, Massachusetts and of the DESY laboratory at Hamburg, Germany, and the 33-BeV proton synchrotron at Brookhaven.

It must be added, on the other hand, that the construction and alignment of the magnet sectors in an AG synchrotron require a much higher precision than in a CG synchrotron. For example, in the 28-BeV AG proton synchrotron of CERN, with a radius of 100 m, the precision required in the alignment of the magnet sectors is 0.3 mm in the vertical direction and 0.6 mm in the radial direction (relative accuracy of 6×10^{-6}). This requirement gives rise to new kinds of problems concerning, for instance, the mechanical stability of the foundations on which the machine rests, but such problems can be solved completely by modern engineering.

In the design usually adopted for AG synchrotrons instead of only two kinds of sectors with indices n_1, n_2 being alternated, a certain number of different kinds of sectors (with different field indices) are alternated according to a certain periodic law. Some straight sections where $\mathbf{B} = 0$ are always included (required for housing the rf cavity and the auxiliary equipment), and there may also be sections where $n = 0$ (B_z uniform) or $n = 1$. From this point of view it can be understood how the "racetrack" (see Figure 1-8), even though it is a weak-focusing synchrotron, can be treated with the same formalism to be derived for AG synchrotrons; this will be done in Section 6-6.

The complete machine can usually be thought of as divided into a certain number of parts, in which the different kinds of sectors always alternate in the same order. Such a part (not further divisible into equal parts) is called a *periodic element* of the machine. As an example, Figure 6-3 shows the behavior of n as a function of the distance along the orbit (measured in radians) in one periodic element (in this case a quadrant) of the 1.5-BeV electron synchrotron of Cornell University. In this machine the length of the straight sections is 91 cm, the radius of the quadrants is 3.81 m, and the ratio between the lengths of a quadrant and of a straight section is about 6.5.

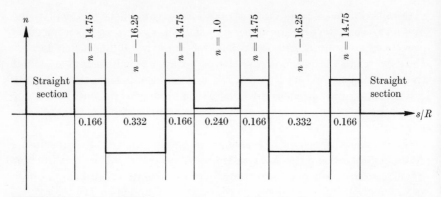

FIGURE 6-3. *The field index as a function of distance along the orbit (measured in units of the radius) for a periodic element of the 1.5-BeV electron synchrotron of Cornell University. The numbers under the s/R axis indicate the lengths of the sectors (inun its of R).*

6-2   ELEMENTS OF MATRIX ALGEBRA

A very convenient formalism for the study of the oscillations in AG synchrotrons makes use of matrix algebra. Therefore, before treating the problem in detail, we recall some elementary results of the theory of matrices, limiting ourselves to those which are used in the theory of accelerators. For a more thorough treatment, see, for example, Bellman (1960).

A square matrix of order n consists of n^2 numbers (real or complex), called *elements* of the matrix, and placed in a table with n rows and n columns. We indicate such a matrix by a capital letter, for instance A, and the element in common to the ith row and kth column by a_{ik}. Since for our purposes only matrices of order $n = 2$ are required we always refer to this case and so the matrix A will be written explicitly as follows:

$$A \equiv \begin{bmatrix} a_{11} & a_{12} \\ a_{21} & a_{22} \end{bmatrix}. \tag{6-5}$$

We call a matrix whose elements are all zero ($a_{ik} = 0$) a *null matrix* and indicate it by [0]; and a matrix whose elements are all zero except those of the principal diagonal which are equal to 1, a *unit matrix*; this matrix is indicated by [1]. So, for $n = 2$,

$$[0] = \begin{bmatrix} 0 & 0 \\ 0 & 0 \end{bmatrix}, \qquad [1] = \begin{bmatrix} 1 & 0 \\ 0 & 1 \end{bmatrix}. \tag{6-6}$$

Given two matrices A and B (whose elements are denoted by a_{ik} and b_{ik}), their sum $A + B$ is defined as the matrix whose elements are

$$(A + B)_{ik} = a_{ik} + b_{ik}. \tag{6-7}$$

Given a number m, the product mA of m times the matrix A is defined as the matrix whose elements are those of A multiplied by m, that is,

$$(mA)_{ik} = ma_{ik}. \tag{6-8}$$

Given two matrices A and B, their product AB is defined as the matrix whose elements are given by

$$(AB)_{ik} = a_{i1}b_{1k} + a_{i2}b_{2k} \tag{6-9}$$

(product "rows by columns"). In general $AB \neq BA$ and it can be that $AB = [0]$ with $A \neq [0]$ and $B \neq [0]$.

One can associate with a square matrix a number which is called its "determinant" and is indicated by det A: it is defined by the usual algebraical rule for the calculation of determinants. It should be noted that (as a consequence of this rule)

$$\det AB = \det A \cdot \det B. \tag{6-10}$$

A square matrix A is called *regular* when det $A \neq 0$ and *singular* when det $A = 0$. If a matrix A is regular there always exists the *inverse matrix* A^{-1}, connected to A by the relation

$$A^{-1}A = AA^{-1} = [1]. \tag{6-11}$$

Another quantity of interest is the sum of the diagonal elements, $a_{11} + a_{22}$, which is called the "trace" of the matrix A and is indicated by tr A.

For our purposes, it is useful to consider also vectors in a two-dimensional space. In a given reference system the components of a vector $\boldsymbol{u}$ will be indicated by u_1, u_2. They can be considered as the elements of a rectangular matrix with two rows and one column, which thus represents the vector completely. Therefore we write

$$\boldsymbol{u} \equiv \begin{bmatrix} u_1 \\ u_2 \end{bmatrix}. \tag{6-12}$$

The product $A\boldsymbol{u}$ of a matrix and a vector is defined as the vector which is obtained by use of the multiplication rule for matrices, Equation 6-9, so that

$$(A\boldsymbol{u})_i = a_{i1}u_1 + a_{i2}u_2. \tag{6-13}$$

The scalar product of two vectors $\boldsymbol{u} \cdot \boldsymbol{v}$ is defined as the number given by the relation

$$\boldsymbol{u} \cdot \boldsymbol{v} = u_1^* v_1 + u_2^* v_2, \tag{6-14}$$

where the asterisk indicates complex conjugation. In particular, the scalar product of a vector $\boldsymbol{u}$ by itself is always a positive quantity, which is indicated by

$$|\boldsymbol{u}|^2 = \boldsymbol{u} \cdot \boldsymbol{u} = |u_1|^2 + |u_2|^2. \tag{6-15}$$

Its square root is called the "magnitude" (or the "length") of the vector $\boldsymbol{u}$.

Given a square matrix A, if there exists a vector $\boldsymbol{u}$ and a number λ such that the vector identity

$$A\boldsymbol{u} = \lambda\boldsymbol{u} \tag{6-16}$$

holds, then $\boldsymbol{u}$ is called an *eigenvector* of A corresponding to the *eigenvalue* λ. Of course, Equation 6-16 defines the eigenvector except for an arbitrary scaling factor.[5] Often the modulus of this factor is fixed by imposing the *condition of normalization*, that is, that the magnitude of $\boldsymbol{u}$ be equal to unity. The phase of the factor remains arbitrary, and it is usually not considered.

It must be noted that, if $\boldsymbol{u}$ is an eigenvector of A corresponding to the eigenvalue λ, it is also an eigenvector of A^m corresponding to the eigenvalue λ^m, for any integer m. Indeed, we have

$$A^m\boldsymbol{u} = A^{m-1}A\boldsymbol{u} = A^{m-1}\lambda\boldsymbol{u} = \lambda A^{m-1}\boldsymbol{u} = \ldots \lambda^m\boldsymbol{u}. \tag{6-17}$$

In order to determine λ and $\boldsymbol{u}$ let us consider the two scalar equations represented by Equation 6-16:

$$\begin{aligned} (a_{11} - \lambda)u_1 + a_{12}u_2 &= 0, \\ a_{21}u_1 + (a_{22} - \lambda)u_2 &= 0. \end{aligned} \tag{6-18}$$

This is a system of linear homogeneous equations in the unknowns u_1, u_2. For this system to have a solution, its determinant must be zero, namely

$$\begin{vmatrix} (a_{11} - \lambda) & a_{12} \\ a_{21} & (a_{22} - \lambda) \end{vmatrix} = 0. \tag{6-19}$$

This is an equation of second degree in λ and it is called the *characteristic equation* of the matrix A. It has two roots λ_1 and λ_2 (which are not necessarily distinct[6]) and to each of these there corresponds an eigenvector

$$\boldsymbol{u}^{(1)} = \begin{bmatrix} u_1^{(1)} \\ u_2^{(1)} \end{bmatrix}, \quad \boldsymbol{u}^{(2)} = \begin{bmatrix} u_1^{(2)} \\ u_2^{(2)} \end{bmatrix}. \tag{6-20}$$

These two eigenvectors constitute a "complete set": this means that every vector $\boldsymbol{w}$ can be expressed as a linear combination of the eigenvectors $\boldsymbol{u}^{(1)}$ and $\boldsymbol{u}^{(2)}$,

$$\boldsymbol{w} = a_1\boldsymbol{u}^{(1)} + a_2\boldsymbol{u}^{(2)}. \tag{6-21}$$

Hence, if a matrix M is such that

$$M\boldsymbol{u}^{(j)} = 0 \qquad \text{for} \quad j = 1, 2, \tag{6-22}$$

---

[5] Apart from this trivial case, it may happen that more than one different eigenvectors correspond to the same eigenvalue. In this case the eigenvalue is called *degenerate*.

[6] When λ_1 and λ_2 coincide, they are degenerate eigenvalues. For simplicity in the present treatment we exclude this case, which would lead to the same conclusions as are obtained by supposing the roots to be distinct.

necessarily $M\boldsymbol{w} = 0$ for any $\boldsymbol{w}$, and so we must have

$$M = [0]. \tag{6-23}$$

If we write out the characteristic equation 6-19 explicitly, we have

$$\lambda^2 - \lambda \operatorname{tr} A + \det A = 0. \tag{6-24}$$

The following properties for the eigenvalues of a matrix follow from well-known theorems for algebraic equations when applied to Equation 6-24:

$$\lambda_1 + \lambda_2 = \operatorname{tr} A, \tag{6-25}$$

$$\lambda_1 \lambda_2 = \det A. \tag{6-26}$$

Finally it must be noted that, if in Equation 6-24 we substitute the matrix A for λ, the relation still holds (as a matrix equation); that is, we have

$$A^2 - A \operatorname{tr} A + [1] \det A = [0]. \tag{6-27}$$

In order to prove this, as we have mentioned, it is sufficient to show that the product of the matrix on the left-hand side of Equation 6-27 by each of the eigenvectors of A, $\boldsymbol{u}^{(1)}$ and $\boldsymbol{u}^{(2)}$, is zero; but this follows immediately from Equation 6-17 and from the fact that λ_1 and λ_2 are roots of Equation 6-24.

6-3 DIAGONALIZATION AND CALCULATION OF THE mth POWER OF A MATRIX

Later in this chapter we shall need to calculate the mth power, A^m, (m integer) of a square matrix A. Therefore in this section we give a general method to calculate this power. First we introduce the concept of diagonalization or reduction to diagonal form of a matrix. A matrix D is called *diagonal* if its elements d_{12} and d_{21} are zero (the matrix [1] is a particular case of diagonal matrix). It is straightforward to verify that the nonvanishing elements d_{11} and d_{22} lying on the principal diagonal of such a matrix coincide with the eigenvalues of the matrix:

$$d_{11} = \lambda_1, \qquad d_{22} = \lambda_2 \tag{6-28}$$

and that the eigenvector corresponding to the eigenvalue λ_j has the jth component equal to 1 and the other component equal to zero. Given an arbitrary matrix A, there corresponds to it in a unique way a diagonal matrix D having the same eigenvalues, that is, the matrix

$$D = \begin{bmatrix} \lambda_1 & 0 \\ 0 & \lambda_2 \end{bmatrix}. \tag{6-29}$$

(As usual, we suppose λ_1 and λ_2 to be distinct.) The operation of finding D for a given A (that is, essentially of finding the eigenvalues of A) is called the "diagonalization" of the matrix A. We now show that D is obtained from A by the relation

$$D = U^{-1}AU, \qquad (6\text{-}30)$$

where U is the matrix[7]

$$U = \begin{bmatrix} u_1^{(1)} & u_1^{(2)} \\ u_2^{(1)} & u_2^{(2)} \end{bmatrix}, \qquad (6\text{-}31)$$

formed by ordering the components of the two eigenvectors of A in adjacent columns. Indeed from the definition of eigenvector, we have

$$\{A - \lambda_i[1]\}u^{(i)} = 0, \qquad i = 1, 2. \qquad (6\text{-}32)$$

The left-hand sides of Equations 6-32 are vectors, that is, matrices with two rows and one column. If we dispose the components of these two vectors in adjacent columns so as to obtain a square matrix S with two rows and two columns, as a consequence of Equations 6-32 we have

$$S = [0]. \qquad (6\text{-}33)$$

However, as can be seen, S can be written in the form

$$S = AU - UD. \qquad (6\text{-}34)$$

By comparing Equations 6-33 and 6-34 and multiplying on the left by U^{-1} we just obtain Equation 6-30. The latter can be written in the equivalent form

$$A = UDU^{-1}. \qquad (6\text{-}35)$$

From this equation it is easy to determine the mth power of the matrix A. If, indeed, we write A in the form of Equation 6-35, we obtain

$$A^m = (UDU^{-1})(UDU^{-1})\cdots(UDU^{-1}) = UD^mU^{-1}. \qquad (6\text{-}36)$$

Now the nth power of the diagonal matrix D can be calculated immediately: it is still a diagonal matrix having $(\lambda_i)^m$ as eigenvalues, so that

$$D^m = \begin{bmatrix} \lambda_1{}^m & 0 \\ 0 & \lambda_2{}^m \end{bmatrix}. \qquad (6\text{-}37)$$

Hence the right-hand side of Equation 6-36 can easily be determined.

Let us now specify the conclusions we have reached for the case (which is of particular interest) where the matrices have real elements and their determinants are equal to unity. A matrix of this kind will be indicated by Δ. From Equation 6-26 it follows that in this case the product of the two eigenvalues λ_1, λ_2 is equal to 1. As the two eigenvalues are roots of the second-

[7] This matrix is always regular if the eigenvalues of A are distinct. For the proof, see Bellman (1960, p. 37).

order equation with real coefficients, Equation 6-24, they may be either both real or complex conjugate. In the latter case, we can write

$$\lambda_1 = e^{i\mu}, \qquad \lambda_2 = e^{-i\mu}, \tag{6-38}$$

with μ real and lying in the interval between 0 and π (these two values are to be excluded if the two eigenvalues are to be distinct). In this case we have

$$D = \begin{bmatrix} e^{i\mu} & 0 \\ 0 & e^{-i\mu} \end{bmatrix}, \qquad D^m = \begin{bmatrix} e^{im\mu} & 0 \\ 0 & e^{-im\mu} \end{bmatrix}. \tag{6-39}$$

If we define a matrix J as

$$J = U \begin{bmatrix} i & 0 \\ 0 & -i \end{bmatrix} U^{-1}, \tag{6-40}$$

from Equations 6-35, 6-36, and 6-39 we obtain (writing Δ for A)

$$\Delta = [1] \cos \mu + J \sin \mu, \tag{6-41}$$

$$\Delta^m = [1] \cos m\mu + J \sin m\mu. \tag{6-42}$$

It must be noted that, for U^{-1} (and hence J) to make sense, it is necessary that the eigenvalues be distinct, that is, that $\sin \mu \neq 0$. This can also be seen directly from Equation 6-41, which gives

$$J = \frac{\Delta - [1] \cos \mu}{\sin \mu}. \tag{6-43}$$

It can be easily seen from Equation 6-40 that

$$J^2 = -[1]. \tag{6-44}$$

Hence if we write the matrix Δ in the form 6-41, the matrix J, although it is a real matrix (as Equation 6-43 shows), plays the same role as the imaginary unit in the ordinary algebra of complex numbers. In particular, formula 6-42 appears as the analog of de Moivre's formula for the mth power of a complex number. This formula will be used later.

6-4   BETATRON OSCILLATIONS IN AN AG SYNCHROTRON. CHARACTERISTIC MATRICES

Let us now return to the study of AG synchrotrons, for which we treat in detail the case of the vertical oscillations (the treatment of the radial oscillations can be obtained by substituting the quantity $1 - n$ for the field index n). Let us consider the motion of a particle in a given sector. If $n > 0$, the vertical displacement is

$$z = z_0 \cos ks + \frac{z_0'}{k} \sin ks, \tag{6-45}$$

where $z_0 = z(0)$ and $z_0' = z'(0)$, the origin of s is at the entrance of the sector, and k is given by Equation 6-2. If $n < 0$, Equation 6-45 still holds but in this case k is imaginary. Let us put

$$k = ik' \qquad (6\text{-}46)$$

so that k' is real, and, using the identities

$$\sin(ix) = i \sinh x; \qquad \cos(ix) = \cosh x, \qquad (6\text{-}47)$$

we can write Equation 6-45 in the form

$$z = z_0 \cosh k's + \frac{z_0'}{k'} \sinh k's. \qquad (6\text{-}48)$$

In the sectors with uniform field ($n = 0$) or in the straight sections without magnetic field, there is no force acting in the vertical direction,[8] and then

$$z = z_0 + z_0's. \qquad (6\text{-}49)$$

The complete trajectory consists of portions of curves of these three kinds. For the continuity of z and z' along the trajectory, the values z_0 and z_0' at the entrance of each section must be equal to the values of z and z' at the exit of the preceding section. These can be obtained in terms of the values at the entrance by means of the corresponding equation 6-45, 6-48, or 6-49, where one puts the length of the sector in place of s. Thus, given z_0 and z_0' for the first sector, the whole trajectory is determined in principle.

We now show how, by applying matrix algebra, we can easily determine z and z' after an arbitrary number of sectors, once z_0 and z_0' are given at the beginning of the trajectory. Let us first consider a focusing sector ($n > 0$) where Equation 6-45 holds, and let us write down also the equation obtained by differentiating it and multiplying it by an arbitrary constant a, having the dimensions of a length.[9] We therefore have the following system:

$$z = z_0 \cos ks + \frac{z_0'}{k} \sin ks,$$
$$az' = -kaz_0 \sin ks + az_0' \cos ks. \qquad (6\text{-}50)$$

[8] It should be noted that, for the radial oscillations, the sectors with $n = 0$ are not comparable to straight sections because in those sectors $k = (1 - n)^{1/2}/R = 1/R$, and so they are focusing. The sectors with $n = 1$ instead are similar to straight sections and produce no focusing.

[9] This constant, introduced for dimensional reasons, will usually be left unspecified; only in some cases, for convenience, a particular value will be chosen (as in Sections 6-6 and 6-12).

The quantities defined by these two equations can be considered as the two components of a vector $u(s)$ defined in a particular representative two-dimensional space

$$u(s) = \begin{bmatrix} z \\ az' \end{bmatrix}. \tag{6-51}$$

This vector completely characterizes the state of the particle (position and inclination of the trajectory) at the abscissa s, as far as the motion in the vertical direction is concerned. Let us now calculate the relation between the values of u at the entrance and at the exit of a focusing sector of length l. If we put $s = 0$ at the entrance and put $u_0 = u(0)$, $u_1 = u(l)$, we have

$$u_1 = \begin{bmatrix} z_1 \\ az_1' \end{bmatrix} = \begin{bmatrix} z_0 \cos kl + \dfrac{z_0'}{k} \sin kl \\ -kaz_0 \sin kl + az_0' \cos kl \end{bmatrix}. \tag{6-52}$$

We can define a matrix Γ_1, characteristic of the sector considered, by means of the relation

$$\Gamma_1 = \begin{bmatrix} \cos \Theta & \dfrac{1}{ka} \sin \Theta \\ -ka \sin \Theta & \cos \Theta \end{bmatrix}. \tag{6-53}$$

where

$$\Theta = kl. \tag{6-54}$$

In this way Equation 6-52 can be written in the form

$$u_1 = \Gamma_1 u_0. \tag{6-55}$$

Thus, given the initial conditions for a sector (expressed by u_0), we obtain the initial conditions for the following sector (expressed by u_1), by multiplying u_0 by Γ_1.

It should be noted that these formulas hold not only for a focusing sector (when k is real) but also for a defocusing one; in this case it is convenient to use Equations 6-46 and 6-47. Thus from Equation 6-48 and its derivative we obtain the matrix Γ_1 relevant to a sector of length l with $n < 0$:

$$\Gamma_1 = \begin{bmatrix} \cosh \Theta' & \dfrac{1}{k'a} \sinh \Theta' \\ k'a \sinh \Theta' & \cosh \Theta' \end{bmatrix}, \tag{6-56}$$

where

$$\Theta' = k'l. \tag{6-57}$$

For a straight section (or a sector with $n = 0$) of length L, the following matrix is similarly obtained from Equation 6-49 (or from Equation 6-53 by letting k tend to zero):

$$\Gamma_1 = \begin{bmatrix} 1 & L/a \\ 0 & 1 \end{bmatrix}. \tag{6-58}$$

The matrix corresponding to a sector is called the "characteristic matrix" of the sector. All the Γ's are matrices of order 2 and have determinant equal to 1. If we apply Equation 6-55 to the next sector, with characteristic matrix Γ_2, we have

$$u_2 = \Gamma_2 u_1, \tag{6-59}$$

where u_2 refers to the exit of the second sector. By substituting Equation 6-55 into Equation 6-59 it follows that

$$u_2 = \Gamma_2 \Gamma_1 u_0. \tag{6-60}$$

Similarly, if u_n is the value of u at the exit of the nth sector, we have

$$u_n = \Gamma_n \Gamma_{n-1} \ldots \Gamma_2 \Gamma_1 u_0, \tag{6-61}$$

where $\Gamma_i (i = 1, 2, \ldots, n)$ is the characteristic matrix of the ith sector. In particular, if we consider the l sectors constituting a periodic element, it is useful to define the matrix Δ (characteristic matrix of the entire periodic element) as follows:

$$\Delta = \Gamma_l \Gamma_{l-1} \ldots \Gamma_2 \Gamma_1. \tag{6-62}$$

As all the Γ_i's have determinant equal to 1, by an obvious extension of Equation 6-10, we obtain

$$\det \Delta = 1. \tag{6-63}$$

It must be noted that, as the machine has a periodic closed structure, the beginning of the periodic element is arbitrary and it is not even necessary that it coincide with the beginning of a sector. By changing the position where the periodic element begins one changes the form of the matrix Δ: however, this choice cannot influence the conclusions of physical interest which will be reached.

Let us call $u_{(m)}$ the value of u after the particle has passed through m consecutive periodic elements. We have

$$u_{(m)} = \Delta^m u_0. \tag{6-64}$$

Obviously also for the radial oscillations a formula of the type of Equation 6-64 will hold, but the matrix Δ will be different.

6-5   THE STABILITY CONDITION FOR BETATRON OSCILLATIONS IN AN AG SYNCHROTRON

We will say that there is "orbital stability" if displacements, both vertical and radial, from the central orbit remain *bounded* as the number of turns in the machine increases. In terms of the representative vectors discussed in the previous section, this means that the magnitude of $u_{(m)}$, both for vertical and for horizontal oscillations, remains bounded while m increases indefinitely. (It should be recalled that, during the acceleration, the particle carries out an enormous number of turns.) For both kinds of oscillation, if λ_1 and λ_2 are the eigenvalues of the matrix Δ and $\boldsymbol{v}_1$, $\boldsymbol{v}_2$ the corresponding eigenvectors, by the property of completeness expressed by Equation 6-21, we can put $\boldsymbol{u}_0$ into the form

$$\boldsymbol{u}_0 = \alpha_1 \boldsymbol{v}_1 + \alpha_2 \boldsymbol{v}_2, \tag{6-65}$$

where α_1 and α_2 are known coefficients. If we use Equation 6-64 and the eigenvector property 6-17, we obtain

$$\boldsymbol{u}_{(m)} = \alpha_1 \Delta^m \boldsymbol{v}_1 + \alpha_2 \Delta^m \boldsymbol{v}_2 = \alpha_1 \lambda_1{}^m \boldsymbol{v}_1 + \alpha_2 \lambda_2{}^m \boldsymbol{v}_2. \tag{6-66}$$

At this point let us take into account that the matrix Δ is of the type discussed in Section 6-3, that is, a matrix of order 2 whose elements are real and whose determinant is equal to 1. The characteristic equation of such a matrix is

$$\lambda^2 - (\operatorname{tr} \Delta)\lambda + 1 = 0. \tag{6-67}$$

Now three cases must be considered:

1. If the roots λ_1 and λ_2 of Equation 6-67 are real and different, one of them is in modulus larger and the other smaller than 1, since their product is 1. In this case, the trajectory is *not* stable; indeed, the mth power of the eigenvalue with modulus greater than 1 increases indefinitely with m and hence, as Equation 6-66 shows, also the magnitude of $\boldsymbol{u}_{(m)}$ increases indefinitely.

2. If λ_1 and λ_2 are complex conjugate, they can be written in the form 6-38; then $\lambda_1{}^m$ and $\lambda_2{}^m$ have modulus equal to one for all m, and hence the magnitude of $\boldsymbol{u}_{(m)}$ remains bounded as m increases and the trajectory is stable.

3. In the intermediate case $\lambda_1 = \lambda_2 = 1$ and the trajectory is theoretically stable, but this case is so close to the unstable range that it must be discarded in practice.

In conclusion, in order to have stability in the vertical direction (and a similar discussion could be made for the radial direction) we must require that the roots of Equation 6-67 be complex, that is, that the discriminant be positive,

$$|\operatorname{tr} \Delta| < 2. \tag{6-68}$$

If this condition is satisfied, the two eigenvalues λ_1 and λ_2 can be written in the form 6-38, namely

$$\lambda_1 = e^{i\mu}, \qquad \lambda_2 = e^{-i\mu}, \tag{6-69}$$

where μ is determined by the condition 6-25, which gives

$$\cos \mu = \tfrac{1}{2} \operatorname{tr} \Delta. \tag{6-70}$$

The expression 6-66 of $u_{(m)}$, which in this case is

$$u_{(m)} = \alpha_1 e^{im\mu} v_1 + \alpha_2 e^{-im\mu} v_2 , \qquad (6\text{-}71)$$

can be written in an alternative form where the resolution 6-65 of the initial vector u_0 does not appear. By substituting directly Equation 6-42 into Equation 6-64, we have

$$u_{(m)} = u_0 \cos m\mu + J u_0 \sin m\mu, \qquad (6\text{-}72)$$

where the matrix J is defined by Equation 6-40 or 6-43.

6-6   APPLICATION OF THE MATRIX FORMALISM TO THE CASE OF A RACETRACK SYNCHROTRON

As we have mentioned in Section 5-8, we shall treat the case of the racetrack synchrotron (that is a CG synchrotron containing straight sections) in this chapter, although it is not a strong-focusing synchrotron: this is justified because this case offers a simple example of the application of the formalism described in the previous sections.

We shall refer to the structure shown in Figure 1-8, where the periodic element consists of the succession of a magnet sector (with $0 < n < 1$) of length l and a straight section of length L. The matrix Γ_1 for the magnet sector is given by Equation 6-53, which, by choosing for convenience $a = 1/k$, becomes

$$\Gamma_1 = \begin{bmatrix} \cos \Theta & \sin \Theta \\ -\sin \Theta & \cos \Theta \end{bmatrix}, \qquad (6\text{-}73)$$

where, as previously (see Equation 6-54),

$$\Theta = kl. \qquad (6\text{-}74)$$

We recall that the expressions for k (see Equation 6-2) are the following:

$$k = \frac{n^{1/2}}{R} \qquad \text{for vertical oscillations,}$$

$$k = \frac{(1 - n)^{1/2}}{R} \quad \text{for radial oscillations.} \qquad (6\text{-}75)$$

Hence, if the racetrack has N magnet sectors (in Figure 1-8, $N = 4$),

$$\Theta = \frac{2\pi}{N} n^{1/2} \qquad \text{for vertical oscillations,}$$

$$\Theta = \frac{2\pi}{N} (1 - n)^{1/2} \quad \text{for radial oscillations.} \qquad (6\text{-}76)$$

It can be seen that, for $0 < n < 1$, Θ is always less than π. The matrix Γ_2 characteristic of the straight section is given by Equation 6-58, which in our case becomes

$$\Gamma_2 = \begin{bmatrix} 1 & kL \\ 0 & 1 \end{bmatrix}. \tag{6-77}$$

In this case $\Delta = \Gamma_2\Gamma_1$ and, by carrying out the multiplication, one obtains

$$\Delta = \begin{bmatrix} \cos\Theta - \xi\sin\Theta & \sin\Theta + \xi\cos\Theta \\ -\sin\Theta & \cos\Theta \end{bmatrix}, \tag{6-78}$$

where we have put

$$\xi = kL. \tag{6-79}$$

The stability condition 6-68 therefore becomes

$$|\, 2\cos\Theta - \xi\sin\Theta\,| < 2 \tag{6-80}$$

and μ is given by (see Equation 6-70)

$$\cos\mu = \tfrac{1}{2}\operatorname{tr}\Delta = \cos\Theta - \tfrac{1}{2}\xi\sin\Theta. \tag{6-81}$$

The condition 6-80 can also be written in the form

$$-1 < \cos\Theta - \tfrac{1}{2}\xi\sin\Theta < 1. \tag{6-82}$$

As $\sin\Theta > 0$, the second of these inequalities is always satisfied. The first inequality instead leads to the condition

$$\frac{\xi}{2} < \frac{1 + \cos\Theta}{\sin\Theta} = \cotan\frac{\Theta}{2}. \tag{6-83}$$

Using Equations 6-74, 6-76, and 6-79 we finally obtain the conditions

$$\frac{L}{2R} < \frac{1}{n^{1/2}}\cotan\frac{\pi n^{1/2}}{N} \qquad\text{for vertical oscillations,}$$

$$\tag{6-84}$$

$$\frac{L}{2R} < \frac{1}{(1-n)^{1/2}}\cotan\frac{\pi(1-n)^{1/2}}{N} \quad\text{for radial oscillations.}$$

The conditions 6-84 give a limitation to the choice of L for a given n (or vice versa) which, however, is not very restrictive in practice. In fact, it is easily seen that the n values imposing the most restrictive condition to L/R are $n = 0$ and $n = 1$, for both of which the most restrictive of the conditions 6-84 reduces to $L/(2R) < \cotan(\pi/N)$. Since, in all practical cases, $N \geq 4$, $L < R$, this condition is largely satisfied.

If the straight sections are short compared with the magnet sectors (usually, L/R is of the order of 0.3), the oscillations will not be very different from the sinusoidal oscillations that would occur in the absence of straight sections.

In Figure 6-4, the solid line schematically shows the behavior of the vertical oscillations $z(s)$ during one entire revolution of the particle in the machine, as a function of the distance s along the unperturbed orbit. The dashed line represents a sinusoidal function $\hat{z}(s)$ of the proper amplitude and frequency, which approximates the actual oscillations. It has been chosen so that it coincides with the actual displacement at the beginning of each periodic

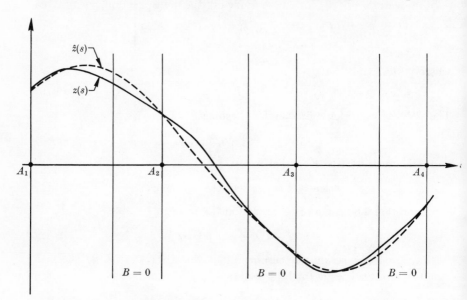

FIGURE 6-4. *The vertical displacement $z(s)$ as a function of distance along the unperturbed orbit in a racetrack synchrotron. The dashed line shows the approximating sinusoid $\hat{z}(s)$, which coincides with $z(s)$ at the points $A_1, A_2, A_3, \ldots$.*

element (points $A_1, A_2, \ldots$ in Figure 6-4). Let us now determine the wave number $\hat{k}$ and the amplitude $\hat{A}$ of this oscillation. Then by comparison with the values derived in the previous chapter for a completely circular synchrotron we can determine the influence of inserting the straight sections. The displacement $z_{(m)}$ at the exit of the mth periodic element is given by the first component of the vector $\boldsymbol{u}_{(m)}$, defined by Equation 6-64. In order to calculate $\boldsymbol{u}_{(m)}$ we shall use Equation 6-72; for this purpose we need to determine J, which, through Equation 6-43 and the expressions 6-78 for Δ and 6-81 for $\cos \mu$, is finally given by

$$J = \frac{\Delta - [1]\cos\mu}{\sin\mu} = \frac{1}{\sin\mu}\begin{bmatrix} -\dfrac{\xi}{2}\sin\Theta & \sin\Theta + \xi\cos\Theta \\ -\sin\Theta & \dfrac{\xi}{2}\sin\Theta \end{bmatrix} \quad (6\text{-}85)$$

If we write out the first component of the right-hand side of Equation 6-72 explicitly, recalling that the components of $\boldsymbol{u}_0$ are z_0 and z_0'/k, we have

$$z_{(m)} = z_0 \cos m\mu + \left(J_{11}z_0 + J_{12}\frac{z_0'}{k}\right) \sin m\mu$$

$$= z_0 \cos m\mu + \left[-z_0\frac{\xi}{2}\sin\Theta + \frac{z_0'}{k}(\sin\Theta + \xi\cos\Theta)\right]\frac{\sin m\mu}{\sin\mu}. \qquad (6\text{-}86)$$

Equation 6-86 can be written in the form

$$z_{(m)} = p \cos m\mu + q \sin m\mu = A \sin(m\mu + b), \qquad (6\text{-}87)$$

where the constants p, q or A, b can be determined by comparison with Equation 6-86.

Let us now introduce the expression of the approximating sinusoid,

$$\hat{z}(s) = \hat{A} \sin(\hat{k}s + \hat{b}), \qquad (6\text{-}88)$$

with the requirement that $\hat{z}(s)$ at the exit of the mth periodic element, that is, for $s = m(l + L)$, be equal to the corresponding $z_{(m)}$ given by Equations 6-86 and 6-87. This is obtained by taking $\hat{A} = A$, $\hat{b} = b$, and

$$\hat{k} = \frac{\mu}{l + L}. \qquad (6\text{-}89)$$

The most interesting case is when ξ is sufficiently small that the expression 6-81 for $\cos\mu$ can be approximated in the form

$$\cos\mu = \cos\Theta - \frac{\xi}{2}\sin\Theta \simeq \cos\left(\Theta + \frac{\xi}{2}\right) \qquad (6\text{-}90)$$

and hence

$$\mu \simeq \Theta + \frac{\xi}{2} = k\left(l + \frac{L}{2}\right), \qquad (6\text{-}91)$$

so that Equation 6-89 becomes

$$\hat{k} = \frac{k}{\Lambda_0}, \qquad (6\text{-}92)$$

where

$$\Lambda_0 = \frac{l + L}{l + L/2} > 1. \qquad (6\text{-}93)$$

It follows that the angular frequency of the vertical betatron oscillations (proportional to k) is decreased by a factor Λ_0 with respect to the case without straight sections:

$$\hat{\omega}_z = \omega_z/\Lambda_0. \qquad (6\text{-}94)$$

The same argument applies to radial oscillations also, and again one finds

$$\hat{\omega}_r = \omega_r/\Lambda_0 . \tag{6-95}$$

Also the angular velocity of revolution is decreased by the presence of straight sections, but by a different factor. As the path of a particle per turn is increased by a factor

$$\Lambda = 1 + \frac{L}{l} > \Lambda_0 , \tag{6-96}$$

we have

$$\hat{\omega} = \omega/\Lambda \tag{6-97}$$

(where ω, as usual, is v/R).

As the frequency of the betatron oscillations is smaller, one expects their amplitude (for given initial conditions) to be larger with respect to the case of a completely circular synchrotron, because of the correspondence mentioned in Section 6-1. The value of the amplitude A in Equation 6-87 (to be derived from Equation 6-86) depends, apart from the parameters of the machine, on the initial conditions z_0 and z_0'. In order to get an idea of the effect, let us suppose $z_0 = 0$; that is, let us consider the case of a particle injected in the median plane but with a velocity slightly divergent from it. In this case, if we express μ by means of Equation 6-91, expand all the quantities to the first order in ξ, and recall that the amplitude A_0 in the absence of straight sections is z_0'/k (see Equation 6-3)[10], we obtain

$$\frac{A}{A_0} \simeq 1 + \frac{\xi}{2} \cotan \Theta > 1. \tag{6-98}$$

Equation 6-98 can be applied to the radial oscillations too, by referring to the second line of the expressions 6-75 and 6-76. As an example, for a four-sector synchrotron with $n = 0.6$, Equation 6-98 gives

$$\frac{A}{A_0} = 1 + 0.144 \frac{L}{R} \quad \text{for vertical oscillations;}$$

$$\frac{A}{A_0} = 1 + 0.207 \frac{L}{R} \quad \text{for radial oscillations.}$$

$$\tag{6-99}$$

It can be seen that the increase of the amplitude is small, so that the presence of the straight sections does not introduce serious problems related to the size of the doughnut and of the magnet.

As far as the phase oscillations in a racetrack synchrotron are concerned, if the straight sections are not too long the discussion of Section 5-2 and the

---

[10] In Equation 6-3, the amplitude was denoted by Z.

following is still valid. The only difference lies in the value of the momentum compaction α, and hence in the constant K, which depends on α through Equation 5-34. The value of α for the racetrack must be calculated directly from Equation 1-38. In this case the total path of a particle per turn in the machine is given by

$$S = 2\pi r + NL, \tag{6-100}$$

and hence, as L is the same for all the trajectories,

$$\frac{dS}{S} = \frac{2\pi dr}{2\pi r + NL} = \frac{dr/r}{1 + NL/2\pi r} \simeq \frac{dr/r}{\Lambda}, \tag{6-101}$$

where in the last step we have put $r \simeq R$ in the denominator (neglecting a higher-order correction). Therefore the momentum compaction in a racetrack, $\hat{\alpha}$, is given by (see Equation 5-39)

$$\hat{\alpha} = \frac{dP/P}{dS/S} = \Lambda \frac{dP/P}{dr/r} = \Lambda (1 - n), \tag{6-102}$$

whereas without straight sections, as we have seen, $\alpha = 1 - n$. Therefore it can be seen that $\hat{\alpha} > \alpha$. The value of the quantity K defined by Equation 5-34 then becomes the following:

$$\hat{K} = 1 + \frac{1}{\beta^2} \left\{ \frac{1}{\Lambda(1 - n)} - 1 \right\}. \tag{6-103}$$

Since $\Lambda > 1$, $\hat{K} < K$; however, the difference is small, and, in all practical cases, never such as to make $\hat{K} < 1$ (this would happen only if $\Lambda > 1/(1 - n)$). Therefore all the results obtained in the previous chapter for the phase oscillations still hold.

As far as the resonances are concerned, the general discussion of Section 5-7 still holds as long as the effective frequencies of revolution and of the vertical and radial oscillations (given by Equations 6-97, 6-94, and 6-95) are considered. Thus Equations 5-81 and 5-82 become, respectively,

$$p\hat{\omega} + q\hat{\omega}_z + r\hat{\omega}_r = 0, \tag{6-104}$$

and

$$p\frac{\Lambda_0}{\Lambda} + qn^{1/2} + r(1 - n)^{1/2} = 0. \tag{6-105}$$

As $\Lambda/\Lambda_0 = 1 + \frac{1}{2}L/l$ is slightly larger than 1, some of the forbidden values of n are slightly modified. However, the values given in Table 5-1 ($p = 0$) remain unaltered.

6-7   A SIMPLE EXAMPLE OF AG SYNCHROTRON.
THE STABILITY DIAGRAM

Let us consider a simple case of an AG synchrotron in which the periodic element consists of only two sectors, with field indexes respectively equal to n_1 and n_2, and both of length l. Let us suppose $n_1 > 1$, $n_2 < -1$ and call $N = 2\pi R/l$ the total number of sectors. We shall first consider the vertical oscillations, and, as usual, put (see Equations 6-2 and 6-46)

$$k_1 = \frac{n_1^{1/2}}{R}, \qquad k_2' = \frac{(-n_2)^{1/2}}{R}. \tag{6-106}$$

The matrix Γ_1 characteristic of the focusing sector (index n_1) will be a matrix of the type given by Equation 6-53, that is,

$$\Gamma_1 = \begin{bmatrix} \cos\Theta_1 & \dfrac{1}{k_1 a}\sin\Theta_1 \\ -k_1 a \sin\Theta_1 & \cos\Theta_1 \end{bmatrix}, \tag{6-107}$$

where we have put (see Equation 6-54)

$$\Theta_1 = k_1 l = \frac{2\pi n_1^{1/2}}{N}. \tag{6-108}$$

The matrix Γ_2 characteristic of the defocusing sector (index n_2) will be a matrix of the type given by Equation 6-56,[11] that is,

$$\Gamma_2 = \begin{bmatrix} \cosh\Theta_2 & \dfrac{1}{k_2 a}\sinh\Theta_2 \\ k_2 a \sinh\Theta_2 & \cosh\Theta_2 \end{bmatrix}, \tag{6-109}$$

where (see Equation 6-57)

$$\Theta_2 = k_2 l = \frac{2\pi}{N}(-n_2)^{1/2}. \tag{6-110}$$

If we carry out the product $\Delta_z = \Gamma_2\Gamma_1$ (where the subscript z indicates that we are referring to the vertical oscillations), we find that the trace of Δ_z is given by

$$\mathrm{tr}\,\Delta_z = 2\cos\Theta_1\cosh\Theta_2 + \left(\frac{k_2}{k_1} - \frac{k_1}{k_2}\right)\sin\Theta_1\sinh\Theta_2, \tag{6-111}$$

or, using Equations 6-108 and 6-110,

$$\mathrm{tr}\,\Delta_z = 2\cos\Theta_1\cosh\Theta_2 + \left(\frac{\Theta_2}{\Theta_1} - \frac{\Theta_1}{\Theta_2}\right)\sin\Theta_1\sinh\Theta_2$$

$$= 2\tau_z(\Theta_1, \Theta_2). \tag{6-112}$$

---

[11] In the following, for simplicity, we suppress the prime in all the quantities referring to the defocusing sectors.

The function $\tau_z(\Theta_1, \Theta_2)$ defined by Equation 6-112 is a universal function of Θ_1 and Θ_2. The stability condition 6-68 requires this function to range between -1 and $+1$. For the study of this condition, let us consider (see Figure 6-5) $\Theta_1{}^2$, $\Theta_2{}^2$ as Cartesian coordinates on a plane, where every machine of the kind we have considered will be represented by a point in the quadrant $\Theta_1{}^2 > 0$, $\Theta_2{}^2 > 0$. On this plane let us trace the curves described by $\tau_z = +1$ and $\tau_z = -1$ (curves a and b of Figure 6-5). The region between these two curves contains all the pairs of values $\Theta_1{}^2$, $\Theta_2{}^2$ which give stability for the vertical oscillations.

Let us now consider the radial oscillations. In this case again we must calculate the characteristic matrix Δ_r of the periodic element for these oscilla-

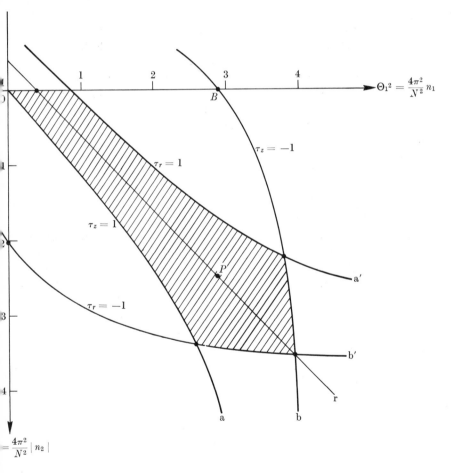

FIGURE 6-5. *The stability diagram for a completely circular AG synchrotron made up with two kinds of sector only, for $N = 10$.*

tions and impose the condition $|\tfrac{1}{2} \operatorname{tr} \Delta_r| = |\tau_r| < 1$. As the beginning of the periodic element is arbitrary, it is convenient to consider now the focusing sector (with index n_2) as the first one, and the defocusing sector (with index n_1) as the second one. Thus the procedure we have followed above remains unaltered, as long as we substitute $1 - n_2$ for n_1 and $1 - n_1$ for n_2, that is, if we use $\Theta_2{}^2 + 4\pi^2/N^2$ instead of $\Theta_1{}^2$ and $\Theta_1{}^2 - 4\pi^2/N^2$ instead of $\Theta_2{}^2$. Therefore

$$\tau_r(\Theta_1{}^2, \Theta_2{}^2) = \tau_z\!\left(\Theta_2{}^2 + \frac{4\pi^2}{N^2}, \Theta_1{}^2 - \frac{4\pi^2}{N^2}\right). \tag{6-113}$$

The transformation described by Equation 6-113 corresponds, in the plane of Figure 6-5, to a reflection with respect to the line r which intercepts two segments of length $4\pi^2/N^2$ on the axes. (Their lengths are usually small compared to the length of the segment AB.) By this symmetry the curves a and b are transformed, respectively, into the curves a' and b' which are just the curves of the equations $\tau_r = \pm 1$. The points lying in the region between the curves a' and b' correspond to machines which give stability for the radial oscillations. The curves drawn in Figure 6-5 constitute the so-called *stability diagram* of the machine, which encloses the region where there is stability both for the radial and for the vertical oscillations (apart from resonance phenomena, which are discussed in Section 6-8). This region is shaded in Figure 6-5; because of its form it is sometimes called the "necktie diagram." Actually the curves drawn in Figure 6-5 have other branches also[12]; therefore we also get other small "islands" of stability, different from the main diagram, for large values of Θ_1 and Θ_2. These regions are never considered in practice because of the large values of the field index required.

In the early theoretical designs of AG synchrotrons, it was thought that N could be made very large so as to remain inside the stability diagram even for very large values of n_1 and $|n_2|$ (of the order of 1000) and to permit an enormous reduction of the size of the doughnut and of the magnet. However, as is shown in the next section, even inside the "necktie" there are restrictions on the choice of the representative point and these become more and more severe as N increases so that the construction of the machine is more and more difficult. Thus the field index cannot be made arbitrarily large. In practice n_1 and $|n_2|$ are chosen of the order of a few hundreds. Often for simplicity in the construction of the magnet (see Section 6-10) one chooses $n_2 = -n_1$: the line in Figure 6-5 along which this condition is satisfied for large values of N practically coincides with r, the line of symmetry of the diagram. On this line, the most "central" position corresponds to $\tau_z = \tau_r = 0$ (the point P in Figure 6-5), which for a sufficiently large N is equivalent to $n_1 = |n_2|$

---

[12] In order to see this, it is sufficient to note that, on the axis $\Theta_2{}^2 = 0$, Equation 6-112 becomes $\tau^2 = \cos \Theta_1 - \Theta_1 \sin\tfrac{1}{2}\Theta_1$, and this expression becomes equal to $+1$ and -1 an infinite number of times as $\Theta_1{}^2$ increases.

$= N^2/16$. It should be noted that, during the operation of the machine, the representative point moves slightly inside the stability diagram, because of effects of partial saturation of the magnet iron, which occur in a different manner in different parts of the magnetic field (as it changes rapidly with radius), and so the value of n changes slightly.

Finally, we must add that also in the AG synchrotron described as an example in this section (and, in general, in all the types of AG synchrotrons), it is possible to apply the procedure, used for the racetrack in Section 6-6, of approximating the behavior of the betatron oscillations by a sinusoidal function of the proper frequency and amplitude. If we consider for example the vertical oscillations, Equation 6-87, which was derived for the racetrack, has a general validity because its dependence on m derives directly from the relation 6-72, independently of the structure of the matrix Δ. Therefore we can again look for an approximate expression for the vertical displacement $z(s)$ of the kind of Equation 6-88, which coincides with the actual displacement at the beginning of each periodic element. In our case, in place of Equation 6-89, for the wave numbers k_z of the vertical oscillations we obtain the expression

$$k_z = \frac{\mu_z}{2l} = \frac{N\mu_z}{4\pi R}, \qquad (6\text{-}114)$$

where $2 \cos \mu_z = \text{tr } \Delta_z$ (see Equation 6-70). From Equation 6-114 we can derive the ratio $\nu_z = \omega_z/\omega$ between the frequency of the vertical oscillations and the frequency of revolution. As the wave number corresponding to the orbital motion in a completely circular machine is given by $1/R$, we find

$$\nu_z = \frac{\omega_z}{\omega} = k_z R = \frac{N\mu_z}{4\pi}. \qquad (6\text{-}115)$$

Similarly, for the radial oscillations

$$\nu_r = \frac{\omega_r}{\omega} = \frac{N\mu_r}{4\pi}. \qquad (6\text{-}116)$$

In the case considered in this section, μ_r and μ_z always lie between 0 and π, because of the stability condition; indeed, the structure of Equation 6-112 shows that, as one moves along a line $\cos \mu_r = \text{const}$, $\cos \mu_z$ assumes once and only once all the values from -1 to 1, and vice versa, so that μ_r and μ_z always lie in the interval $(0, \pi)$. It follows that the ratios given by Equations 6-115 and 6-116 are increasing functions of N and for N of the order of 10 and for reasonable choices of μ_r and μ_z they are already larger than 1. Figure 6-6 shows the behavior of the vertical oscillations in an AG synchrotron with many sectors: the dashed line indicates the approximating sinusoid and the wiggles of the actual motion are exhibited.

It is convenient at this point to generalize formulas 6-115 and 6-116 to the case of an arbitrary AG structure. Referring again to the treatment of Section 6-6 of the vertical oscillations, it is easily seen that the formula for the wave number k_z, in general, is given by

$$k_z = \frac{\mu_z}{S_0},$$ (6-117)

where S_0 is the length of the periodic element. On the other hand, the wave number of the orbital motion is given by

$$k_0 = \frac{2\pi}{S} = \frac{2\pi}{MS_0},$$ (6-118)

where M is the number of periodic elements and S the total path of the particles in one revolution. From Equations 6-117 and 6-118 it follows that

$$\nu_z = \frac{\omega_z}{\omega} = \frac{k_z}{k_0} = \frac{M\mu_z}{2\pi}.$$ (6-119)

Similarly, for the radial oscillations

$$\nu_r = \frac{\omega_r}{\omega} = \frac{M\mu_r}{2\pi}.$$ (6-120)

If we specialize Equations 6-119 and 6-120 to the case described in this section we again obtain Equations 6-115 and 6-116. It should be noted that for periodic

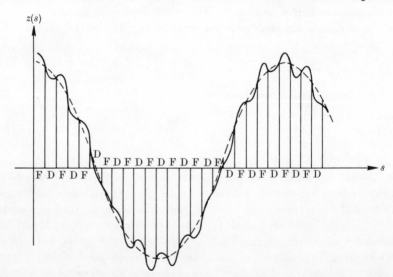

FIGURE 6-6.   *The vertical displacement $z(s)$ as a function of the distance s along the unperturbed orbit for a 28-sector AG synchrotron. The letters F and D indicate the alternating focusing and defocusing sectors.*

elements of a complicated structure containing many sectors, even if M becomes small but N is unaltered, the frequency ratios ν_z and ν_r remain the same. In general, indeed, it is not true that the quantities μ_r and μ_z are necessarily less than π: they can be larger than π for periodic elements with a complicated structure containing more than one sector of the same kind. More precisely, if a periodic element contains r sectors of the same kind, the μ's will lie between 0 and $r\pi$. In order to understand this in a simple case, let us consider the succession of two periodic elements of the machine described in this section as a new periodic element: this is certainly possible if the total number of sectors in the machine is a multiple of 4. In this case, for both kinds of oscillations, the new characteristic matrix is $\Delta' = \Delta^2$, and, from Equation 6-42, it can be seen that everything goes as before if μ is substituted by $\mu' = 2\mu$. The stability condition becomes $|\cos \mu'| < 1$: the stability diagram of Figure 6-5 remains the same but its boundary contains only lines $\cos \mu' = +1$; the lines $\cos \mu' = -1$ are inside the necktie, and if we move along a curve $\cos \mu_r' = \text{const}$, $\cos \mu_z'$ goes from 1 to -1 and again from -1 to 1, that is, μ_z' goes from 0 to 2π. Let us now imagine that a short straight section is inserted between the couple of adjacent elements considered. In this way the periodic element is no longer divisible, but the value of μ' cannot be substantially different. In conclusion, if the periodic element is made more complicated, μ increases by practically the same factor as M decreases so that in Equations 6-119 and 6-120 the value of the ratio does not change significantly.

6-8 ERRORS OF ALIGNMENT AND RESONANCES

We have mentioned in Section 6-1 that in AG synchrotrons the precision of the construction and assembly of the magnet has a great importance. In this section we specify this concept quantitatively and at the same time we study the influence of the resonances between the betatron oscillations and the orbital motion (which already have been discussed for the CG synchrotron in Section 5-7). The most important error of assembly is misalignment in position (both radial and vertical) of the magnet sectors. In each sector the position of the equilibrium orbit with respect to the magnet is well defined: it is the arc of circle lying in the median plane, where the magnetic field has at each instant of time the required value with respect to the energy of the particles. The errors of alignment result in the fact that the ends of the parts of equilibrium orbit in two adjacent sectors[13] do not coincide, and the corresponding tangents are not parallel. The error of alignment between the hth sector and the next can be defined by giving the displacement ϵ_h and the

---

[13] The same argument can be extended to the case where there is a straight section between the two sectors.

angular divergence ψ_h (see Figure 6-7) at the connection between the two sectors, both in the vertical and in the radial directions. (All the following treatment can be applied to either direction.) If we put $\tan \psi_h = \epsilon_h'$, we can introduce the two-dimensional vector

$$\boldsymbol{p}_h = \begin{bmatrix} \epsilon_h \\ a\epsilon_h' \end{bmatrix} \tag{6-121}$$

(where a is the factor, of the dimensions of a length, introduced in Section 6-4). This vector represents the alignment error completely. Of course ϵ and ϵ' are small quantities. Let us study the effect of the alignment errors on the motion of the particles in a very simple case; the results obtained can easily

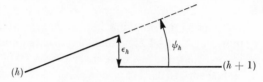

FIGURE 6-7. *Diagram illustrating the alignment errors between the h-th sector and the next.*

be generalized (Sands and Touschek, 1953). Let us suppose that alignment errors are present only at one point in the machine, that is, where the particles pass from a certain sector to the next, and let us assume this point as the beginning of a periodic element. Since there is only one vector $\boldsymbol{p}$ we drop the subscript. Then if Δ is the characteristic matrix and M the number of periodic elements, after one turn we have (see Equation 6-64)

$$\boldsymbol{u}_{(M)} = \Delta^M \boldsymbol{u}_0 + \boldsymbol{p}, \tag{6-122}$$

and after two turns

$$\boldsymbol{u}_{(2M)} = \Delta^M \boldsymbol{u}_{(M)} + \boldsymbol{p} = \Delta^{2M} \boldsymbol{u}_0 + (\Delta^M + [1])\boldsymbol{p}. \tag{6-123}$$

Similarly, after m turns (that is, after mM periodic elements) we have

$$\boldsymbol{u}_{(mM)} = \Delta^{mM} \boldsymbol{u}_0 + D^{(m)}\boldsymbol{p}, \tag{6-124}$$

where

$$D^{(m)} = \Delta^{(m-1)M} + \Delta^{(m-2)M} + \ldots + \Delta^M + [1]. \tag{6-125}$$

In order to have stability of the trajectory it is no longer sufficient that the condition 6-68 be satisfied: we must also require the magnitude of the vector $D^{(m)}\boldsymbol{p}$ to remain bounded as m increases. If this is not verified, even a small alignment error would eventually cause the particles to hit against the walls of the vacuum chamber.

Let us expand the vector $\boldsymbol{p}$ in terms of the eigenvectors $\boldsymbol{v}_1$ and $\boldsymbol{v}_2$ of Δ (see Equation 6-65):

$$\boldsymbol{p} = c_1\boldsymbol{v}_1 + c_2\boldsymbol{v}_2 . \tag{6-126}$$

As the corresponding eigenvalues are $e^{i\mu}$ and $e^{-i\mu}$, we have

$$D^{(m)}\boldsymbol{p} = c_1\boldsymbol{v}_1[e^{i(m-1)M\mu} + e^{i(m-2)M\mu} + \ldots + e^{iM\mu} + 1]$$
$$+ c_2\boldsymbol{v}_2[e^{-i(m-1)M\mu} + e^{-i(m-2)M\mu} + \ldots + e^{-iM\mu} + 1], \tag{6-127}$$

and, if we sum the geometric series in the brackets,

$$D^{(m)}\boldsymbol{p} = \frac{e^{imM\mu} - 1}{e^{iM\mu} - 1} c_1\boldsymbol{v}_1 + \frac{e^{-imM\mu} - 1}{e^{-iM\mu} - 1} c_2\boldsymbol{v}_2 , \tag{6-128}$$

which can also be written as

$$D^{(m)}\boldsymbol{p} = \frac{\sin \frac{1}{2}mM\mu}{\sin \frac{1}{2}M\mu} \{e^{i(m-1)M\mu/2} c_1\boldsymbol{v}_1 + e^{-i(m-1)M\mu/2} c_2\boldsymbol{v}_2\}. \tag{6-129}$$

The magnitude of the vector in brackets is always bounded (of the same order as the magnitude of $\boldsymbol{p}$). The coefficient of the vector instead remains bounded in modulus only if $\sin \frac{1}{2}M\mu \neq 0$, that is, if $\frac{1}{2}M\mu \neq h\pi$, where h is an integer. If instead

$$\mu = h\frac{2\pi}{M} , \qquad h = 0, 1, 2, \ldots, \tag{6-130}$$

this coefficient is equal to m and hence the magnitude of $D^{(m)}\boldsymbol{p}$ increases proportionally to the number of turns. Thus the machine must be designed so that the condition 6-130 is *not* satisfied either for the vertical or for the radial motion.

Let us see, for the simple case considered in the previous section, how the condition 6-130 influences the structure of the stability diagram of Figure 6-5. In this case, as $M = N/2$, Equation 6-130 becomes

$$\mu = h\frac{4\pi}{N} , \qquad h = 0, 1, 2, \ldots. \tag{6-131}$$

As μ can have values between 0 and π, both for the radial and for the vertical motion, Equation 6-131 corresponds to two families of curves (whose number is the maximum integer contained in $N/4$), which always include the boundary curves described by $\mu = 0$, while they may or may not include the other boundary curves described by $\mu = \pi$. Thus the stability region of Figure 6-5 is covered by a net of "forbidden lines" corresponding to Equation 6-130 or 6-131. Figure 6-8 shows this for the case of a large value of N.

The choice of the representative point of the machine becomes more difficult: the point must possibly be chosen at the center of one of the diamonds contained in the necktie of Figure 6-8, and care must be taken that, if the representative point moves during the acceleration phase, it never crosses one of the forbidden lines.

Since the forbidden lines become more dense as M increases, it is not possible in practice to increase the number of elements beyond a certain limit (as we mentioned in the previous section). As N is limited, and (from the stability diagram) also n/N^2 is limited, there derives also a limitation for the field index n.

It is interesting to note that the condition 6-130 or 6-131 corresponds exactly to the existence of the so-called "integral resonances" between the betatron oscillations (radial or vertical) and the orbital motion. Indeed, by substituting Equation 6-130 into Equations 6-119 and 6-120, we obtain

$$\nu_r = h, \quad \text{or} \quad \nu_z = h, \qquad h = 0, 1, 2, \ldots . \qquad (6\text{-}132)$$

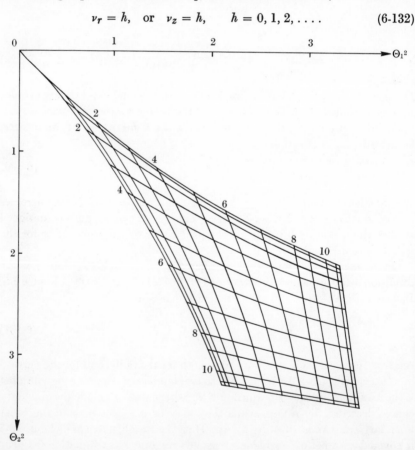

FIGURE 6-8. *The stability diagram for an AG synchrotron with 48 sectors, showing the "forbidden" lines corresponding to the integral resonances. The values of h (defined in Equation 6-131) are indicated for each line.*

This type of resonance is by far the most dangerous in AG synchrotrons. It should be noted that this resonance cannot occur in ordinary synchrotrons because, by the stability condition, ν_r and ν_z must fall between 0 and 1. The other resonances between betatron oscillations and orbital motion, for which the frequency ratio is a simple, nonintegral, rational number (especially if the ratio is a half-integer), should be avoided, but they are not as dangerous as the integral resonances for the stability of the beam. The lines representing the half-integral resonances further divide up the diamonds of Figure 6-8 and they introduce more restrictions on the choice of the representative point. If the representative point, as it moves during the acceleration cycle, crosses these lines, provided the transition is sufficiently fast, the beam is not disturbed significantly. The same argument applies to the so-called "sum resonances," where $\nu_r + \nu_z$ is an integer. Resonances between radial and vertical oscillations, which in ordinary synchrotrons are the most dangerous, in this case are not important: their coupling, indeed, is weak because the oscillations are not really sinusoidal. In practice, indeed, the common choice of $n_1 = |n_2|$ leads to $\omega_r \simeq \omega_z$ in synchrotrons with many sectors. In some cases one prefers to correct the effects of these resonances by means of appropriate weak compensating magnetic fields. In any case, even if one keeps away from the resonances, it is necessary to reduce the errors of alignment and inhomogeneities of the magnetic field inside each sector as far as possible, because each of these effects enhances the amplitude of the oscillations, as we have shown above. Thus we see why the enormous precision mentioned at the beginning of this chapter is required. In the assembly of the magnets it is convenient to distribute the different parts of which they consist randomly among them, so as to average out any errors of manufacture or any differences in quality of the materials. The effects of any residual inhomogeneities can be corrected by auxiliary magnets (such as the quadrupole lenses described in Appendix 1), placed in the straight sections.

6-9 PHASE OSCILLATIONS IN AN AG SYNCHROTRON.
THE TRANSITION ENERGY

In an AG synchrotron the mechanism of particle acceleration is the same as in a constant-gradient synchrotron. Thus the considerations developed in the previous chapter still hold and, in particular, the concepts of synchronous particle, phase of a particle, and synchrotron oscillations. All the formulas which refer to the analysis of these oscillations are also still valid. The only important difference with respect to the case already treated consists in the value of the quantity K (defined by Equation 5-34), which appears in the expression for the frequency Ω of these oscillations (see Equation 5-70). With the notation of Section 5-6 we have

$$\Omega = \omega \left(- \frac{|q| UKk}{2\pi E_s} \cos \varphi_s \right)^{1/2} \tag{6-133}$$

(where we have taken into account that $u = U \sin \varphi_s$ and $\cos \varphi_s < 0$). The difference in the value of K for ordinary and for AG synchrotrons derives from the difference in the value of the momentum compaction α. Already, in the case of the racetrack we have seen that the presence of the straight sections changes the value of α; however, in this case the change is small, α is still less than 1, and the nature of the oscillations remains the same. For the AG synchrotron instead it is found that $\alpha > 1$ and usually of the order of some units. Thus (see Equation 5-34) K changes rather strongly during the acceleration cycle and it passes from negative to positive values across the value zero. This value is reached at the energy, called *transition energy*, where $\gamma^2 = \alpha$ (as we have discussed in Section 1-10).

The proof that $\alpha > 1$ and the explicit calculation of α are rather laborious, even for a periodic element with a simple structure, and we omit it. The details of such a calculation can be found in Livingston and Blewett (1962, Section 15-6) or in Livingood (1961, Section 12-5). In the limit of a large value of N, it can be shown that α is given by the square of the ratio ν_r between the frequency of the radial betatron oscillations and the orbital frequency

$$\alpha = \nu_r{}^2 = \left(\frac{\omega_r}{\omega} \right)^2. \tag{6-134}$$

It is interesting to note that the relation 6-134 holds exactly in the case of constant-gradient and racetrack synchrotrons, as can be checked from Equations 5-39 and 6-102. This analogy may explain the physical meaning of Equation 6-134 from a qualitative point of view. The derivation of Equation 6-134 for large values of N, starting from the explicit formula for α, can be found in Livingood (1961, Section 12-5). As we have shown, $\omega_r > \omega$ and thus $\alpha > 1$.

When Equation 6-134 holds, Equation 5-34 can be written (using Equation 1-7) as

$$K = \frac{1}{\beta^2} \left\{ \frac{1}{\nu_r{}^2} - \left(\frac{E_0}{E} \right)^2 \right\}, \tag{6-135}$$

and the transition energy E_t, where $K = 0$, is given by

$$E_t = \nu_r E_0. \tag{6-136}$$

Since K changes sign when the particles reach the energy E_t, we find that for $E < E_t$ we have stability (that is, a real Ω) not for cos $\varphi_s < 0$ but for cos $\varphi_s > 0$ (see Equation 6-133). Thus before reaching the transition energy the particles must encounter an accelerating electric field increasing with time, as in the linear accelerator; above the transition energy they must encounter an electric field decreasing with time, as in constant-gradient synchrotrons.

When the particles reach the transition energy, there is no longer phase stability. This is a very delicate moment in the operation of the machine because at this point the bunches tend to dissolve and the oscillation amplitude increases strongly. In order to avoid the loss of an enormous fraction of the particles it is necessary, when they cross the transition energy, for the phase of the electric field in the rf cavity to change abruptly. In this case the amplitude of the synchrotron oscillations remains bounded, even if it does have a maximum (see the qualitative diagram of Figure 6-9). Under the usual conditions of operation, if the phase jump of the oscillator is sufficiently fast, the total amplitude of the oscillations is not larger than just after injection: thus there is no need to examine again the question of the size of the vacuum chamber.

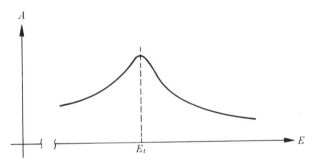

FIGURE 6-9. *Schematic diagram of the amplitude A of the synchrotron oscillations as a function of energy, near the transition energy.*

In order to avoid the difficulties of the transition, it is convenient (if possible) to inject the particles at an energy already larger than E_t. This can usually be done in the electron synchrotrons, where the transition energy is of the order of 2 to 5 MeV.

As far as the damping of radial synchrotron oscillations is concerned, their amplitude (by Equations 5-73 and 5-80) is proportional to $\Omega^{3/2}$ and so decreases during the acceleration as in constant-gradient synchrotrons. When the energy is very high ($\gamma \gg 1$), $K \simeq 1/\alpha$ and, as this quantity is very much smaller in AG synchrotrons than in ordinary synchrotrons, we can see that the use of the alternating gradient leads to a great reduction of the amplitude of the radial synchrotron oscillations.

6-10 SOME PROBLEMS OF THE STRUCTURE AND OPERATION OF AG SYNCHROTRONS

As we have mentioned previously, the magnet elements of an AG synchrotron have much smaller dimensions and weight than those of a CG synchrotron of the same energy. In general the magnets are C-shaped, as shown in Figure 5-1; in order to give the magnetic field the rapid variation required in the radial direction, the pole taper is greatly enhanced (see Figure 6-10). In practice, it is possible to use only one kind of magnet element (such as the one of Figure 6-10a) if the C is turned alternately toward the

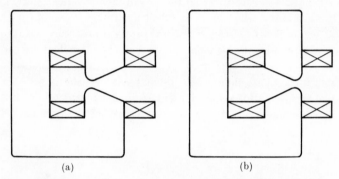

(a)   (b)

FIGURE 6-10.   *Schematic magnet designs for the AG synchrotron.*

inside and the outside of the machine. Thus one obtains a field which increases or decreases rapidly with radius, and the values of the field index are equal and opposite. Because of the rapid variation of the field in the radial direction the magnetic field cannot reach the limit of saturation on the principal orbit; there would first be saturation in the regions (inside or outside the orbit) where the field is stronger than on the principal orbit, and then the value of n would be altered. For the largest machines the maximum magnetic field obtained on the equilibrium orbit is about 1.3 Wb/m^2. Usually the machine contains many straight sections in which are inserted all the auxiliary devices, such as rf cavities, vacuum pumps, inflector, targets, and focusing magnets (magnetic quadrupole lenses; see Appendix 1). A straight section can be inserted between a focusing and a defocusing sector, as is shown in Figure 6-11a. The arrangement most frequently used is illustrated in Figure 6-11b: The straight sections are placed between two sectors of the same kind, and different sectors are in direct contact. We can think of this design as being derived from that of the completely circular machine described in Section 6-7 by cutting each sector in two equal parts (so as to obtain "half-magnets") and inserting a straight section in between the two parts. This design ensures a greater symmetry of the trajectories.

Finally we note that the enormous precision required in the alignment of
the magnets is also necessary in their construction. The dissipative effects of
eddy currents, residual field, and so on, must be the same for all the components of the magnet. For this purpose, as mentioned in Section 6-8, it is
important not to use the laminations produced in the same batch for a single
magnet, but to shuffle all those produced in different batches. If necessary,
electric circuits can be used to compensate any residual inhomogeneity.

Concerning the problems connected with the rf cavity, the magnet supply,
the injection (always at high energy), and beam extraction, the considerations
developed in Sections 5-8 to 5-10 for the ordinary synchrotron are still valid.
However, in the AG case, as the magnet is smaller and hence absorbs less
power, the repetition time can be made shorter: one can avoid the use of a
pulsed magnet supply (as is shown in Figure 5-16) and use, instead, a sinusoidal power supply (with a frequency of 30–60 cps, for electron synchrotrons)
or a saw-tooth supply (with a period of a few seconds, for proton synchrotrons).

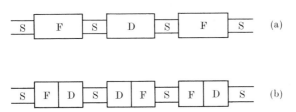

FIGURE 6-11. *Typical magnet arrangements for AG synchrotrons showing the placement
of the straight sections* S, *the focusing sectors,* F, *and the defocusing sectors* D.

Also in AG electron synchrotrons radiation losses are very important and
they place a practical limit to the energy which can be obtained with this
kind of machine. At a given energy, radiation losses can be reduced by increasing the radius of the machine, and correspondingly decreasing the
magnetic field. With present technology, it seems possible to design an AG
electron synchrotron even for 50 BeV; such a machine should have a very
large radius (about 1 km, like the superhigh-energy proton synchrotrons
described below) and a very low magnetic field. In proton AG synchrotrons,
instead, the radiation losses are quite negligible in all practical cases.

We close this section by briefly mentioning the problems connected with
the construction of "superhigh-energy" proton synchrotrons (from 200 to
about 1000 BeV), for which there already exist detailed preliminary studies
(see, for instance, Johnsen, 1965; Keefe, 1965).

A synchrotron of this type (of course with an AG structure) is not substantially different, in principle, from the largest proton synchrotrons already
operating; only its diameter must be much larger (of the order of some kilo-
meters), because it increases roughly proportionally to the energy. For some

problems, the details of the solutions will be different: for example, the high-energy injection will be made at about 8 BeV, in order to overcome the transition energy; therefore, the injector itself will be a smaller synchrotron ("booster ring"). Another problem which may arise (Symon *et al.*, 1965) is the possible occurrence of resonances also between the synchrotron oscillations and the orbital motion. Indeed, for such large rings, the harmonic number k must be very high, and this may make the value of the ratio Ω/ω_s (Equation 5-71) of order unity.

6-11   THE FRINGING-FIELD EFFECTS AND THE ZERO-GRADIENT SYNCHROTRON

In the theory of the racetrack synchrotron developed in Section 6-6, we have supposed that at the edges of a magnet sector the magnetic field vanishes abruptly, so that the terminal cross sections of the magnet sector are discontinuity surfaces for the field. Furthermore, we have supposed that inside the magnet sector the field is the same function of r, z in any meridian section, even in those very near to the edges. Obviously, these are only approximations: in practice, as one moves along the principal orbit (or any line parallel to it) the field components remain practically constant inside the sector region far from the edges, but they decrease steadily to practically zero in a transition region, extending from each side of the terminal cross section for a distance of the order of the width of the gap between the poles. In this region the magnetic field (called "fringing field") is no longer contained in the meridian plane (r, z) but may also have a component normal to this plane, and its dependence on r, z is different from that inside the magnet. These facts have a negligible effect on the motion of the particles if the terminal surface of the magnet sector coincides, as usual, with a meridian plane, but may have a remarkable focusing or defocusing effect if instead the terminal surface of the magnet is made oblique. Since this effect has received an important application, we shall now give a short outline of its theory.

Figure 6-12 shows a cross section of a uniform-field magnet with a vertical plane tangential to the principal orbit (and practically containing it): the

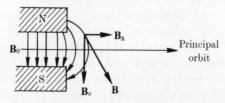

FIGURE 6-12.   *Schematic diagram of the longitudinal cross section of a magnet showing the fringing field. For the notation, see text.*

fringing field, beside the vertical component $\mathbf{B}_v$ which acts on the particles in the same way as the guiding field $\mathbf{B}_0$, also has a horizontal component $\mathbf{B}_h$ (vanishing in the median plane), which is always normal to the terminal surface of the magnet element. This surface can be normal to the principal orbit or also slightly oblique (for reasons that we shall soon see). Figure 6-13 shows a cross section of the magnet with the median plane showing the different possible orientations of the terminal surface. In ordinary magnets (Figure 6-13b), where the terminal surface is perpendicular to the principal orbit and

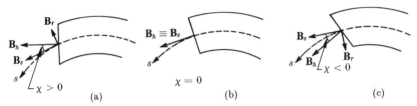

FIGURE 6-13. *Median-plane cross sections of magnet sectors showing the horizontal components of the magnetic field for the case of* (a) *an outward slanted magnet,* (b) *no slant, and* (c) *an inward slanted magnet. For the notation, see text.*

coincides with a transverse cross section, the component $\mathbf{B}_h$ is entirely in the direction of the particle motion and hence it has no effect on the beam. If, instead, between the normal to the terminal surface and the principal orbit there is an angle χ (which we define as positive when, outside the magnet, this normal is external to the orbit as in Figure 6-13a, and as negative in the opposite case as in Figure 6-13c), the field $\mathbf{B}_h$, in addition to the component $\mathbf{B}_s$ along the principal orbit, has a component $\mathbf{B}_r$ in the radial direction (see Figures 6-13a and 6-13c). The projections of $\mathbf{B}_h$ on the s and r directions are given by

$$B_s = B_h \cos \chi,$$
$$B_r = B_h \sin \chi. \tag{6-137}$$

Here B_r can be positive (Figure 6-13a) or negative (Figure 6-13c) according to the sign of χ, and it causes a deviation of the trajectory which may accordingly have a focusing or a defocusing effect. We have seen that in an ordinary synchrotron ($0 < n < 1$) in order for it to be focusing, $\mathbf{B}_r$ must be directed outward: this corresponds to the case of Figure 6-13a. However, near the edge of the magnet the field changes rapidly with r (because even near the principal orbit, if one moves radially, for a certain r one goes out of the magnet); therefore the situation is similar to that of the high-gradient sectors, such as those used in AG synchrotrons. Thus in the case of Figure 6-13a (χ positive, magnet slanted outward) there is vertical focusing and radial defocusing at the magnet edge; in the case of Figure 6-13c (χ negative, magnet slanted inward) there is radial focusing and vertical defocusing at the edge. The same effect also exists when the particle enters the sector instead of leaving it. Hence if all the sectors of a racetrack synchrotron are shaped in one of the ways we have considered (see Figures 6-14a and 6-14b) we can obtain an additional vertical or horizontal focusing (together with a corresponding horizontal or vertical defocusing, respectively).

On the other hand, also intuitively, the synchrotron of Figure 6-14a can be considered as equivalent to a synchrotron with $n > 0$, and the synchrotron of Figure 6-14b, to a synchrotron with $n < 0$. Indeed in one turn a particle which describes a more internal orbit will follow a *longer* path inside the magnetic field in the case of Figure 6-14a and a *shorter* path in the case of Figure 6-14b. Thus on the average over one turn, the particles will see a magnetic field decreasing outward in the first case and increasing in the second case.

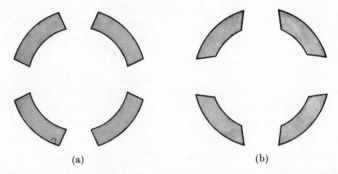

(a)   (b)

FIGURE 6-14. *Schematic diagram of four-sector racetrack synchrotrons having* (a) *outward slanted magnets, and* (b) *inward slanted magnets.*

The existence of this effect has permitted the design of the so-called zero-gradient synchrotron (ZGS), of which until 1966 only one example had been built: the 12.5-BeV proton synchrotron of the Argonne Laboratory, near Chicago (Crewe, 1959; Teng, 1963, 1965). The ZGS is a racetrack synchrotron with many sectors (eight in the Argonne machine), where the field is uniform ($n = 0$, and hence the name) and the magnets have slant edges as in the diagram of Figure 6-14a, in such a way as to ensure the vertical focusing which is not provided inside the magnets. The parameters of the machine can be chosen in such a way that the radial defocusing effect of the edges is smaller than the focusing effect ($n = 0$) inside the sectors; thus a trajectory which is stable in both directions is obtained.

The great advantage of using a uniform magnetic field consists in the fact that stronger magnetic fields can be obtained on the equilibrium orbit (without some other part of the magnetic circuit being saturated); therefore for a given energy the size of the machine can be reduced. In the case of the Argonne synchrotron the maximum field on the orbit is 2.15 Wb/m² and the diameter of the machine is 60 m (see Table 1-3).

6-12 BETATRON OSCILLATIONS IN THE ZERO-GRADIENT SYNCHROTRON

We now give a schematic treatment of the betatron oscillations in the ZGS. As it is a racetrack type of synchrotron, it is convenient to use matrix algebra. We must, however, take into account the focusing and defocusing effect of the edges explicitly, and introduce a characteristic matrix also for the edges. If the distance over which the trajectory is subjected to the edge effect is small with respect to the length of the sector, the position (both radial and vertical) of the particle will practically remain the same, whereas its velocity will have a sharp deflection. We shall show that, in this approximation, both in the radial and in the vertical direction, this deflection is proportional to the distance of the particle from the unperturbed orbit (as for a ray of light in a thin lens) and we can write

$$\Delta z' = -z/f_z,$$
$$\Delta x' = -x/f_x, \tag{6-138}$$

where the prime indicates differentiation with respect to the distance s along the unperturbed orbit and the two constants f_z, f_x, are called "focal lengths," because of the optical analogy. We shall prove this separately for the two cases, and show that $f_z = -f_x$.

For the vertical oscillations the equation of motion in the z direction, at the magnet edge, is

$$m_v \ddot{z} = - \mid q \mid vB_r = - \mid q \mid vB_h \sin \chi \tag{6-139}$$

(with the notations illustrated in Figure 6-13). If we introduce the variable s and note that $ds = v \, dt$, Equation 6-139 becomes

$$z'' + \frac{\mid q \mid B_h}{m_v v} \sin \chi = 0. \tag{6-140}$$

The quantity B_h is a function of s and z (but not of r). If we integrate Equation 6-140 with respect to s, across the magnet edge (from s_1 to s_2, say) and suppose that B_h is zero outside this interval, we obtain

$$\Delta z' = - \frac{\mid q \mid \sin \chi}{m_v v} \int_{s_1}^{s_2} B_h(s, z) \, ds, \tag{6-141}$$

where we have called $\Delta z'$ the variation of the inclination of the trajectory. The integral of Equation 6-141 is proportional to z: this can be seen by considering the circuit $ABCDA$ of Figure 6-15 (which shows a vertical cross section of the magnet similar to Figure 6-12). As there are no currents linking the circuit $\oint \mathbf{B} \cdot d\mathbf{l} = 0$ around it; but the contribution to the circulation of $\mathbf{B}$ is zero both along BC (because it is well outside the magnet, where $\mathbf{B} = 0$) and along CD (because, by symmetry, $B_h = 0$ in the median plane). Thus

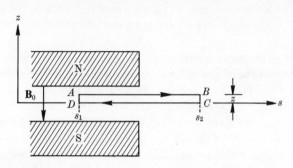

FIGURE 6-15. *Vertical cross section of a synchrotron magnet illustrating the path of integration $ABCD$ (see text).*

we have $\int_{AB} \mathbf{B} \cdot d\mathbf{l} + \int_{DA} \mathbf{B} \cdot d\mathbf{l} = 0$, or $\int_{s_1}^{s_2} B_s \, ds - B_0 z = 0$, and, using Equation 6-137,

$$\int_{s_1}^{s_2} B_h \, ds = \frac{B_0}{\cos \chi} z. \tag{6-142}$$

Substituting this into Equation 6-141, we obtain

$$\Delta z' = -\frac{|q| B_0 \tan \chi}{m_v v} z = -\frac{\tan \chi}{R} z, \tag{6-143}$$

since the condition for a circular orbit is $P = m_v v = |q| R B_0$. By comparing this equation with the first of Equations 6-138, we obtain

$$f_z = \frac{R}{\tan \chi}. \tag{6-144}$$

For the radial oscillations, let us consider two trajectories a and b in the median plane (see Figure 6-16), the former along the principal orbit, the latter (in its part inside the magnet), parallel to the other and displaced by a distance x in the radial direction. Outside the magnet, the two trajectories are straight lines, but no longer parallel, because the trajectory a has been deflected by the field through the arc d, while the other has not. Obviously, the angle η between the two is given by

$$\eta = \frac{d}{R} \simeq \frac{x \tan \chi}{R}, \tag{6-145}$$

where both x and χ must be taken with their signs. Thus we have

$$\Delta x' \simeq \eta = \frac{x \tan \chi}{R}, \qquad (6\text{-}146)$$

so that, from the second of Equations 6-138, we obtain

$$f_x = -\frac{R}{\tan \chi}. \qquad (6\text{-}147)$$

Thus we have shown that the radial and vertical focal lengths are constants, equal and opposite.

If, as usual, we use the indices 0 and 1 for quantities before and after the transition across a slant edge, we have the following relations for the vertical displacement z:

$$z_1 = z_0 ,$$
$$z_1' = z_0' - \frac{z_0}{f_z}, \qquad (6\text{-}148)$$

so that the characteristic matrix of the edge for vertical oscillations is given by

$$\Gamma_{ez} = \begin{bmatrix} 1 & 0 \\ -\dfrac{a}{f_z} & 1 \end{bmatrix} \qquad (6\text{-}149)$$

The same holds for the radial oscillations if we substitute f_x for f_z.

We can now construct the matrix Δ_z of the periodic element of a ZGS as the ordered product of the characteristic matrices of the edge, the magnet sector, another edge, and finally the straight section.

Let us carry out the calculation for the vertical oscillations first. Since for these $k = n^{1/2}/R = 0$, we cannot choose $a = 1/k$ as in Section 6-6: we

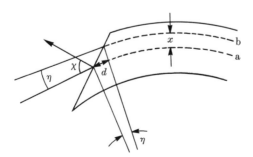

FIGURE 6-16. *Schematic diagram of the median-plane section of a slanted synchrotron magnet, defining the angle χ and the arc d.*

choose instead $a = R$. Thus the matrix 6-149, characteristic of an edge, becomes, using Equation 6-144,

$$\Gamma_{ez} = \begin{bmatrix} 1 & 0 \\ -\tan\chi & 1 \end{bmatrix}. \tag{6-150}$$

The matrix characteristic of the straight section is given by Equation 6-58, that is,

$$\Gamma_{sz} = \begin{bmatrix} 1 & L/R \\ 0 & 1 \end{bmatrix}. \tag{6-151}$$

For the magnet sector, remembering (Section 6-4) that for $n = 0$ it behaves like a straight section of length l, we have similarly

$$\Gamma_{mz} = \begin{bmatrix} 1 & l/R \\ 0 & 1 \end{bmatrix}. \tag{6-152}$$

By carrying out the product and for convenience putting

$$\frac{L}{R} = \xi,$$

$$\frac{l}{R} = \frac{2\pi}{N} = \rho, \tag{6-153}$$

N being the number of magnet sectors, we obtain

$$\Delta_z = \Gamma_{ez}\Gamma_{mz}\Gamma_{ez}\Gamma_{sz} = \begin{bmatrix} 1 & 0 \\ -\tan\chi & 1 \end{bmatrix}\begin{bmatrix} 1 & \rho \\ 0 & 1 \end{bmatrix}\begin{bmatrix} 1 & 0 \\ -\tan\chi & 1 \end{bmatrix}\begin{bmatrix} 1 & \xi \\ 0 & 1 \end{bmatrix}$$

$$= \begin{bmatrix} 1 - \rho\tan\chi & \rho + (1 - \rho\tan\chi)\xi \\ -(2 - \rho\tan\chi)\tan\chi & 1 - \rho\tan\chi - (2 - \rho\tan\chi)\xi\tan\chi \end{bmatrix}. \tag{6-154}$$

From the trace of this matrix we get the stability condition for the vertical oscillations (see Equation 6-68), that is,

$$-1 < 1 - \rho\tan\chi - \left(1 - \frac{\rho}{2}\tan\chi\right)\xi\tan\chi < 1. \tag{6-155}$$

This condition is not at all restrictive on χ: for $N = 8$ and with the usual choice of ξ (of the order of 1/3 or 1/4), we find that χ can be chosen inside a wide interval (of the order of 60°).

For the radial oscillations, Equations 6-75 and 6-76, with $n = 0$, give $k = 1/R$, $\Theta = 2\pi/N = \rho$: so we can use for the magnet the matrix 6-73 with ρ in the place of Θ. Calculating as before the matrices Γ_{er} and Γ_{sr}, we obtain

$$\Delta_r = \Gamma_{er}\Gamma_{mr}\Gamma_{er}\Gamma_{sr}$$

$$= \begin{bmatrix} 1 & 0 \\ \tan \chi & 1 \end{bmatrix} \begin{bmatrix} \cos \rho & \sin \rho \\ -\sin \rho & \cos \rho \end{bmatrix} \begin{bmatrix} 1 & 0 \\ \tan \chi & 1 \end{bmatrix} \begin{bmatrix} 1 & \xi \\ 0 & 1 \end{bmatrix}$$

$$= \begin{bmatrix} \cos \rho + \sin \rho \tan \chi \\ 2 \cos \rho \tan \chi - (1 - \tan^2 \chi) \sin \rho \end{bmatrix.$$

$$\left. \begin{matrix} \sin \rho + \xi(\cos \rho + \sin \rho \tan \chi) \\ \cos \rho + \sin \rho \tan \chi + \xi[2 \cos \rho \tan \chi - \sin \rho(1 - \tan^2 \chi)] \end{matrix} \right]. \qquad (6\text{-}156)$$

Hence the stability condition for the radial oscillations is

$$-1 < \cos \rho + \sin \rho \tan \chi + \xi[\cos \rho \tan \chi - \tfrac{1}{2} \sin \rho(1 - \tan^2 \chi)] < 1. \tag{6-157}$$

It can be seen that, for small values of ξ, this condition is satisfied by $\chi < \rho/2 = \pi/N$. This limitation is more stringent than the one set by the vertical oscillations; however, the allowed range of χ is still very wide.

As far as the frequency of the betatron oscillations is concerned, the general considerations developed in Section 6-7 are still valid. It can be derived from Equations 6-119 and 6-120 that in this case too ω_r/ω and ω_z/ω are usually less than 1. (In the Argonne machine the values of these ratios are about 3/4 and 7/8, respectively.)

For the synchrotron oscillations in the ZGS, the same considerations hold as in the CG synchrotron and in the racetrack. The value of the momentum compaction α, because of the edge effect, is less than the value 1 which one would have for a CG synchrotron with zero gradient (without vertical stability) and it is of the same order of magnitude as in an ordinary constant-gradient synchrotron ($\alpha = 0.6$ in the Argonne synchrotron). For an explicit derivation of the expression of α, see Livingood (1961, p. 84). The behavior of the synchrotron oscillations in the zero-gradient synchrotron is therefore similar to that discussed in Chapter 5 for the constant-gradient synchrotron.

CHAPTER 7

THE CYCLOTRON,
THE SYNCHROCYCLOTRON,
AND THE MICROTRON

7-1 ORBIT STABILITY IN A FIXED-FREQUENCY CYCLOTRON

The principle of operation of a fixed-frequency cyclotron has been already treated in Section 1-6. In this chapter we give a more detailed treatment of the subject making use of some of the concepts introduced in the previous chapters, such as orbit stability (Section 4-4) and the phase of a particle (Section 5-2).

As far as orbit stability is concerned, it must be noted that in the cyclotron vertical stability is necessary so that ions emitted by the source in a direction not perfectly horizontal will not hit against the top or bottom surfaces of the "dees" and be lost, thus reducing the intensity of the useful beam to practically zero. Two mechanisms are provided to ensure vertical stability.

First of all, the magnetic field, which in the elementary description of Section 1-6 was supposed to be perfectly uniform, is made instead slightly decreasing in the radial direction, with a field index n (defined as usual by Equation 4-2) that is much smaller than in the betatrons and synchrotrons. At the center n is zero and it is made to increase almost linearly toward the outer regions, reaching a value of the order of 0.1 at the border of the useful region; outside this the magnetic field decreases very rapidly (fringing field) with values of n of the order of 1. Figure 7-1 shows the behavior of B and n with radial distance in a typical cyclotron.

The radial decrease of B (as has been proved in Section 4-4) gives rise to a restoring force which attracts the particles toward the median plane, and therefore there occur vertical oscillations of angular frequency $\omega_z = n^{1/2}\omega$ (see Equation 4-47), where ω is the angular velocity of the particle. This "focusing effect" is very weak in the central zone and increases gradually toward the periphery, but it is always much weaker than in the weak-focusing synchrotron because of the small value of n. Higher values of n are excluded by the necessity of keeping ω almost constant, in order to ensure the fulfillment of the resonance condition for the fixed-frequency cyclotron (see Section 1-6). We discuss in the next section how the imperfection of the resonance produced by the nonuniformity of the field affects the operation of the cyclotron. Incidentally, we remark that the small value of n ensures a good radial stability.

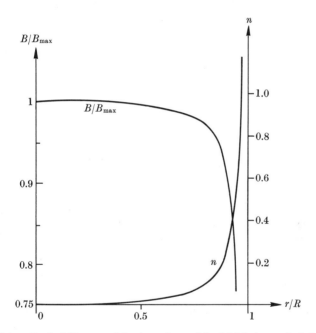

FIGURE 7-1. *Typical diagram of the dependence of the field index and of the magnetic field on radius in a fixed-frequency cyclotron. R is the radius of the magnet poles.*

The second mechanism contributing to vertical stability is an *electric* focusing effect acting on the particle every time it crosses the gap between the dees. This effect is essentially similar to the "electrostatic lens" effect which we have considered in Section 2-1 for the electrostatic accelerators and can be understood by examining the diagram of Figure 7-2, which is essentially the same as the one shown in Figure 2-3. It is seen that the electric field produces a focusing effect on the trajectory of the particle when it crosses the first half of the gap and a defocusing effect when it crosses the second half.

If the electric field is constant in time the focusing effect is always dominant, as has been noted in Section 2-1, but in the present case we must take into account that the electric field changes during the transit of the particle. Clearly, if the field is decreasing, the net focusing effect is enhanced, and in the opposite case it is reduced (as is shown in Figure 7-2) or even inverted. This dependence of the electric focusing on the phase of the electric field at the instant of crossing the gap puts some limitations on the range of useful phases of crossing, as will be seen in the next section.

The electric focusing mechanism is obviously the more effective the slower are the particles, and hence it is more important in the central part of the machine, just where the magnetic focusing is less effective. As the particle moves outward and gains energy, electric focusing is gradually replaced by magnetic focusing, and so vertical stability is constantly assured.

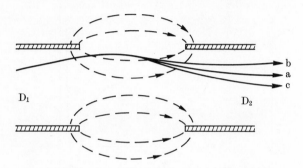

FIGURE 7-2. *Figure illustrating the focusing at the gap between the dees* (D_1 *and* D_2) *with typical trajectories (exaggerated) for an electric field* (a) *constant in time,* (b) *increasing in time, and* (c) *decreasing in time. Lines of force of the electric field are shown as dotted lines.*

7-2 THE VARIATION OF THE PHASE IN THE CYCLOTRON

Let us refer to Figure 7-3, which shows schematically the first part of a particle trajectory in a cyclotron. We introduce the azimuthal angle θ of the particle, measured from the median section of the gap, and assume that the voltage difference $V(t)$ between the two electrodes D_2 and D_1 is given by

$$V(t) = U \sin \omega_e t, \tag{7-1}$$

where $U > 0$ and ω_e is a constant, given approximately by Equation 1-31.[1]

---

[1] Formula 1-31 for the magnetic resonance frequency is often written in an empirical form which is useful for determining its value for the different kinds of particle accelerated in a cyclotron. For example, for the frequency $\nu_e = \omega_e/2\pi$ we have $\nu_e = 1.52B$ for protons, and $\nu_e = 0.76B$ for deuterons and α particles, if we measure ν_e in megacycles per second and B in kilogauss (1 kG = 0.1 Wb/m²). For values of B between 10 and 20 kG we have frequencies between 15 and 30 Mc/sec for protons and 7.5 and 15 Mc/sec for deuterons, i.e., short-wave radio frequencies.

Let us define the phase φ of a particle as in the synchrotron (with $\omega_e = $ const) by

$$\varphi = \omega_e t - \theta. \tag{7-2}$$

The energy gain L_e at the mth transit is (for positive q)

$$L_e = (-1)^m qV, \tag{7-3}$$

where V is taken at the time of transit. Hence, using Equations 7-1 and 7-2 with $\theta = m\pi$ ($m = 1, 2 \ldots$), we have

$$L_e = qU \sin \varphi. \tag{7-4}$$

If we differentiate Equation 7-2 with respect to time and put, as previously, $\dot{\theta} = \omega$ (the angular velocity of the particle), we obtain

$$\dot{\varphi} = \omega_e - \omega. \tag{7-5}$$

The value of ω can be related to the particle energy and to the value of the magnetic field, by means of Equations 1-30 and 1-7. Thus we obtain

$$\omega = c^2 q \, \frac{B}{E} \tag{7-6}$$

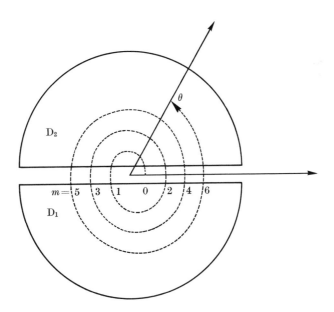

FIGURE 7-3. *Diagram of particle orbits in a cyclotron. The width of the gap between the dees (D_1 and D_2) has been exaggerated.*

(where $B > 0$ is the magnetic field intensity and E as usual is the total energy of the particle), and if we substitute Equation 7-6 into 7-5 we have

$$\dot{\varphi} = \omega_e - c^2 q \frac{B}{E}. \tag{7-7}$$

From Equation 7-7 it can be seen that in the fixed-frequency cyclotron ($\omega_e = $ const) there cannot be a synchronous particle for which φ remains constant. Indeed, as E increases along the trajectory and B remains constant or decreases slightly (see the previous section), $\dot{\varphi}$ cannot be identically zero but it increases and it can only cross the value zero (if ω_e is chosen within the proper interval). It follows that φ will first decrease, then pass through a minimum when $\dot{\varphi} = 0$, and finally it will increase. As we will see, these variations are not at all negligible: the range of φ during the entire acceleration cycle can be of the order of π and the highest efficiency of the machine is obtained by choosing this range conveniently.

In order to study the phase variations in the cyclotron easily, let us make the following simplifying assumptions:

1. The magnetic field is uniform along the entire trajectory.
2. The accelerating gap has an infinitesimal width.
3. The phase variation (which actually takes place suddenly at the gap transits) can be approximated by a continuous variation, linear over a turn (this approximation is of the same kind as the one used for the synchrotron and described schematically by Figure 5-3).

We shall later discuss the modifications introduced if we consider the real situation rather than this simple model. From assumption 3, it follows that for the phase change in a transit across the gap we can write

$$\Delta\varphi \simeq \dot{\varphi} \frac{\pi}{\omega} \tag{7-8}$$

and, using Equations 7-5 and 7-6,

$$\Delta\varphi = \pi \left(\frac{\omega_e}{\omega} - 1 \right) = \pi \left(\frac{\omega_e E}{c^2 q B} - 1 \right), \tag{7-9}$$

and hence

$$\frac{d\varphi}{dE} \simeq \frac{\Delta\varphi}{L_e} = \frac{\pi}{qU \sin \varphi} \left(\frac{\omega_e E}{c^2 q B} - 1 \right), \tag{7-10}$$

that is,

$$d\cos\varphi = -\frac{\pi}{qU} \left(\frac{\omega_e E}{c^2 q B} - 1 \right) dE. \tag{7-11}$$

This is the phase equation for the cyclotron. If B is a constant (assumption 1), Equation 7-11 can be integrated immediately and gives

$$\cos \varphi = \cos \varphi_0 - \frac{\pi}{qU}\left[\frac{\omega e}{2c^2qB}(E^2 - E_0{}^2) - (E - E_0)\right], \qquad (7\text{-}12)$$

where we have called φ_0 the initial phase (which depends on the instant of injection) and we have taken into account that at the injection the particles have practically no velocity, that is, E is equal to the rest energy E_0. If we introduce the kinetic energy $T = E - E_0$ and put

$$\omega_0 = c^2 q \frac{B}{E_0} \qquad (7\text{-}13)$$

(ω_0 is the nonrelativistic magnetic resonance frequency given by Equation 1-31), then Equation 7-12 can be rewritten as

$$\cos \varphi = \cos \varphi_0 + \frac{\pi}{qU}\left(1 - \frac{\omega e}{\omega_0}\right)T - \frac{\pi}{2qUE_0}\frac{\omega e}{\omega_0}T^2. \qquad (7\text{-}14)$$

If we represent $\cos \varphi$ graphically as a function of T for a given value of the machine parameters, Equation 7-14, for different values of $\cos \varphi_0$, gives a family of parabolas concave downward, which differ only by a displacement along the ordinate axis (see Figure 7-4). From this figure it can be seen that, in the region of T having physical meaning ($T > 0$), it can occur that for some values of $\cos \varphi_0$ (with $|\cos \varphi_0| < 1$) there are energies for which Equation 7-14 would give $|\cos \varphi| > 1$ and hence have no meaning. This occurs in all cases, whatever the value of $\cos \varphi_0$, when T is sufficiently large. Actually,

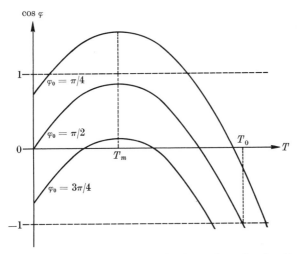

FIGURE 7-4. *Plot of $\cos \varphi$ as a function of T for three values of φ_0 (see Equation 7-14).*

what happens is that when $|\cos\varphi| \simeq 1$, $\sin\varphi \simeq 0$ and hence $L_e \simeq 0$ (see Equation 7-4), so that Equation 7-10 is no longer valid. When the parabola reaches the point where $|\cos\varphi| = 1$, the particle encounters zero electric field in the gap, so that it is not accelerated and it remains on an orbit of constant radius. If we want the particle to reach the end of the acceleration cycle, we must require that the expression 7-14 always be included between -1 and $+1$. This means that not all the values of φ_0 can be accepted and that, for a given φ_0, the final energy T_f reached by the particles cannot exceed the limiting value T_0 for which the expression 7-14 becomes definitely less than -1. (In Figure 7-4 we have shown T_0 for the curve of initial phase $\varphi_0 = \pi/2$.)

We must now remember that since the source emits ions continuously, φ_0 has all the possible values, but only those ions can be used which are emitted in time intervals corresponding to values of φ_0 which are "acceptable," in the sense discussed above. Thus the machine parameters must be chosen in such a way that the range of acceptable values of φ_0 is the largest. For this purpose obviously the frequency of the accelerating field must *not* be exactly equal to the nonrelativistic resonance frequency ω_0, given by Equation 7-13, but it must be chosen slightly smaller, so that the precise resonance condition does not occur at the beginning of the acceleration, but at some intermediate stage. If indeed we had $\omega_e = \omega_0$, in Equation 7-14 the linear term in T would be zero and the parabolas would have the shape shown in Figure 7-5a. Here the limiting energy T_0 for a given φ_0 is small and the range of initial phases for which the particles can reach a given final energy T_f (useful range) is small. If instead we choose $\omega_e < \omega_0$, the position T_m of maximum of the curves $\cos\varphi\,(T)$ falls within the acceleration range (see Figure 7-5b), and as $\cos\varphi$ first increases and then decreases, the particle remains in the machine a longer time and it can reach a higher energy. Usually ω_e is chosen in such a way that the position T_m of the maximum falls at about one half of the final energy T_f (see Figure 7-5b). Thus the useful range of initial phases is the greatest and a larger intensity can be obtained. As we have

$$T_m = E_0\left(\frac{\omega_0}{\omega_e} - 1\right),\qquad(7\text{-}15)$$

the condition $T_m = \tfrac{1}{2}T_f$ gives

$$\omega_e = \frac{\omega_0}{1 + T_f/2E_0} \simeq \omega_0\left(1 - \frac{T_f}{2E_0}\right).\qquad(7\text{-}16)$$

In practice, the difference between ω_e and ω_0 turns out to be of the order of 1%.

Let us now examine how the conclusions that we have reached are modified if we abandon the simplifying assumptions used previously. If the magnetic field has a radial dependence, Equation 7-11 cannot be integrated directly. The parabolas of Figure 7-4 are replaced by curves calculated by means of a

numerical integration. However, as the variation of B is slow, essentially the
same behavior is obtained as shown in Figure 7-4. Of greater importance is the
effect of the finite width of the gap. Indeed the particles emitted by the source
have a very low velocity so that during the first turn they do not penetrate

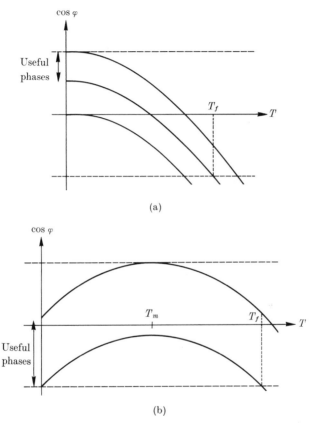

(a)

(b)

FIGURE 7-5.   *The cos φ-T diagram for a given final energy* T_f, *showing the range of
useful phases* (a) *for* $\omega_e = \omega_0$ *(that is,* $T_m = 0$) *and* (b) *for* $T_m = \frac{1}{2}T_f$.

inside one of the dees and they are subjected simultaneously to the action of
the electric and of the magnetic field. Under these conditions, as can be seen
from an explicit calculation (see, for example, Livingston and Blewett, 1962,
Section 6-4), the trajectory has the shape of a spiral and furthermore the
particles (emitted with all possible initial phases) bunch around the particle
emitted when the electric field is maximum, whose initial phase is $\varphi_0 = \pi/2$.[2]

[2] A partial penetration inside the dees during the first turn does not essentially change
this situation. For a detailed discussion of this effect, see Livingston and Blewett (1962,
Section 6-4).

Later when the orbit radius increases and the time spent inside the dees is great compared with the transit time across the gap, the approximation of negligible gap width is justified. The initial bunching of the particles around the one with $\varphi_0 = \pi/2$ leads to the fact that not all the initial phases are equally probable, but the values of $\cos \varphi_0$ around zero are strongly favored. It is therefore important that in Figures 7-4 or 7-5b the curve corresponding to $\varphi_0 = \pi/2$ be entirely within the useful zone $|\cos \varphi| < 1$ so that most of the particles are accelerated to the final energy.

It is necessary at this point to mention a further limitation to the variation of the phase during the increase of the energy. In the previous section we have seen that, if the particles encounter an accelerating electric field which increases in time, there is a defocusing effect (in the vertical direction). If this effect is greater than the focusing due to the magnetic field gradient, the trajectory becomes unstable and the particles are lost. A detailed study of the problem of the vertical focusing in the cyclotron has been carried out by M. E. Rose (1938).[3] It was found that the angular frequency of the vertical oscillations is given by the formula

$$\omega_z{}^2 = \omega^2 \left(n - \frac{qU}{\pi T} \cos \varphi \right), \qquad (7\text{-}17)$$

where the phase corresponds to the times of transit across the gap. The first term on the right-hand side represents the usual magnetic focusing effect as in the synchrotron, while the second term gives the effect of the electric focusing. It can be seen that, if $\cos \varphi > 0$, the particle encounters an electric field increasing in time, and thus there is electric defocusing, and vice versa. Furthermore, the electric-focusing term is important only at low energies. The condition for the stability of the orbit is that the right-hand side of Equation 7-17 should be positive. Therefore the condition

$$\cos \varphi \leq \frac{\pi T n}{qU} \qquad (7\text{-}18)$$

gives another limitation to the variation of the phase with energy. In the diagram of Figure 7-4 the equality of the expression 7-18 would be represented by a curve which in the zone of interest is practically a straight line r through the origin (see Figure 7-6). The region above this line is a zone of vertical instability which must not be crossed by the curve of phase variation against energy. Figure 7-6 illustrates with an example the influence of the condition for vertical stability on the choice of the initial phase φ_0. It can be seen that in general this condition is not compatible with positive values of $\cos \varphi_0$ in Equation 7-14 (curve a). Instead the curves, like curve b, corresponding to

---

[3] A later study by B. L. Cohen (1953) computes some corrective terms to Equation 7-17 below.

cos $\varphi_0 \leq 0$, (if they lie inside the strip $-1 \leq \cos \varphi \leq 1$) never cross the zone of vertical instability, at least for the parameters commonly used in cyclotrons.

It should be noted that also the analysis of the vertical stability summarized here is not valid for the first few turns because of the finite width of the gap. However, the qualitative consideration still holds, that the greatest loss of particles against the walls occurs in this initial stage of the acceleration cycle.

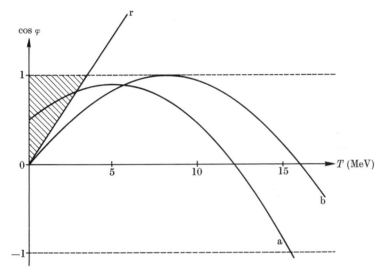

FIGURE 7-6. *The cos φ-T diagram showing the regions of vertical instability (shaded) limited by the straight line* r *(given by Equation 7-18), together with two typical curves,* a *and* b. *Curve* a *is incompatible with the stability condition; curve* b *instead is only limited by the condition* $|\cos \varphi| \leqslant 1$ *and it is not influenced by the stability condition. Data used:* $E_0 = 1$ *BeV,* $qU = 100$ *keV,* $n = 0.01$; *for curve* a, $\omega_e/\omega_0 = 0.995$, $\varphi_0 = \pi/3$; *for curve* b, $\omega_e/\omega_0 = 0.992$, $\varphi_0 = \pi/2$.

7-3   THE MAXIMUM OBTAINABLE ENERGY IN A CYCLOTRON

A consequence of the phase variations of a particle in a cyclotron, described in the previous section, is that, once the accelerating voltage U is fixed, there is a maximum particle energy which it is not possible to exceed, even with the use of a magnet of arbitrarily large radius. This, as we have discussed in Section 1-6, is essentially due to the loss of synchronism caused by the relativistic increase of mass. Let us again refer to the schematic case treated in the previous section. As Figure 7-4 shows, for a given initial phase φ_0, the kinetic energy obtained cannot exceed the value T_0 for which cos $\varphi = -1$ (on the descending branch of the parabola). Furthermore it can be seen that, for a given maximum value cos φ_m of cos φ, T_0 increases when cos φ_0 decreases and it is the greatest when $\cos \varphi_0 = -1$. In order that T_0 be the greatest possible it is necessary that the parameters of the machine be chosen in such a way that, at the maximum of the parabola ($T = T_m$), $\cos \varphi = 1$. It can indeed be shown directly (from the equation of the parabola) that no other parabola reaches as high an energy T_0. Thus the greatest possible value for T_0, T^*, is determined by the curve shown in Figure 7-7.[4] The value of T^* can be obtained

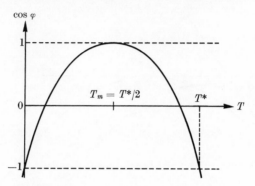

FIGURE 7-7. *Diagram showing the $\cos\varphi$-T parabola giving the maximum possible value T_0, T^*.*

from Equation 7-14 (with $\cos \varphi_0 = -1$) by requiring that the right-hand side be equal to 1 for $T = T_m = \frac{1}{2}T^*$ and to -1 for $T = T^*$. From these two equations we can eliminate the ratio ω_ℓ/ω_0 and obtain T^* as a function of U and E_0 only. In this way we obtain the following relation:

$$\frac{\pi T^{*2}}{qUE_0(1 + T^*/2E_0)} = 16. \tag{7-19}$$

If in the denominator we neglect T^* with respect to $2E_0$ (indeed we shall see that T^* is of the order of a few tens of million electron volts, whereas for the particles accelerated in cyclotrons, E_0 is of the order of 1 BeV) we obtain

$$T^* \simeq 4\left(\frac{qUE_0}{\pi}\right)^{1/2}. \tag{7-20}$$

Numerically this formula can be written

$$T^* = 2.16\sqrt{U} \quad \text{for protons,}$$
$$T^* = 3.08\sqrt{U} \quad \text{for deuterons} \tag{7-21}$$

[4] For this curve ($\cos \varphi_0 < 0$) the vertical stability condition is satisfied (see the previous section).

(U in kilovolts, T^* in million electron volts).[5] With the voltages of the order of 100–200 kV used in practice, one obtains values of T^* between 22 and 30 MeV for protons and between 31 and 43 MeV for deuterons. Equation 7-20 can also be interpreted in terms of the minimum voltage U_{min} required to reach a given energy T_f; that is, we must have

$$U > U_{min} = \frac{\pi T_f^2}{16 q E_0} \,. \tag{7-22}$$

However, it is important to note that the values of T^* and of U_{min} given by Equations 7-20 and 7-22 have only a theoretical significance. With reference to Equation 7-20, for example, it is obvious that a cyclotron must always be designed for an energy less than the value given by the equation. Indeed the

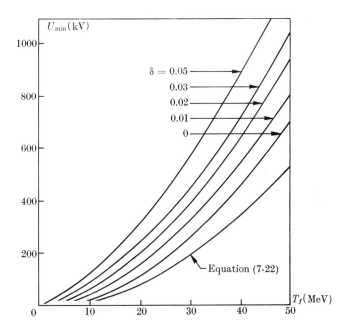

FIGURE 7-8. *Diagram of the minimum dee voltage U_{min} required to obtain a given proton energy for a magnetic field variation given by $B = B_0 [1 - \delta (r/R)]$. These curves are taken from a paper by B. L. Cohen (1953), and take account of all the effects which influence the motion of the particles in the cyclotron. For comparison, the curve corresponding to Equation 7-22, derived from the schematic case described in Section 7-2, is shown.*

[5] This formula again shows that a cyclotron is not convenient for accelerating electrons. Indeed, for an electron Equation 7-20 gives $T^* = 0.05 U^{1/2}$ (in the same units), and the use of the more exact equation 7-19 (since here T^* is of the order of E_0) does not change this result significantly.

case of Figure 7-7 corresponds to zero intensity (the range of the useful initial phases has zero width) and furthermore, as a result of the initial phase bunching around $\pi/2$ and of the effect of the decrease of magnetic field, the situation of Figure 7-7 does not occur in practice. However, the treatment we have given shows how the energy obtainable with a cyclotron is intrinsically limited by the value of the accelerating voltage, which must therefore be rather high. In qualitative terms, as there is a certain loss of synchronism (phase jump) at each transit across the gap, it is necessary to reduce the number of transits as far as possible, and hence, for a given final energy, to increase the energy given to the particle at each transit, that is, to increase the value of U.

A detailed study of the minimum value of the voltage U required to reach a certain energy, by including the effect of the variation of the magnetic field, can be found in the work of B. L. Cohen mentioned above (Cohen, 1953). Figure 7-8 shows a graph of the resulting $U_{\min}$ as a function of T_f for various rates of falloff of the magnetic field; the curve corresponding to Equation 7-22 is included for comparison.

7-4   THE DESIGN AND THE TECHNICAL PROBLEMS
OF THE CYCLOTRON

In the design of a cyclotron one of the most important problems is the construction and the supply of the oscillating circuit producing the accelerating voltage between the dees. As the dees have capacitance to earth and also between themselves, one could think of coupling them inductively with the rf generator (see Figure 7-9, where L must be chosen so that $\omega_e = (LC)^{-1/2}$, if C is the equivalent capacity of the system of dees). This method, however, is not practical both because the values of L required are too low and hence the coupling with the generator is weak, and because radiation losses would be

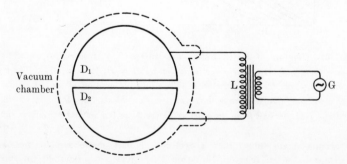

FIGURE 7-9.   *Schematic diagram of a cyclotron dee system, where the dees* D_1, D_2 *are coupled inductively to an ac generator,* G.

high. In all modern cyclotrons the dees are excited by means of two coaxial transmission lines T_1 and T_2 (see Figure 7-10) terminated for quarter-wave operation. The outer conductor of these lines is the vacuum-chamber wall (metallic or metallized) and the inner conductor is a metal bar (called the "dee stem"), which also provides the mechanical support of the dees. The two lines are connected to the generator directly, or by means of coupling loops (see Figure 7-10). Thus ohmic and radiation losses are reduced and voltages up to 200 kV or more can be obtained between the dees.

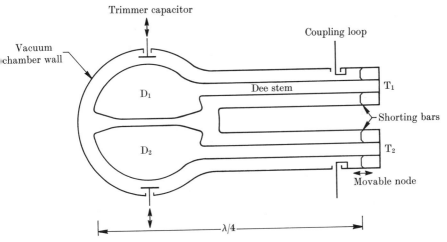

FIGURE 7-10. *Schematic diagram of a cyclotron dee system using transmission lines* (T_1, T_2) *with quarter-wave operation for the supply of the high-voltage accelerating potential between the dees* D_1, D_2.

As the frequency of the oscillating circuit must be determined with great precision (in Section 7-2 we have seen that a change of 0.1% in ω_e produces a great modification in the behavior of the phase of the particles), it is necessary to introduce some devices for its control. A rough adjustment is obtained by means of mobile metal diaphragms ("shorting bars") on the dee stems with which it is possible to control the length of the transmission line (see Figure 7-10). The precise adjustment is obtained by means of a variable trimmer capacitor which slightly modifies the capacitance of the dee system. In modern cyclotrons it is possible to carry out these adjustments without a shutdown of the machine.

In order to reduce the ohmic energy losses, all the conductors are made of copper. However, a large amount of energy is always dissipated in the oscillating circuit and therefore an efficient cooling system is required. Water cooling is generally used and the water tubes are welded to the metal surfaces of the cyclotron. In order to avoid changes in the capacitance of the system it is necessary to stabilize the temperature of the cooling water (sometimes to within 1 °C).

The cyclotron magnet must produce a field constant in time; therefore it is not made of laminations. Indeed, the various forgings of which it consists are made as large as possible, so that a small number of them suffices for the construction of the whole magnet. In order to avoid magnetic field distortions, a high precision (of the order of 1/50000) is required for the parallelism of the magnet poles. The height of the vacuum chamber is smaller than the gap width between the magnet poles and it rests on small bronze or brass supports so as to leave a clearance between the pole surfaces and the lids of the vacuum chamber. In this space soft-iron shims are placed in order to correct possible errors in the magnetic field and to ensure the correct decrease of magnetic field with radius. The shims used to correct the n value have the shape of disks or rings; those used to correct the azimuthal inhomogeneities have the shape of sectors or wedges. In all cyclotrons the use of shims is necessary to obtain the desired magnetic field with the precision required. In the earlier cyclotrons the shimming was obtained by trial and error, but now it is computed theoretically after an accurate measurement of the magnetic field point by point inside the vacuum chamber. Instead of iron shims it is possible to use correcting coils excited with the proper currents.

In some cases it is required to extract the beam of particles from the vacuum chamber. For this purpose one can use an electrostatic system formed by two electrodes in the shape of parallel vertical plates bent along a cylindrical surface and placed inside one of the dees near the peripheral wall (see Figure 7-11). The inner electrode (called the "septum") is connected electrically to the dee surrounding it; the outer electrode (called the "deflector") is kept at a high negative potential (of the order of 50 kV) and it is supported by an isolated metal bar passing through the dee stem. The septum has the form of a wedge and it is rather thin (see Figure 7-11), so that even if it is hit by the beam, it splits it into two parts (one of which penetrates inside the deflector system and is extracted) without being strongly damaged.

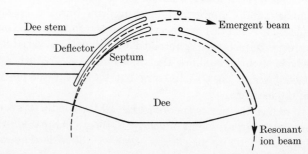

FIGURE 7-11. *Schematic diagram of the deflecting system used in the cyclotron to extract the beam.*

Once inside this system, the beam is deflected toward a window in the vacuum chamber closed by a thin foil. The construction of the deflecting system offers some technical difficulties both for the insulation of the deflector and for the wear of the septum which is subject to strong particle bombardment; furthermore, also the deflecting system requires water cooling to carry away the energy dissipated in it. A simple way of reducing the wear of the septum is to cut a slot in it, in the median plane: thus the zone of impact of the beam against the septum is no longer on the edge of the latter and the electric field inside the extraction channel is not strongly disturbed. Of course in order to increase the extraction efficiency the trajectories of particles on successive turns must be separated as far as possible. For this purpose the particles are extracted when their phase is again $\pi/2$, so that the particles encounter the field at the peak value, and, as a consequence of Equation 1-17, there is the maximum separation between two successive orbits. In this way (see Figure 7-12) one does not use the entire range of energies allowed for the phase variation (and the final energy is T_{f1} in Figure 7-12). If instead the particles are made to hit a target inside the vacuum chamber, the orbit separation is no longer so important and the acceleration can be pursued, in the same conditions, up to the maximum possible energy (T_{f2} in Figure 7-12).

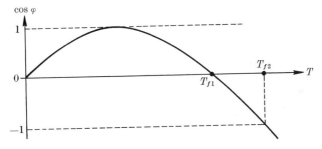

FIGURE 7-12. *Schematic* $\cos \varphi$-T *diagram for* $\cos \varphi_0 = 0$, *illustrating the maximum energy for the extracted beam,* T_{f1}, *and the maximum energy for an internal target,* T_{f2}.

Usually the beam-extraction efficiency in a cyclotron is never larger than 25% and values of about 15% are commonly reached. A typical value of the extracted beam intensity is of the order of 100 μA starting from a resonant beam of about 600 μA.

Other technical problems in the cyclotron are created by the electrical discharges that can occur inside the machine (for example, the phenomenon called "multipacting," which is discussed in Section 8-11). Furthermore in the cyclotron the operation of outgassing is laborious, owing to the presence of large metal surfaces. For this reason it is necessary to avoid any construction (such as soft soldering) which can easily give rise to gas sputtering.

The subject of ion sources is treated in Section 7-9.

7-5 MULTIPLE-PROJECTILE AND VARIABLE-ENERGY
OPERATION OF A CYCLOTRON

The same cyclotron, as can be seen from Equation 1-31, can accelerate ions of different mass and charge as long as they have the same ratio q/m. Thus a cyclotron for protons cannot be used for any other kind of particle. However, a cyclotron for deuterons can also be used to accelerate α particles (He^{++}) or molecular hydrogen ions (H_2^+). (Of course for α particles the final energy is twice as large as for deuterons.) The slight variations of the radio frequency needed in order to change from one case to the other (due to the imperfect identity of q/m) are within the range of the control systems described in the previous section. This is one of the reasons that the majority of the fixed-frequency cyclotrons operating at present (1966) are designed for deuterons.

Large changes of the frequency, such as to allow the acceleration of particles with substantially different values of q/m, are not possible in practice. Equally not practical is the idea of reducing the magnetic field, even by a small amount, so as to obtain, when required, particles of energy less than the maximum. This can only be done in the smaller cyclotrons where the magnetic field is everywhere far from saturation. If the field is near to saturation a change of its value involves reconstruction of the whole system of auxiliary magnetic shims, and this is a complicated and laborious operation.

A use of the cyclotron that is of increasing interest is the acceleration of ions heavier than helium, which are used for the production of certain nuclear reactions and in particular to obtain some transuranic elements. Indeed, with present techniques it is possible to build sources of sufficient intensity. Some kinds of heavy ions can be accelerated in cyclotrons built for light particles: This occurs either when q/m is the same (for instance, a C_{12}^{3+} ion can be accelerated in a cyclotron designed for He^+ ions) or when the so-called "harmonic operation" can be used. We have harmonic operation when the time required for a heavy ion to carry out a half-circle inside one of the dees is an *odd* multiple of the half-period of the rf oscillation. In this case it is easy to verify that the particle is again accelerated at each transit as in the normal operation. In this case formula 1-31 is changed to

$$\omega_e = h\frac{qB}{m}, \qquad h = 3, 5, 7, \ldots . \qquad (7\text{-}23)$$

For example, a cyclotron for protons can accelerate He_3^+ ions on the third harmonic.

In any case, it is always possible to adapt existing cyclotrons or to design new ones specifically for the acceleration of heavy ions.

7-6 THE SYNCHROCYCLOTRON

As we have mentioned in Section 1-7, the structure of a synchrocyclotron does not differ greatly from that of a fixed-frequency cyclotron. As the energy obtained is higher, also its size is greater (in the larger synchrocyclotrons, the magnet poles have a diameter of some meters). The two major differences with respect to the cyclotron which are characteristic of the synchrocyclotron are (1) the modulation of the frequency, which is made to decrease in order to follow the effects of the relativistic increase of mass and of the radial decrease of magnetic field, and (2) the much smaller value of the accelerating voltage U (of the order of 10 kV instead of 100 kV), such that the particles carry out a much greater number of turns inside the machine (of the order of 10,000 instead of 100, and up to 50,000 in the larger synchrocyclotrons). As a consequence of these two differences, many of the conclusions reached in the previous sections must be modified. As a result of the frequency modulation, the phase of the particles does not change during the acceleration in the way described in Section 7-2, but rather its behavior is similar to that in the synchrotron (see Equation 5-8, with $k=1$). Indeed, for the synchrocyclotron (as for the synchrotron) it is possible to define a synchronous particle (s.p.) for which $\dot{\varphi}$, given by Equation 7-7, is identically zero, and it is possible to follow through the same arguments as in Chapter 5 for the synchrotron and to reach the same conclusions.[6] Thus again the particles are bunched around the s.p., about which they carry out phase oscillations and radial "synchrotron" oscillations (with a frequency about 1000 times less than the rotation frequency). We find that the zone of phase stability is the one where the accelerating electric field is decreasing in time ($\pi/2 < \varphi_s < \pi$) and that the momentum compaction α has the same value $(1 - n)$ as in the synchrotron. As there is phase stability and the phase can remain limited as the energy increases, it is no longer necessary for the peak voltage U to be larger than a certain minimum value as occurs in the cyclotron, where at most we can use a single phase oscillation (see Section 7-3), into which we must fit the entire acceleration required. Thus in the synchrocyclotron much smaller values of U are used (point (2) at the beginning of this section) so that problems of insulation and power are much less important.

Again we have betatron oscillations superimposed on the synchrotron oscillations, and their frequency depends on the parameters of the machine as in the cyclotron. It must be noted that, as U is rather small, the electrostatic focusing term in Equation 7-17 is always very small and hence it is necessary to continue the field gradient (with a field index of the order of 0.02 to 0.05) up to the center of the machine. Another important consequence of

---

[6] The formulas valid for the synchrocyclotron are not exactly the same as those derived for the synchrotron, because the particle is accelerated twice in each turn. The corresponding modifications can be easily derived (see Bohm and Foldy, 1947).

point (2) is that, as the particles follow a very tight spiral and so stay a long time in all the parts of the magnetic field, the resonance effects described in Section 5-7 for the synchrotron have great importance. In particular the resonance between radial and vertical oscillations corresponding to $n = 0.2$ (see Table 5-1) is very dangerous. Experiments have shown (see, for example, Henrich *et al.*, 1949) that when the particles cross a region where $n = 0.2$ the synchrocyclotron beam is practically destroyed: the few surviving particles are eliminated by the resonance (between radial or vertical oscillations and the orbital motion) which occurs at $n = 0.25$. The resonance between radial and vertical oscillations occurring at $n = 0.1$ does not disturb the beam significantly. It is therefore necessary for the particles to be accelerated within a radius less than the one where $n = 0.2$. As the field index increases rapidly only at the edge of the magnet (see Figure 7-1), the radius at which acceleration is stopped is only slightly less than the magnet radius.

The synchronous phase φ_s (which satisfies an expression of the kind of Equation 5-19) is chosen of the order of $150°-160°$ as in the synchrotron, and so the resulting accelerating field is about one half of the peak value. However, we must remember that at the beginning of the acceleration the particles are practically all concentrated around the phase $\varphi = 90°$ because of the initial phase bunching described above for the cyclotron. As this phase always falls inside the stability zone, practically all the particles emitted during the useful time for acceleration are captured (apart from the losses due to the vertical betatron oscillations or to collisions with molecules of the residual gas).

In conclusion, the difference of intensity between the cyclotron and the synchrocyclotron is mainly due to the fact that the cyclotron has a practically continuous operation, whereas the synchrocyclotron accelerates only the particles emitted in a certain time interval Δt at the beginning of the frequency-modulation cycle (see Figure 7-13). The ratio of the intensities for the two

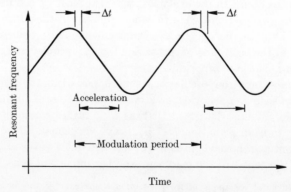

FIGURE 7-13. *Typical frequency-modulation cycle showing the time interval Δt when injected particles are accepted.*

kinds of machine is therefore given by the duty cycle of the synchrocyclotron, that is, by the ratio of Δt and the period of the modulation cycle. This ratio is of the order of 1%; the average currents obtained in the resonant beam are of the order from 0.1 to 1.0 μA and exceptionally up to 2 μA. Recent improvements in technical devices give hope that higher values may be reached.

Finally, it must be noted that the synchrocyclotron can be used for the so-called "stochastic acceleration," which has a satisfactory efficiency and gives continuous instead of pulsed operation. For this kind of acceleration (first proposed by Burshtein *et al.* (1955), p. 3), the frequency of the rf system is modulated by random noise (instead of a regular signal), the noise spectrum covering the whole interval of frequency modulation in an ordinary synchrocyclotron, and the ion source has continuous operation (instead of pulsed operation, as in the ordinary synchrocyclotron; see the following section). Under these conditions the ions are subject to random acceleration and deceleration, but there are always some ions for which the synchronism condition is satisfied by the particular frequency encountered; hence the ions gain energy on the average, and some of them reach the final energy even if in an irregular way. The principle has been tested by R. Keller, L. Dick, and M. Fidecaro (1959), who have obtained 1 μA of 4.4-MeV protons in a cyclotron of 50-cm diameter.

7-7 TECHNICAL PROBLEMS OF THE SYNCHROCYCLOTRON

The differences in the operation of the synchrocyclotron with respect to the cyclotron lead to differences in the solutions of many of the problems described in Section 7-4. In particular, as the voltage U required in the former is low there is no need for two dees at opposite potentials to produce the rf electric field. Only one dee is used and the accelerating voltage is applied between this and the vacuum chamber. To the vacuum chamber are attached (see Figure 7-14) two electrodes facing the dee, which simulate the entrance of the second dee (a "dummy dee"), and so the electric field has a distribution similar to the one existing in the cyclotron.

The frequency modulation is usually obtained by means of a capacitor whose capacitance changes periodically (with a frequency from 60 to 2000 cps). Often a rotating multibladed capacitor is used. This capacitor is inserted in the rf oscillating circuit and usually it is placed outside the magnetic field of the machine. However, as it must operate in a vacuum in order to avoid electrical discharges, it usually has its own vacuum chamber. A modern method of frequency modulation consists in changing the capacitance of the oscillating circuit by means of a vibrating reed; in this way it is also possible to increase the duty cycle.

Because of construction problems connected with the large size of the machine, the vacuum chamber in the synchrocyclotron does not have separate lids as in the cyclotron: the evacuated volume is limited by the surfaces of the pole pieces to which a vacuum-tight side wall is sealed. Thus there are no shimming gaps and the magnet pole tips must be machined with great precision; any corrective shims must be welded to the pole surfaces.

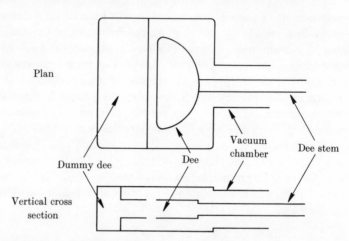

FIGURE 7-14. *Schematic structure of a synchrocyclotron using a dummy dee.*

The beam cannot be extracted with the method described above for the cyclotron, because the separation between successive orbits is small and the septum would intercept the entire beam. To extract the beam, the distance between consecutive orbits is increased by means of carefully designed local perturbations of the magnetic field (for instance, by using the magnetic peeler described in Section 4-6) in such a way that the beam can penetrate in a region where the magnetic field is shielded out, so that it is no longer deviated and it can leave the machine. Extraction efficiencies of a few percent have been obtained in this way.

Details on the ion sources are given in Section 7-9. The only difference with respect to the cyclotron is that the source has pulsed operation and it only emits ions during the useful time for acceleration (Δt in Figure 7-13).[7]

Finally it must be noted that, as a consequence of the modulation of the radio frequency and as the technical difficulties in the construction of the oscillating circuit are not so severe, it is possible to accelerate different kinds of particles in the same synchrocyclotron. The magnetic field is kept constant, while the range of frequency modulation is altered as well as the final energies

---

[7] Of course for stochastic acceleration the operation of the source is not pulsed (see the previous section).

of the particles. Usually, to accelerate particles with different values of q/m (such as protons and deuterons) the modulation ratio must be approximately $2:1$ or $3:1$.

7-8 THE MICROTRON

The microtron is an electron accelerator which has the feature in common with the cyclotron that the particles are accelerated by a fixed-frequency resonant cavity and they move in a constant magnetic field where they describe circular trajectories of increasing radius. The concept of the microtron is due to Veksler (1944a,b; 1945); a schematic plan of the machine is shown in Figure 7-15. The electrons follow circular orbits tangential to the axis of the

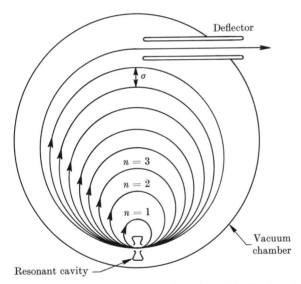

FIGURE 7-15. *Schematic diagram of particle orbits in the microtron.*

cavity. As they are accelerated at each transit across the cavity, the radius of the orbit and the time τ required for one turn both increase. If we use the subscript n to denote quantities referring to a particle during the nth turn, we have (using Equation 7-6)

$$\tau_n = \frac{2\pi}{\omega_n} = \frac{2\pi}{c^2 eB} E_n, \qquad n = 1, 2, \ldots, \qquad (7\text{-}24)$$

(where $-e$ is the charge of the electron). If we want the electron to encounter the field of the cavity always in the same phase (such as to accelerate it), the time τ_n (for all n) must be an integral multiple of the period T_e of the accelerating electric field. The electrons to be accelerated are obtained directly by field emission from the walls of the cavity. As their initial kinetic energy is practically zero we shall have (for the electrons satisfying the synchronism condition)

$$E_n = E_0 + neU \sin \varphi, \qquad n = 1, 2, \ldots, \tag{7-25}$$

where U is the peak value of the accelerating voltage and φ is the (constant) phase[8] with which the electrons cross the cavity. From Equations 7-24 and 7-25 we obtain

$$\tau_n - \tau_{n-1} = \frac{2\pi}{c^2 eB}(E_n - E_{n-1}) = \frac{2\pi}{c^2 B} U \sin \varphi. \tag{7-26}$$

The synchronism condition for the times of rotation (so that the phase φ remains constant) is satisfied if the quantity $(\tau_n - \tau_{n-1})$ given by Equation 7-26 is an integral multiple, h_1, say, of T_e, that is,

$$\frac{2\pi U \sin \varphi}{c^2 B} = h_1 T_e, \tag{7-27}$$

and if τ_1 itself is an integral multiple, h_2, say, of T_e, that is,

$$\tau_1 = \frac{2\pi}{c^2 eB}(E_0 + eU \sin \varphi) = h_2 T_e. \tag{7-28}$$

From Equations 7-27 and 7-28 we obtain

$$U \sin \varphi = \frac{E_0}{e}\frac{h_1}{h_2 - h_1} ; \tag{7-29}$$

$$\omega_e = \frac{2\pi}{T_e} = \frac{c^2 Be}{E_0}(h_2 - h_1). \tag{7-30}$$

As ω_e must be positive, we must have $h_2 > h_1$. As the minimum value of $(h_2 - h_1)$ is 1, it can be seen that in practical cases ω_e falls in the range of centimeter microwaves. For example, for $B = 0.1$ Wb/m², $h_2 - h_1 = 1$, we obtain $\nu_e = \omega_e/2\pi = 2.8 \times 10^9$ cps ($\lambda = 10.7$ cm). For frequencies of this order of magnitude, however, high voltages are required: for $h_1 = 1$, $h_2 = 2$ (these are the smallest possible values of h_1 and h_2, and the motion of an electron under these conditions is schematically shown in Figure 7-16), we obtain $U \geq E_0/e = 511$ kV. Such high voltages can be obtained by modern microwave technology. Smaller values of U can be chosen if $(h_2 - h_1) > 1$.

[8] The phase for the microtron is again defined by Equation 7-2, if one measures the angular distance θ from the cavity and assumes the expression 7-1 (with $U > 0$) for the accelerating voltage. In all the present considerations the transit time across the cavity is neglected.

In this case higher frequencies must be used. Usually one prefers to use a high value of U because this results in a greater separation between successive orbits and a smaller number of turns inside the machine. Under these conditions the problems of beam stability and extraction are greatly simplified (as will be discussed later).

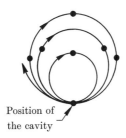

Position of
the cavity

FIGURE 7-16. *Schematic diagram of the first three orbits in a microtron with $h_1 = 1$, $h_2 = 2$. The distances between two successive dots along the orbit are covered by the electron in a time equal to the period of the resonant cavity.*

As the microtron is essentially a weak-focusing accelerator, there is phase stability in this machine also. The synchronous phase, defined by Equation 7-29 (once the parameters of the machine are fixed), is again stable when it falls in the region of decreasing electric field, that is, between $\pi/2$ and π. The problem of the vertical stability of the beam is more serious because the uniform magnetic field does not produce vertical focusing, and the focusing effect on the transits across the cavity (when the electric field is decreasing; see Section 7-1) is small. For this reason the magnet must be built with great precision. As the number of rotations of the particles in the machine is small (of the order of 10 for energies of a few million electron volts), the absence of vertical focusing does not cause loss of the particles injected tangentially or with a small deviation from the median plane. All the other particles are lost, and therefore there is a low efficiency of extraction from the source (of the order of 1%). However, recent technological developments have succeeded in overcoming this difficulty and in obtaining large currents, by designing suitable sources which inject the electrons in the required direction and which broaden the range of accepted initial phases (see, for example, Kapitza, 1965).

A pulse from the machine consists of a succession of short bunches, of the size of about $\lambda/20$, which follow each other at a distance of one wavelength λ. The microtron has the advantage that electrons of different energy are "localized" in sharply distinct regions, that is, the beam is always very narrow with respect to the distance between two successive orbits, and the more so the greater the peak voltage U (or, in equivalent terms, the lower the frequency ω_e). The distance between successive orbits can easily be computed from Equation 7-26 by using Equation 7-27 and by recalling that $\tau_n = \pi d_n/v_n$, where d_n is the diameter of the nth orbit and v_n the velocity of the particles describing it. We therefore obtain

$$\frac{d_n}{v_n} - \frac{d_{n-1}}{v_{n-1}} = \frac{2h_1}{\omega_e}. \tag{7-31}$$

In the ultrarelativistic limit, which is reached very soon, $v_n \simeq v_{n-1} \simeq c$, and the orbit spacing becomes constant (see Figure 7-15). The maximum separation σ between two successive orbits is

$$\sigma = 2h_1 \frac{c}{\omega_e} = h_1 \frac{\lambda}{\pi}. \tag{7-32}$$

It can be seen that, for values of λ of a few centimeters, σ is sufficiently large with respect to the spread of the beam to allow an easy extraction, with a small loss of electrons. It is sufficient to put a deflector (a magnetic one, for instance) in correspondence with the outermost orbit (see Figure 7-15).

The extracted beam is quite intense (pulse currents from 20 to 100 mA, average currents of about 10^2 μA) and very homogeneous in energy. For this reason microtrons are very suitable as injectors for larger machines. Energies from a few to about 30 MeV have been obtained up to now; for a review of the data of the operating machines, see Kapitza (1965). In the larger microtrons, slight inhomogeneities of the magnetic field may be introduced in order to improve the stability of the beam.

The accelerating cavity is fed from outside by means of a waveguide, with pulsed operation, because of the large power involved. It must be noted that it is possible to change the final energy in a microtron by injecting the electrons with a certain kinetic energy T_0. In this case in Equation 7-28 E_0 must be replaced by $(E_0 + T_0)$ and the same substitution occurs in Equations 7-29 and 7-30. It is therefore necessary to adjust the value of the magnetic field. In this way the total final energy reached (not the kinetic energy) is increased by a factor $(1 + T_0/E_0)$.

The treatment given above shows that the microtron, with the practical design described in this section, cannot be used to accelerate protons. Indeed, as E_0 in this case is very large, Equation 7-29 would require values of U of about 10^9 V.

7-9   ION SOURCES FOR CYCLOTRONS

As we have mentioned in Section 1-11, ion sources for cyclotrons must be designed with great care if reasonable intensities are required; these sources, indeed, must operate in a region where strong electric and magnetic fields are present.

In the early cyclotrons a simple hot filament, placed near the lower lid of the vacuum chamber, was used with the purpose of producing electrons: these were deviated by the magnetic field in such a way as to follow a helicoidal path in the vertical direction. (This helix was rather tight because the magnetic field was strong and the speed of the electrons low.) Thus a beam of electrons was obtained, whose overall motion was parallel to the magnetic field. These electrons produced ions by collisions with the molecules of the gas which was injected near the filament. It was necessary for the gas pressure (which was the same in the whole machine) to be sufficiently high to give a reasonable intensity but not so high as to produce appreciable scattering of the accelerated ion beam by collisions. Thus very low intensities were obtained.

In order to avoid this difficulty, sources have been built inside which the gas pressure can be higher than the pressure in the vacuum chamber. High-voltage sources cannot be used because of the presence of the alternating field between the dees, and in cyclotrons only low-voltage (arc) sources and oscillating-electron sources are used.

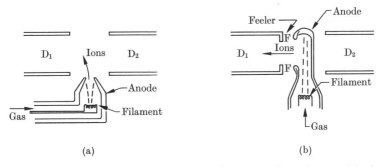

FIGURE 7-17.   *Schematic diagrams of arc-type ion sources for cyclotrons:* (a) *simple-arc source*; (b) *hooded-arc source.*

A simple kind of arc source is shown in Figure 7-17a. The principle of operation is the same as that of the source shown in Figure 1-13, with the difference that the exit hole of the ions can be made large (in order to increase the intensity), because the magnetic field limits the dispersion of the electron beam. A greater amount of gas also gets through the hole but it does not give trouble if there is an efficient differential pumping. In this type of source, the ions are emitted at all azimuths. One can imagine modifying it (see Figure 7-17b) in such a way that, for a given area of the exit aperture, the ions leave the source in the azimuthal direction the most convenient for acceleration. The arc is formed in a cylindrical anode which has a thin vertical slit (FF in the figure), oriented in the direction of one of the dees. At the entrance of this dee, in correspondence with the source, there may be some metallic protruding lips (feelers) whose purpose is to enhance the electric field at the source and so to focus the ions leaving it. However the use of the feelers introduces a vertical component of the velocity which may cause trouble because at the beginning of the acceleration the vertical focusing is weak (see Section 7-2). In fixed-frequency cyclotrons it is preferable to use two vertical bars (called "pullers"), placed across the opening of the dee (see Figure 7-18), for focusing the emitted ions. The pullers can also be placed at larger radial distances, outside the particle orbits, in order to intercept the parasitic ions which in any case would never reach the end of the acceleration phase. The pullers cannot be used in the synchrocyclotron, where the orbit spacing is too small.

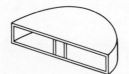

FIGURE 7-18. *Schematic diagram of a dee showing the position of the pullers.*

Concerning the oscillating-electron sources, the only point to be added to the considerations of Section 1-11 is that in the case of cyclotrons the magnetic field required by the source (see Figure 1-14) is the field of the machine itself.

In general modern sources give a useful resonant beam of the order of 500 μA with a dissipation of about 0.5 kW. The arc voltage is usually between 100 and 200 V, with a current of a few amperes. The main problem of these sources is the short lifetime of the filament (of the order of 100 hours for tungsten filaments) and of the arc anode (often made of graphite). It must therefore be possible to remove the source from the machine easily, without deterioration of the vacuum. Furthermore the source must be well cooled in order to dissipate the heat produced by the discharge.

CHAPTER 8

THE LINEAR ACCELERATOR

By Dr. M. Puglisi*

8-1 INTRODUCTION. BEAM STABILITY IN A LINAC

The principle of operation of a linear accelerator (linac) has been described in Section 1-5, where we have indicated the differences in construction and operation between a linac for heavy particles (such as protons) and one for electrons.

In this chapter the operation of the linac will be treated in greater detail with special emphasis on the electron machines, which at present appear to be the only accelerators capable of producing electron beams of very high energies—indeed the circular machines are greatly limited by radiation losses (see Section 5-8). On the other hand, at present proton linacs are practically only used as injectors for larger machines, as they give a high beam intensity and good collimation, whereas for the production of nuclear reactions other machines seem to be more convenient, both for low and for high energies.

The construction of a linear accelerator presents great technical problems because the operation of the machine requires an rf system of enormous power. For this reason, although the principle of the operation of these machines has been known since 1930, high-energy linacs were only built after World War II, when the experience gained in radar technology permitted the construction of resonant cavities and microwave generators (klystrons) capable of producing sufficiently large powers. This is one of the most typical cases of a close connection between technological and scientific progress.

* Professor of Radio Engineering at the University of Palermo, Italy.

In Section 1-9 we have seen that the principle of phase stability holds also for the linac and that the synchronous phase φ_s must lie between 0 and $\pi/2$, that is, the particles must encounter an accelerating electric field which is increasing in time. The description of the phenomenon given in Section 1-9 is sufficient for the purpose of this book; the conclusions reached also hold for the (traveling-wave) electron linacs, even if, in this case, an intuitive representation is less immediate. Figure 8-1 shows the profile of the accelerating electric field along the direction of propagation (z axis) "frozen" at a certain instant of time t. An accelerated electron (traveling together with the wave) having a stable phase lies in a position between A and B (at C, for example) so that it is, as it were, "pushed" ahead by the crest of the propagating wave. It can be seen that, under these conditions, at a fixed point in the accelerator ($z = z_0$) the electric field *increases* in time as the electron goes by.

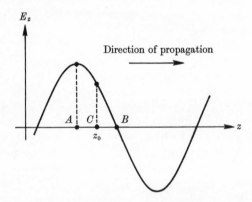

FIGURE 8-1. *Diagram of the accelerating electric field as a function of the distance z along the linac at a given instant of time. If the direction of propagation is the one shown, positions between A and B correspond to phase stability.*

We shall discuss in more detail the question of the *transverse stability* of the accelerated beam. (It is obvious that, as the system has cylindrical symmetry, all the transverse directions are equivalent.) In a linac the longitudinal (phase) stability and the transverse stability are incompatible. This can be understood in a general way by noting that, in a reference system moving together with the synchronous particle at a certain instant, a phase-stable particle is practically at rest, and then the only forces acting on it are those associated with the electrostatic field. In this field there can be no position of stable equilibrium. Indeed this position would correspond to a minimum of the potential, but this can have no minima or maxima except at the boundary because it is a harmonic function. Thus, in the quarter-periods where there is longitudinal (phase) stability, there is transverse instability and vice versa.

The transverse instability in an accelerator with discontinuous acceleration (proton linac) can also be considered in the following way. A particle crossing the accelerating gap as the electric field is increasing is subject to the same kind of net defocusing effect, due to the radial component of electric field, that occurs in the gap between the dees of a cyclotron (see Section 7-1 and Figure 7-2). However, it can be shown (see, for example, Livingood, 1961, p. 283) that in a linac because of the presence of the magnetic field of the electromagnetic wave, the transverse instability goes like $(1 - \beta^2)$ and hence becomes negligible for ultrarelativistic particles. Hence in electron linacs this problem (which is further discussed in Section 8-5) does not give great trouble. In proton linacs, however, where the particles are far from the ultrarelativistic limit, the transverse instability is serious and it must be corrected by special devices, which are discussed in Section 8-13.

In order to conclude this introduction, we mention some alternative designs for linear accelerators. A possibility that has been studied and experimented with, but is not used now, is to excite an electron linac with a standing wave instead of a traveling wave. A standing wave can be considered as the superposition of two equal waves traveling in opposite directions; therefore in these machines the particles are accelerated by the component propagating in the direction of the motion, whereas the other component produces a very rapid succession of accelerations and decelerations which on the average have no effect. In those machines the power carried by the reverse wave is wasted. However, as in traveling-wave accelerators too there is a large dissipation of power (see Section 8-9), this is not the reason that traveling-wave accelerators are preferred.

The reason is that at present (1966) the generators most suitable to feed a resonating structure (that is, a structure in which standing waves can exist) are magnetrons, and these generators are less convenient in practice than klystrons because they produce less power and are more difficult to operate. Klystrons, on the other hand, having recently undergone a great technological development are the most suitable generators for feeding the structures in which only traveling waves are allowed (matched loads). The existing standing-wave linacs were built before this development of klystron technology, and, once the problems of operation have been overcome, they have a good efficiency.

Another important version of the electron linac is the one that allows the acceleration of electrons and positrons in the same machine. These machines are very important as injectors for storage rings (see Chapter 9). The beam of accelerated positrons is obtained by inserting a target in the path of the electron beam at an intermediate distance (one third of the accelerator length, for instance) and by adjusting the second part of the machine so that the positrons produced by conversion can be accelerated. The positron beam thus produced has a lower energy than the electron beam, because of the shorter path, and above all it has a much lower intensity owing to the small conversion efficiency (of the order of 10^{-3}). The most significant example of a machine of this kind is the 20-BeV accelerator at Stanford (see Section 1-5), which can also produce 13-BeV positrons. It is expected that study of the operation of such machines will yield further information on the efficiency of the conversion process, for which a complete theory is still lacking.

In this chapter we first describe the electron linacs which use the continuous acceleration provided by a traveling electromagnetic wave (Sections 8-2 to 8-11); then we consider the heavy-particle linacs where the particles are accelerated discontinuously at the gaps between successive drift tubes (Sections 8-12, 8-13). Since the traveling waves which accelerate the electrons propagate within structures that can be considered as special types of waveguides (see Section 1-5), part of this chapter (Sections 8-6 to 8-8) contains some elements of the theory of waveguides.

8-2 ELEMENTARY NOTIONS ON WAVE PROPAGATION

In the following sections, where the electron linacs are treated, use will be made of a formalism which is of common use for the phenomena of wave propagation. Let us consider a quantity $F(z, t)$, which propagates without attenuation along the positive direction of the z axis, according to a sinusoidal law of the kind

$$F(z,t) = F_0 \cos(kz - \omega t), \qquad (8\text{-}1)$$

where F_0, k, ω are positive constants which represent the amplitude of the wave, its wave number, and its angular frequency, respectively. (If λ and ν are the wavelength and the frequency of the wave, respectively, then $k = 2\pi/\lambda$, $\omega = 2\pi\nu$.) The phase velocity v_p of the wave is defined by

$$v_p = \frac{\omega}{k} = \lambda\nu. \qquad (8\text{-}2)$$

It can be verified that an observer traveling with a velocity v_p along the z axis does not see any change in the quantity F, that is, in the argument $(kz - \omega t)$. Equation 8-1 can always be written in the form[1]

$$F = \text{Re}[F_0 \exp i(kz - \omega t)]. \qquad (8\text{-}3)$$

If the quantity F is used only in linear operations (including thus differentiation and integration), at each step the operation of taking the real part can

---

[1] The same holds if a sine instead of a cosine appears in Equation 8-1: in this case the imaginary part must be taken in Equation 8-3. It is also possible to use an expression where the sign of the phase argument is changed, that is, like $\exp i(\omega t - kz)$.

be exchanged with all the others. Therefore we can eliminate the symbol Re
in Equation 8-3 and write directly

$$F = F_0 \exp i(kz - \omega t), \qquad (8\text{-}4)$$

assuming implicitly that, at each step, in order to obtain the quantity with
physical meaning, we must take the real part of the (complex) expressions
containing F. This procedure is very useful in practice because of the greater
ease of manipulating exponentials. This is especially clear when we wish to
treat the general case of the superposition of many sinusoidal waves which in
general propagate with different wavelengths, frequencies, and velocities.
Again using the symbol $F(z, t)$, we can always write the quantity in the
form (for a superposition of waves traveling without attenuation)[2]

$$F(z, t) = \int_{-\infty}^{+\infty} A(\omega) \exp i(kz - \omega t) \, d\omega. \qquad (8\text{-}5)$$

In this expression, $k = k(\omega)$ must be considered a function of ω (*dispersion
relation*) determined by the laws governing the propagation of the waves.
(For example, for an electromagnetic wave propagating in a homogeneous,
infinite, nondispersive medium, $|v_p| = $ const and $k = $ const $\times \omega$.) $A(\omega)$ is the
(usually complex) amplitude of the wave having angular frequency ω and
wave number $k(\omega)$. It should be noted that in Equation 8-5 also negative
values of ω may appear. These correspond to waves which propagate in the
negative direction of the z axis, for which Equation 8-4 has the form

$$F = F_0 \exp i(kz + |\omega| t). \qquad (8\text{-}6)$$

As most systems are symmetrical with respect to a reversal of the direction
of propagation, usually $k(\omega) = k(-\omega)$.

An important characteristic velocity, the group velocity v_g, is defined in
terms of the function $k(\omega)$ by

$$v_g(\omega) = \left(\frac{dk}{d\omega}\right)^{-1} \qquad (8\text{-}7)$$

(or, if ω is considered a function of k, $v_g(\omega) = d\omega/dk$). The importance of the
group velocity is that it represents the velocity of the center of a wave packet
(such as is represented by an expression like Equation 8-5 where $A(\omega) \neq 0$
only over a certain narrow frequency range); v_g is also the velocity of propagation of the energy of a physical wave packet.

In many practical cases, in expressions like Equation 8-4 the factor
$\exp(-i\omega t)$, which is always the same, can be understood and is not explicitly
written. Thus a traveling wave is completely described by its spatial part

---

[2] In this case, k is a real quantity. In general, however, for a dissipative medium,
waves are attenuated along the direction of propagation and then k also has an imaginary part.

exp (ikz); the sign of k determines the direction of propagation; its modulus, all the other characteristic quantities. The formalism described above can readily be generalized to the propagation of a signal in an arbitrary direction in three-dimensional space; however, this is not required in the present chapter.

8-3   CONDITIONS FOR TRAVELING-WAVE ACCELERATION

We now wish to examine the conditions that must be satisfied for a traveling electromagnetic wave to give energy continuously to a particle in a linac. Two important conditions must be satisfied. In the first place, the electric field associated with the wave must have an axial component in the direction of propagation. Second, the axial electric field seen by the particle must always (or for most of the time) have the same sign, such as to accelerate the particle. The first condition implies (as we shall examine in detail later) that the so-called TM waves must be used for particle acceleration (see Section 8-6). The second condition has an important consequence: it implies that the particle velocity and the phase velocity of the wave should be approximately equal. This can be seen in the following way.

If we call $\varphi = \omega t - kz$ the phase of the wave, then the angular frequency seen by a stationary observer ($z = $ const) is given by $\partial\varphi/\partial t = \omega$, but the angular frequency seen by an observer moving with a velocity v is given by $\omega' = d\varphi/dt' = \omega dt/dt' - k\,dz/dt' = (\omega - kv)dt/dt'$ where t' is the time measured in the reference system of this observer. Since (see, for instance, Panofsky and Phillips, 1962, p. 290) $dt/dt' = (1 - \beta^2)^{-1/2} = \gamma$, by using Equation 8-2, we find

$$\omega' = \omega\gamma\left(1 - \frac{v}{v_p}\right). \qquad (8\text{-}8)$$

This difference is simply the Doppler effect. Thus if $v = v_p$ the particles see an accelerating field with a constant phase, that is, a field which does not oscillate at all ($\omega' = 0$). If instead v is even slightly different from v_p, the particles see a field which oscillates at the high frequency ω', of the order of $\gamma\omega$. In this case the average acceleration would be very small. The condition that the accelerating field seen by the particle should always be of the same sign implies that $\omega' \ll \omega$ and so, from Equation 8-8,

$$v \simeq v_p. \qquad (8\text{-}9)$$

As the laws of relativistic mechanics require that $v \leq c$, it follows from the matching condition 8-9 that in order for an electromagnetic wave to accelerate a particle continuously it must satisfy the condition that

$$v_p \leq c. \qquad (8\text{-}10)$$

We shall show in the following sections that there are special metallic structures (loaded waveguides) which allow the propagation of electromagnetic waves having not only a nonzero axial component of electric field but also a phase velocity less than or equal to c.

8-4 PARTICLE MOTION IN THE ELECTRON LINAC. THE CAPTURE CONDITION

The behavior of the accelerating electric field as a function of the distance along the axis of the machine is always very complicated both for machines with discontinuous acceleration and for those with continuous acceleration. However, for the latter if one refers to the synchronous particle (s.p.), the problem can be simplified by considering the case of a particle in motion in a uniform field whose value is precisely that seen by the s.p. Let m, $\pm e$, β be respectively the rest mass, the charge[3], and the "normalized velocity" ($\beta = v/c$; see Section 1-2) of the particle, and let E_z be the magnitude of the accelerating electric field. Then the relativistic equation of motion (Equation 1-2) is

$$\frac{d}{dt}\left(\frac{mc}{(1 - \beta^2)^{1/2}}\beta\right) = eE_z, \tag{8-11}$$

and, if E_z is a constant, this can be integrated to give

$$\frac{\beta}{(1 - \beta^2)^{1/2}} - \frac{\beta_0}{(1 - \beta_0{}^2)^{1/2}} = \frac{eE_z}{mc}t, \tag{8-12}$$

where $\beta = \beta_0$ for $t = 0$. This equation will be used in order to derive the so-called "capture condition," which is of great importance in the design of electron linacs.

As we have seen in the previous section, in order to maintain the synchronism between the particle motion and the propagation of the traveling wave, we must have $v \simeq v_p$ at each point. In an electron linac we have $v \simeq c$ almost everywhere and so it is sufficient to design a waveguide where the phase velocity is constant and equal to c. However, at the injection and during the first part of the acceleration the particle velocity is less than c, for the values of the injection energy used in practice. Instead of modulating the phase velocity in the first part of the acceleration (which is a difficult problem), let us see for which conditions particles injected directly into a wave traveling with a phase velocity c are in the region of stable phases (see Section 1-9). In this case the particles are "captured" by the wave and they reach the end of the acceleration cycle carrying out phase oscillations about the s.p.

[3] The quantity $e > 0$ is the absolute value of the electron charge (1.6021×10^{-19} coulomb): the linac theory, developed here, only refers to electrons and positrons.

We therefore suppose that a wave propagates inside the accelerator with a phase velocity equal to c, that the accelerating electric field is in the direction of propagation and has a sinusoidal behavior in time, and that its amplitude E_{z0} is constant along the trajectory. Then, if E_z is the field seen by the particle, we define the phase angle φ between the wave and the particle by means of the relation

$$E_z = E_{z0} \sin \varphi. \tag{8-13}$$

If v is the particle velocity, then

$$dl = (c - v) \, dt \tag{8-14}$$

is the difference in path between the wave and the particle in the time dt. This path difference can also be expressed in terms of the phase difference $d\varphi$, that is,

$$dl = \frac{\lambda_g}{2\pi} d\varphi, \tag{8-15}$$

where $\lambda_g = 2\pi/k_g$ is the wavelength inside the waveguide. From Equations 8-14 and 8-15, with $v = \beta c$, we obtain

$$\frac{d\varphi}{dt} = \frac{2\pi c}{\lambda_g} (1 - \beta). \tag{8-16}$$

This equation relates the rate of change of the phase to the instantaneous (normalized) velocity of the particle. Let us now again consider the equation of motion, Equation 8-11. If we substitute into it Equation 8-13 for E_z, we have

$$\frac{d}{dt} \left(\frac{\beta}{(1 - \beta^2)^{1/2}} \right) = \frac{eE_{z0}}{mc} \sin \varphi, \tag{8-17}$$

and, if we put

$$\beta = \cos \alpha, \tag{8-18}$$

this becomes

$$\frac{d\alpha}{dt} = - \frac{eE_{z0}}{mc} \sin \varphi \sin^2 \alpha. \tag{8-19}$$

Let us use the substitution 8-18 in Equation 8-16 and put

$$\frac{d\varphi}{dt} = \frac{d\varphi}{d\alpha} \frac{d\alpha}{dt}:$$

if we now substitute for $d\alpha/dt$ the expression given by Equation 8-19, we obtain

$$-\sin \varphi \, d\varphi = \frac{2\pi}{\lambda_g} \frac{mc^2}{eE_{z0}} \frac{1 - \cos \alpha}{\sin^2 \alpha} d\alpha, \tag{8-20}$$

and, by integrating from the time t to the initial time $t = 0$ (where $\varphi = \varphi_0$ and $\alpha = \alpha_0$),

$$\cos \varphi - \cos \varphi_0 = \frac{2\pi}{\lambda_g} \frac{mc^2}{eE_{z0}} \left[\tan \frac{\alpha}{2} - \tan \frac{\alpha_0}{2} \right]. \tag{8-21}$$

If we now recall that

$$\tan \frac{\alpha}{2} = \left(\frac{1 - \cos \alpha}{1 + \cos \alpha} \right)^{1/2} = \left(\frac{1 - \beta}{1 + \beta} \right)^{1/2}, \tag{8-22}$$

and suppose that at the time t the particle is already ultrarelativistic ($\beta \approx 1$), from Equations 8-21 and 8-22 we have

$$\cos \varphi_0 - \cos \varphi = \frac{2\pi}{\lambda_g} \frac{mc^2}{eE_{z0}} \left(\frac{1 - \beta_0}{1 + \beta_0} \right)^{1/2}. \tag{8-23}$$

Since the left-hand side of this equation cannot be greater than 2, we must have

$$E_{z0} \geq \frac{\pi mc^2}{\lambda_g e} \left(\frac{1 - \beta_0}{1 + \beta_0} \right)^{1/2}. \tag{8-24}$$

Thus we see that the "capture condition" (Equation 8-24, relating the peak electric field, the rf wavelength in the guide, and the initial velocity) must be satisfied for it to be possible to capture the particles injected at a velocity less than the phase velocity. It is obvious that the condition 8-24 becomes less restrictive as β_0 increases; however, to reach values of E_{z0} and λ_g obtainable in practice it is not necessary to use enormous injection energies. For example, for $\lambda_g = 10$ cm and an injection energy of 150 keV, the condition 8-24 gives $E_{z0} \geq 7.6 \times 10^6$ V/m, a technically accessible value.

Thus with injection energies of the order of 100–200 keV it is possible to build linacs (for electrons and positrons) where the phase velocity is a constant even in the first sections of the accelerator. For protons or other heavy particles the condition 8-24 would give prohibitive values for the required electric field; therefore for these particles accelerating fields with variable phase velocity must be used. This greatly complicates the design of the machine and in practice machines with discontinuous acceleration are preferred (see Section 8-12) for heavy particles.

8-5   THE RELATIVISTIC CONTRACTION OF AN ELECTRON LINAC AND THE TRANSVERSE INSTABILITY

We have already mentioned, in Section 8-1, that in a linac there is transverse instability and that this effect becomes negligible for ultrarelativistic particles. We now discuss this point further and show how the question can be considered from a different point of view, taking into account the "Lorentz contraction" required by the theory of relativity. Indeed, as the velocity of the electron increases, in the frame of reference where it is at rest (the rest frame), the total length of the linac seen by the particle decreases owing to the relativistic contraction of length. Thus any cause that tends to displace the electron from the machine axis produces an effect which is progressively smaller.

Let us calculate the apparent length of the accelerator seen by the electron. If dz is an element of the electron path in the frame of reference of the machine (the laboratory frame), the corresponding element of path dz' in the rest frame, according to a well-known formula of relativity (see, for example, Panofsky and Phillips, 1962, p. 283), is given by

$$dz' = dz(1 - \beta^2)^{1/2}. \tag{8-25}$$

From Equation 1-7 we have

$$(1 - \beta^2)^{-1} = \left(\frac{E}{E_0}\right)^2, \tag{8-26}$$

and by substituting into Equation 8-25 we obtain

$$dz' = \frac{E_0}{E} dz. \tag{8-27}$$

On the other hand, the energy is related to the distance z which the particle travels (if we suppose the particle to be subject to a constant accelerating electric field E_z along its whole trajectory; see Section 8-4) by the expression

$$E = E_i + eE_z z, \tag{8-28}$$

where $E_i = E_0 + T_0$ is the total initial energy, if we call T_0 the injection (kinetic) energy. If we integrate Equation 8-27, after substituting Equation 8-28 in it, over the entire length L of the linac, we obtain the apparent length L'

$$L' = \int_0^L \frac{E_0\, dz}{E_i + eE_z z} = \frac{E_0}{eE_z} \log \frac{E_f}{E_i}, \tag{8-29}$$

where $E_f = E_i + eE_z L$ is the total final energy. When $T_0 \ll E_0$, this expression becomes simply

$$L' = L \frac{E_0}{T_f} \log\left(1 + \frac{T_f}{E_0}\right), \tag{8-30}$$

where $T_f \approx eE_z L$ is the final kinetic energy.

It can be seen that the apparent length for high-energy machines is much less than the real length. For example, for a machine of 100 m length which accelerates electrons to 1 BeV, Equation 8-30 gives an apparent length $L' = 39$ cm. Over such a small distance some vertical instability can be tolerated. It can be shown (see, for instance, Livingston and Blewett, 1962, Section 10-3) that as a first approximation, valid in a region very near the axis, there is practically no radial electric field in the rest frame of an ultrarelativistic electron (see also Section 8-1). Thus the final displacement in the radial direction depends only on the initial conditions. If we call r the radial distance in the electron rest frame (equal to that in the laboratory frame, because there is no relativistic contraction in directions transverse to the motion), we have

$$r \simeq r_i + \left(\frac{dr}{dz'}\right)_i z' \leq r_i + \left(\frac{dr}{dz'}\right)_i L', \qquad (8\text{-}31)$$

where the index i refers to the initial conditions. In the example given above, if the beam diameter must remain less than 2 cm, it can be seen that (for $r_i = 0$) one could theoretically tolerate an initial deflection of the beam from the axis up to 1.5 degree. However, at the beginning of the acceleration the electrons are not ultrarelativistic and the defocusing force is not negligible even in the rest frame. In practice, a well-collimated beam is injected into the linac, and magnetic focusing devices (see Section 8-10) are placed along the trajectory.

8-6 ELEMENTS OF THE THEORY OF WAVEGUIDES

A waveguide consists, in the most general case, of a metal duct filled with a dielectric (which may be air or also a vacuum). Such an object is called a waveguide because under certain conditions electromagnetic waves can propagate in it and they are "guided" by the metal walls. The theory of waveguides of an arbitrary shape is extremely complex. The simplest kind of waveguide consists of a cylindrical metal tube filled with a homogeneous dielectric; it is called a uniform waveguide and it is of great importance in the field of communication systems, but (for reasons that will be discussed later) it cannot be used in a linear accelerator. More complex types of waveguides, called "loaded waveguides" can be obtained from a uniform waveguide by adding a periodic perturbation along the system. This kind of waveguide is used in the field of high-frequency generators and amplifiers and in the field of linear accelerators. The simplest kind of loaded waveguide (see Figure 8-2) is obtained from a circular uniform waveguide by adding a series of disks with circular holes at the center (also called "irises"), placed at equal distances along the tube. We first treat the theory of the uniform circular waveguide, as it will be useful for understanding the principle of operation of a loaded waveguide. Some of the results obtained for the former can be carried over approximately to the latter.

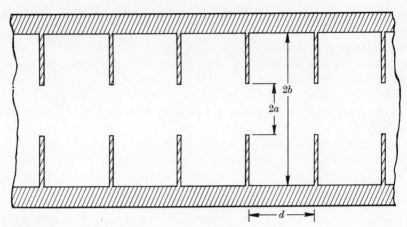

FIGURE 8-2. *Section of part of a circular waveguide loaded with circular irises.*

For a perfect,[4] homogeneous dielectric with dielectric constant ϵ and magnetic permeability μ, Maxwell's equations are (in the mks system of units)

$$\operatorname{div} \mathbf{E} = 0,$$

$$\operatorname{div} \mathbf{H} = 0,$$

$$\operatorname{curl} \mathbf{E} = -\mu \frac{\partial \mathbf{H}}{\partial t}, \qquad (8\text{-}32)$$

$$\operatorname{curl} \mathbf{H} = \epsilon \frac{\partial \mathbf{E}}{\partial t}.$$

In the case of the vacuum, the dielectric constant and magnetic permeability of free space, ϵ_0 and μ_0, satisfy the relation

$$\epsilon_0 \mu_0 = 1/c^2. \qquad (8\text{-}33)$$

Now we can use the vectorial identity

$$\operatorname{curl} \operatorname{curl} \mathbf{A} = \operatorname{grad} \operatorname{div} \mathbf{A} - \nabla^2 \mathbf{A}, \qquad (8\text{-}34)$$

where the operator ∇^2 is defined (in Cartesian coordinates) by

$$\nabla^2 = \frac{\partial^2}{\partial x^2} + \frac{\partial^2}{\partial y^2} + \frac{\partial^2}{\partial z^2}, \qquad (8\text{-}35)$$

and in Equation 8-34 it is intended that $(\nabla^2 \mathbf{A})_x = \nabla^2(A_x)$, and so on. In

---

[4] A perfect dielectric has no free charges, zero electric conductivity, and ϵ and μ are constant in time and independent of the amplitude of the electromagnetic field.

this way, we can eliminate either $\mathbf{H}$ or $\mathbf{E}$ from Maxwell's equations 8-32, and we obtain the wave equations

$$\nabla^2 \mathbf{E} = \epsilon\mu \frac{\partial^2 \mathbf{E}}{\partial t^2} \qquad (8\text{-}36)$$

and

$$\nabla^2 \mathbf{H} = \epsilon\mu \frac{\partial^2 \mathbf{H}}{\partial t^2}, \qquad (8\text{-}37)$$

which describe waves whose free-space propagation velocity is equal to $(\epsilon\mu)^{-1/2}$ (in the vacuum, this velocity is c).

If cylindrical coordinates (r, θ, z) are used, it can be shown (by considering directly Equation 8-34 in cylindrical coordinates) that the z components of Equations 8-36 and 8-37 retain the same form, with

$$\nabla^2 E_z = \left(\frac{\partial^2}{\partial r^2} + \frac{1}{r}\frac{\partial}{\partial r} + \frac{1}{r^2}\frac{\partial^2}{\partial \theta^2} + \frac{\partial^2}{\partial z^2} \right) E_z, \qquad (8\text{-}38)$$

(and similarly for H_z), but this is not true for the r and θ components.

We shall look for solutions of the form (see Section 8-2, in particular footnote 1)

$$\mathbf{E} = \mathbf{E}(r, \theta) \exp i(\omega t - k_g z), \qquad (8\text{-}39)$$

where the angular frequency ω is a real assigned quantity and the wave number in the guide k_g (sometimes called the "propagation constant") can be real or complex and will be determined later. With the form 8-39, Equation 8-36 gives

$$\nabla^2 E_z = -k^2 E_z, \qquad (8\text{-}40)$$

where the free-space wave number k is given by

$$k^2 = \omega^2 \epsilon\mu. \qquad (8\text{-}41)$$

If we call $\nabla^2(r, \theta)$ the transverse part of the operator ∇^2 of Equation 8-38, that is,

$$\nabla^2(r, \theta) = \frac{\partial^2}{\partial r^2} + \frac{1}{r}\frac{\partial}{\partial r} + \frac{1}{r^2}\frac{\partial^2}{\partial \theta^2}, \qquad (8\text{-}42)$$

and note that from Equation 8-39 it follows

$$\frac{\partial^2 E_z}{\partial z^2} = -k_g{}^2 E_z, \qquad (8\text{-}43)$$

it can be seen that Equation 8-40 can be written as

$$\nabla^2(r, \theta) E_z = -k_c{}^2 E_z, \qquad (8\text{-}44)$$

where we have put

$$k_c{}^2 = k^2 - k_g{}^2. \qquad (8\text{-}45)$$

Similarly, if **H** also has the form 8-39, the equation for H_z,

$$\nabla^2(r, \theta)H_z = -k_c{}^2 H_z, \tag{8-46}$$

similar to Equation 8-44, follows from Equation 8-37. If we recall that, with this form, $\partial/\partial z = -ik_g$, and if we use Equation 8-45, the following four equations can be obtained from the r and θ components of the last two Maxwell equations (8-32):

$$
\begin{aligned}
E_r &= -\frac{1}{k_c{}^2}\left[ik_g \frac{\partial E_z}{\partial r} + \frac{i\omega\mu}{r}\frac{\partial H_z}{\partial \theta} \right], \\[1em]
E_\theta &= \frac{1}{k_c{}^2}\left[-\frac{ik_g}{r}\frac{\partial E_z}{\partial \theta} + i\omega\mu \frac{\partial H_z}{\partial r} \right], \\[1em]
H_r &= \frac{1}{k_c{}^2}\left[\frac{i\omega\epsilon}{r}\frac{\partial E_z}{\partial \theta} - ik_g \frac{\partial H_z}{\partial r} \right], \\[1em]
H_\theta &= -\frac{1}{k_c{}^2}\left[i\omega\epsilon \frac{\partial E_z}{\partial r} + \frac{ik_g}{r}\frac{\partial H_z}{\partial \theta} \right].
\end{aligned}
\tag{8-47}
$$

Thus, if we find solutions E_z and H_z of Equations 8-44 and 8-46 we can use Equations 8-47 to obtain the remaining components of **E** and **H**. From Equations 8-47 it can be seen that we cannot simultaneously have $E_z = 0$, $H_z = 0$ (unless $k_c{}^2 = k^2 - k_g{}^2 = 0$); otherwise $\mathbf{E} = \mathbf{H} \equiv 0$. As the equations are linear, the general solution, where both E_z and H_z are different from zero, can be obtained from the sum of two simpler kinds of solution: One, called "transverse magnetic mode" (TM), has $H_z = 0$; the other, called "transverse electric mode" (TE), has $E_z = 0$. Thus in a TM mode the magnetic field is normal to the direction of propagation and similarly in a TE mode the electric field is normal to the direction of propagation. Obviously TE modes cannot be used to accelerate particles because the longitudinal component of the electric field is zero; therefore in the following we only consider TM modes. (However, the treatment of the TE modes is quite similar, as is obvious from the symmetry of **E** and **H** in Equations 8-44 and 8-46.) For a TM mode, Equation 8-46 is identically satisfied, because

$$H_z = 0. \tag{8-48}$$

We therefore look for a solution of Equation 8-44 inside a cylindrical guide of radius a, with the boundary condition that at the wall $(r = a)$, which is supposed to be a very good conductor, the tangential component of the electric field is zero, that is,

$$E_z = E_\theta = 0, \quad \text{for} \quad r = a. \tag{8-49}$$

The solutions of Equation 8-44 can be found by the method of separation of variables. Let us put

$$E_z(r, \theta) = R(r)\Theta(\theta), \tag{8-50}$$

where R is only a function of r and Θ only of θ. Then, if we substitute this form of E_z into Equation 8-44 with the explicit form 8-42 of $\nabla^2(r, \theta)$, and multiply the equation by $r^2(R\Theta)^{-1}$, we obtain

$$\frac{R''}{R} r^2 + \frac{R'}{R} r + r^2 k_c^2 = -\frac{\Theta''}{\Theta}, \qquad (8\text{-}51)$$

where a prime indicates differentiation. As the two sides of Equation 8-51 depend on different variables they must both be equal to a constant, which we call n^2 (because, as we shall see, this constant must be positive). Thus from Equation 8-51 we obtain the following system:

$$R'' + \frac{R'}{r} + \left(k_c^2 - \frac{n^2}{r^2}\right)R = 0, \qquad (8\text{-}52)$$

$$\Theta'' + n^2\Theta = 0. \qquad (8\text{-}53)$$

The general solution of Equation 8-53 is (with C, D arbitrary constants)

$$\Theta(\theta) = C \cos n\theta + D \sin n\theta. \qquad (8\text{-}54)$$

As Θ must be a periodic function of θ, with period 2π, it can be seen that n must be a (real) integer (hence, as we have mentioned, $n^2 > 0$). For integer n, two independent solutions of Equation 8-52 are the well-known Bessel functions of first and second kind (of order n), $J_n(k_c r)$ and $N_n(k_c r)$, respectively, and the general solution of the equation is a linear combination of these two functions; that is,

$$R(r) = AJ_n(k_c r) + BN_n(k_c r). \qquad (8\text{-}55)$$

The function $N_n(k_c r)$ is singular for $r = 0$ and as we require the solution $R(r)$ to be regular for $0 \le r \le a$ we must have $B = 0$: therefore the solution (see Equation 8-50) is a linear combination of terms (modes) of the form

$$E_z = AJ_n(k_c r) [C \cos n\theta + D \sin n\theta] \exp i(\omega t - k_g z), \qquad (8\text{-}56)$$

where $n = 0, 1, 2, \ldots$. If now the boundary condition 8-49 is to be satisfied (for all values of θ and z) we must have

$$J_n(k_c a) = 0. \qquad (8\text{-}57)$$

The function $J_n(w)$ goes through zero an infinite number of times as its argument increases from zero to infinity. Therefore, if we call w_{nh} the hth zero[5] of J_n, the condition 8-57 implies

$$k_c a = w_{nh}. \qquad (8\text{-}58)$$

---

[5] The values of w_{nh} for the first values of n and h are tabulated in many books (see, for example, McLachlan, 1961).

Thus the subscript n describes the azimuthal variation of E_z (and also determines the order of the Bessel function) and the subscript h determines the scale of the radial distribution of E_z. The subscript h is obviously equal to the number of times that $E_z = 0$ as r increases from 0 to a. In order to specify completely the mode considered, the subscripts n and h are added to the notation TM, that is, TM_{nh}.

The condition 8-58 has some very important consequences. Using Equations 8-45 and 8-41, we have for the condition 8-58

$$\frac{\omega^2}{c^2} - k_g{}^2 = \left(\frac{w_{nh}}{a}\right)^2, \qquad (8\text{-}59)$$

where we have assumed $\epsilon\mu = c^{-2}$, because we are interested in the case where the waveguide is completely evacuated. This assumption will be maintained in the following.

The relation 8-59, which is called the *dispersion relation* for the TM_{nh} mode for a circular waveguide of radius a, determines the propagation constant k_g for a given ω and a given mode. From Equation 8-59 it can be seen that if $k_g{}^2 \geq 0$,

$$\frac{\omega}{c} \geq \frac{w_{nh}}{a} . \qquad (8\text{-}60)$$

If the inequality 8-60 does not hold, then $k_g{}^2 < 0$, and k_g is imaginary, and (see Equation 8-39) there is no propagation but the "wave" is attenuated. Therefore Equation 8-60 determines a cutoff frequency ω_c, given by

$$\omega_c = \frac{c}{a} w_{nh}, \qquad (8\text{-}61)$$

and a cutoff wavelength λ_c (corresponding to the wave number k_c), given by

$$\lambda_c = \frac{2\pi}{k_c} = 2\pi \frac{a}{w_{nh}} , \qquad (8\text{-}62)$$

such that only waves with $\omega > \omega_c$, $k > k_c$, and (free-space) wavelength $\lambda < \lambda_c$ can be propagated without attenuation. Hence the guide wavenumber k_g can be written in the form

$$k_g = k\left[1 - \left(\frac{\omega_c}{\omega}\right)^2\right]^{1/2} = k\left[1 - \left(\frac{k_c}{k}\right)^2\right]^{1/2} \qquad (8\text{-}63)$$

and the phase velocity v_p is therefore

$$v_p = \frac{\omega}{k_g} = \frac{c}{[1 - (\omega_c/\omega)^2]^{1/2}} = \frac{c}{[1 - (k_c/k)^2]^{1/2}} . \qquad (8\text{-}64)$$

From this equation, if we put $\beta_p = v_p/c$, we obtain

$$k_c{}^2 = k^2 \left(1 - \frac{1}{\beta_p{}^2}\right).\tag{8-65}$$

From Equation 8-64 or 8-65 it can be seen that the phase velocity is always *greater* than c, and this is the reason why uniform waveguides cannot be used to accelerate particles. As we shall see, if such a waveguide is loaded periodically the phase velocity can be reduced below c.

The most important and also the simplest transverse magnetic mode is the TM_{01} mode, which has no azimuthal dependence and no zeros between $r = 0$ and $r = a$. As $w_{01} = 2.405\ldots$ and therefore $k_c = 2.405/a$, for the TM_{01} mode we have

$$\lambda_c = \frac{2\pi}{k_c} = 2.61a,\tag{8-66}$$

and

$$E_z = E_{z0} J_0 \left(2.405 \frac{r}{a}\right) e^{i\varphi},\tag{8-67}$$

where E_{z0} is the peak field on the axis, and we have called φ the phase factor,

$$\varphi = \omega t - k_g z.\tag{8-68}$$

From Equations 8-47 we can now obtain the remaining components of the electromagnetic field. For the TM_{01} mode $\partial/\partial\theta = 0$ and so $E_\theta = 0$, $H_r = 0$, and

$$E_r = -\frac{ik_g}{k_c{}^2}\frac{\partial E_z}{\partial r} = ik_g \frac{a}{2.405} E_{z0} J_1\left(2.405 \frac{r}{a}\right) e^{i\varphi};\tag{8-69}$$

$$H_\theta = -\frac{i\omega\epsilon_0}{k_c{}^2}\frac{\partial E_z}{\partial r} = i\omega\epsilon_0 \frac{a}{2.405} E_{z0} J_1\left(2.405 \frac{r}{a}\right) e^{i\varphi}.\tag{8-70}$$

Therefore the lines of force of the magnetic field are circles, $r = $ const, and those of the electric field lie in the planes $\theta = $ const (see Figure 8-3).

We now look for solutions of the wave equation 8-36 which represent waves with a phase velocity less than $c(\beta_p < 1)$. We must of course abandon the boundary conditions 8-49 corresponding to a smooth wall: indeed, we shall examine precisely what kind of boundary condition allows the propagation of waves with $\beta_p < 1$.

In the previous discussion we implicitly assumed $k_c{}^2 > 0$ in the definition 8-45, and indeed this must be so (as will soon be clear) if we have to satisfy the conditions 8-49. However, from Equation 8-65 it can be seen that, in order to have $\beta_p < 1$, we must have $k_c{}^2 < 0$; therefore it is interesting to examine the consequences of this inequality. If k_c is imaginary it is convenient to use instead a real quantity k_c' defined by

$$k_c' = -ik_c. \qquad (8\text{-}71)$$

In this case all the equations derived previously still hold (and in particular Equation 8-56 still represents solutions of the wave equation) however, we

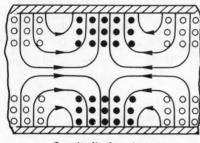
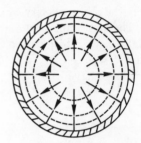

Longitudinal section   Transverse section

FIGURE 8-3. *Diagram of the lines of force of the electric and magnetic fields for the* TM_{01} *mode in a uniform waveguide of circular cross section.*

now have to consider Bessel functions of an imaginary argument. Therefore it is convenient to use the modified Bessel functions (of the first kind) I_n, which are functions of a real variable x defined by

$$J_n(ix) = i^n I_n(x) \qquad (8\text{-}72)$$

(see, for example, McLachlan, 1961). By using this definition, the simple solution considered previously (see Equations 8-67, 8-69, and 8-70) can be written in the form

$$E_z = E_{z0} J_0(ik_c'r)e^{i\varphi} = E_{z0} I_0(k_c'r)e^{i\varphi}, \qquad (8\text{-}73)$$

$$E_r = \frac{k_g}{k_c'} E_{z0} J_1(ik_c'r)e^{i\varphi} = \frac{ik_g}{k_c'} E_{z0} I_1(k_c'r)e^{i\varphi}, \qquad (8\text{-}74)$$

$$H_\theta = \frac{\omega\epsilon_0}{k_c'} E_{z0} J_1(ik_c'r)e^{i\varphi} = \frac{i\omega\epsilon_0}{k_c'} E_{z0} I_1(k_c'r)e^{i\varphi}, \qquad (8\text{-}75)$$

where $\varphi = \omega t - k_g z$ (Equation 8-68). The modified Bessel functions of the first kind increase monotonically with the argument and they can vanish only if the argument is zero. It is easy to understand that a cylindrical conducting surface cannot give the appropriate boundary conditions for Equations 8-73, 8-74, and 8-75, which demand E_z to be different from zero on the boundary.

On the other hand, by eliminating t and z (that is, φ) from Equations 8-73 and 8-75 by dividing them side by side, and by making $r = a$, we get the relation

$$\left(\frac{E_z}{H_\theta}\right)_{r=a} = -i\,\frac{k_c'}{\omega\epsilon_0}\,\frac{I_0(k_c'a)}{I_1(k_c'a)}\,. \tag{8-76}$$

From Equation 8-76 we can infer that the hypothetical boundary surface suitable for the propagation of the wave (with $\beta_p < 1$) defined by Equations 8-73, 8-74, and 8-75 should be a surface with reactive properties, as can be seen from the imaginary value of the right-hand side of Equation 8-76. We shall see later a special structure, the iris-loaded waveguide, which, in an approximate manner, can provide the reactive boundary conditions suitable for the propagation of waves having $\beta_p < 1$ (see Section 8-8). A similar condition can be obtained from Equations 8-73 and 8-74.

It must be noted that, from the properties of the modified Bessel functions of very small argument, we have $I_0(z) \approx 1$, $I_1(z) \approx z/2$ for $z \ll 1$. Consequently, if k_c' is so small that $k_c'a \ll 1$, we get

$$\left(\frac{E_r}{E_z}\right)_{r=a} = \frac{ik_g}{k_c'}\,\frac{I_1(k_c'a)}{I_0(k_c'a)} \simeq \frac{ik_ga}{2} \simeq \frac{ika}{2}\,, \tag{8-77}$$

and therefore at the wall the component E_r may be made much smaller in modulus than E_z if ka is made sufficiently small.[6]

8-7 SOME INTUITIVE CONSIDERATIONS ON THE IRIS-LOADED WAVEGUIDE: THE ω-k_g DIAGRAM

Let us consider the dispersion relation 8-59 and its representation on the (ω, k_g) plane (see Figure 8-4), which is a hyperbola whose asymptotes pass through the origin. For a point P on the hyperbola, if we draw the tangent at P and the line through P and the origin, it is obvious that, if these lines form angles α_g and α_p, respectively, with the k_g axis, we have

$$\tan \alpha_g = \frac{d\omega}{dk_g} = v_g\,, \tag{8-78}$$

$$\tan \alpha_p = \frac{\omega}{k_g} = v_p\,, \tag{8-79}$$

where v_g is the group velocity defined by Equation 8-7. If $\omega \to \infty$, also P moves away to infinity along the hyperbola, the tangent coincides with the asymptote, and (see Equation 8-59) $v_g = v_p = c$. It is obvious from Figure

---

[6] The importance of the limit $k_c' \to 0$ is that this corresponds to $k \simeq k_g$ (see Equations 8-45 and 8-71), i.e., $v_p \simeq c$.

8-4, as we have seen directly from the equations, that for a finite ω, $\tan \alpha_p > c$ and $\tan \alpha_g < c$ and therefore

$$v_g < c < v_p . \tag{8-80}$$

It can also be seen that below $\omega_c = cw_{01}/a$ no propagation is possible.

Let us now consider a circular waveguide, of radius b, to be loaded with thin metal disks (see Figure 8-2) placed at distance d apart and each having a hole of diameter $2a$. First of all, let us suppose $(b - a) \ll b$, so that at least for a certain band of frequencies (as we shall see) the irises constitute a small perturbation and the behavior of the loaded waveguide is nearly equal to that of the corresponding uniform waveguide.

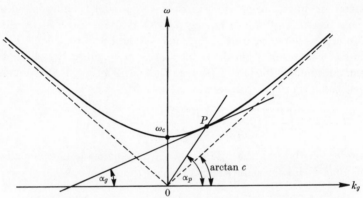

FIGURE 8-4. *The ω-k_g diagram for a uniform circular waveguide.*

As a wave propagates inside the loaded waveguide, at each iris it is partly reflected. However, if the wavelength is long compared with $(b - a)$, that is, if k_g is sufficiently small, a very small fraction of the wave is reflected and the corresponding dispersion relation tends to that of the uniform waveguide. Consequently the cutoff frequency is again approximately given by Equation 8-61 (however, here we call it ω_{c1} because, as we shall see, new cutoff frequencies exist now), and the form of the ω-k_g curve remains almost unaltered, for $\omega \approx \omega_{c1}$. As the frequency is increased (above ω_{c1}), the wavelength decreases, a larger fraction of the wave is reflected at each iris, and the interference between incident and reflected waves becomes stronger, until, when $\lambda_g = 2d$, we obtain purely stationary waves (the cavities consisting of the spaces between irises are at resonance). Therefore, for $k_g d = \pi$, the group velocity is zero and the tangent to the ω-k_g curve must be horizontal. We can therefore understand why the dispersion curve for the loaded waveguide has the form of the lower curve in Figure 8-5[7]: as k_g approaches zero it tends to the uniform-

[7] Of course, the precise form of the dispersion curve depends on the values of a, b, and d, and on the thickness of the irises; however, the general shape is the one shown in the figure.

waveguide curve (upper curve), but as k_g increases it deviates from this curve (the sooner, the greater $(b - a)/b$ is), and the derivative decreases, until it becomes zero for $k_g d = \pi$, where the frequency is ω_{c2}. It is now obvious that there are frequencies between ω_{c1} and ω_{c2}, such as the frequency ω^* in Figure 8-5, for which $\tan \alpha_p < c$ on the loaded-waveguide diagram. Thus it can be seen that in a loaded waveguide, for some frequencies, the phase velocity is less than c and therefore these structures can be used to accelerate particles. It must be noted that where $v_p \lesssim c$ the group velocity is very low: in linac waveguides usually $v_g/v_p \simeq 10^{-2}$.

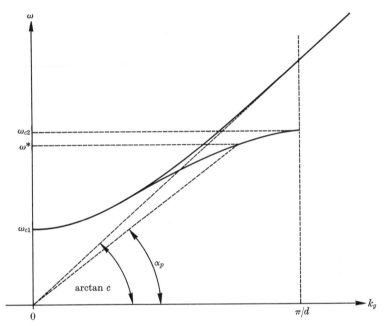

FIGURE 8-5.   *The ω-k_g diagram for a uniform circular waveguide (upper curve) and for the same guide loaded with irises with a spacing d. The frequency ω^* is a typical frequency for which $v_p = \tan \alpha_p < c$ in the loaded waveguide.*

Actually the ω-k_g diagram for a loaded waveguide has many branches (an infinite number) and the full diagram has the form shown in Figure 8-6 (see, for instance, Beck, 1958, p. 44). From this diagram, sometimes called the Brillouin diagram, it can be seen that there are frequency ranges such as the one between ω_{c2} and ω_{c3} (called "stop bands") where no propagation is possible, alternating with ranges such as the one between ω_{c3} and ω_{c4} ("pass-bands") where there is propagation. However, only the part of the diagram shown in Figure 8-5 is used for accelerating particles. The remaining branches correspond to $v_p > c$, or to values of v_p which are too small, or to values of

λ which also are too small in practice. The branches of the Brillouin diagram that are not used for particle acceleration are important because some of the energy of the wave sent into the waveguide for particle acceleration goes into these undesired modes and is therefore wasted, and furthermore the stability of the beam deteriorates (see the discussion in Section 8-11).

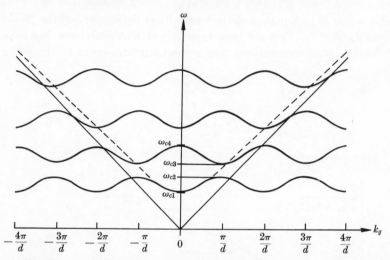

FIGURE 8-6.   *The full dispersion curve (Brillouin diagram) for a loaded waveguide with iris spacing equal to d. The dotted curve is the hyperbola corresponding to the uniform waveguide of the same diameter.*

8-8   THE FREQUENCY EQUATION

For a loaded waveguide, it is difficult in practice to derive the precise theoretical dispersion relation, which is a complicated function of the geometrical parameters. However, it is possible to obtain an approximate but simple relation between the frequency and the dimensions of the waveguide when the phase velocity is equal to c. This relation, called the *frequency equation*, is very important in the design of a waveguide for a linear accelerator: it is used to obtain a first estimate of the required dimensions, a, b, d, and the disk thickness s. However, before construction of the waveguide, usually a model is built and the precise dispersion relation is measured experimentally.

Before deriving the frequency equation, let us consider the so-called short-circuited radial transmission line. This consists of a cylindrical metal box (see Figure 8-7) which can be excited near the axis in such a way that an electromagnetic wave propagates radially, the electric field being purely axial and the magnetic field purely azimuthal, and both independent of θ and z. As can be verified by substituting into Maxwell's equations (or into

Equations 8-44, 8-46, and 8-47, which are equivalent), the electric and magnetic fields are given, respectively, by

$$E_z = [AJ_0(kr) + BN_0(kr)]e^{i\omega t}, \tag{8-81}$$

$$H_\theta = -\frac{i\omega\epsilon_0}{k^2}\frac{\partial E_z}{\partial r} = \frac{i\omega\epsilon_0}{k}[AJ_1(kr) + BN_1(kr)]e^{i\omega t}, \tag{8-82}$$

where[8] $k = \omega/c$ as in Equation 8-41, A and B are constants, and the Bessel functions J_0, N_0, J_1, N_1 have been encountered previously; see Equation 8-55.[9] As the radial transmission line is short-circuited, that is, there is a

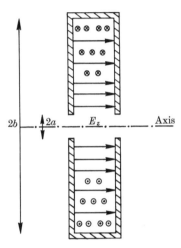

FIGURE 8-7. *Section through the axis of symmetry of a short-circuited radial transmission line showing the lines of force of the electric and magnetic fields.*

metal boundary at a certain radius (at $r = b$, say), at this point the electric field must be zero and we have

$$AJ_0(kb) + BN_0(kb) = 0. \tag{8-83}$$

Therefore, if we put $C = A/N_0(kb)$, Equations 8-81 and 8-82 can be written in the form

$$E_z = C[N_0(kb)J_0(kr) - J_0(kb)N_0(kr)]e^{i\omega t}, \tag{8-84}$$

$$H_\theta = \frac{i\omega\epsilon_0}{k}C[N_0(kb)J_1(kr) - J_0(kb)N_1(kr)]e^{i\omega t}. \tag{8-85}$$

[8] We again assume a vacuum. It is straightforward to obtain the equations for the general case.

[9] In this case we retain the Bessel function of second kind, N_0, because the solution may be singular for $r = 0$.

Finally we find that, at $r = a$,

$$\left(\frac{E_z}{H_\theta}\right)_{r=a} = -\frac{ik}{\omega\epsilon_0} \frac{[N_0(kb)J_0(ka) - J_0(kb)N_0(ka)]}{[N_0(kb)J_1(ka) - J_0(kb)N_1(ka)]}. \tag{8-86}$$

Thus we see that a radial transmission line produces at its inner boundary ($r = a$) a value of E_z/H_θ which is precisely of the form (see Equation 8-76) required in order to allow the propagation of electromagnetic waves with $v_p < c$ inside a cylinder of radius a; that is, $(E_z/H_\theta)_{r=a}$ is an imaginary number.

Let us therefore again consider an iris-loaded waveguide (like the one which has been described in the previous section and is shown in Figure 8-2). We can consider two regions of space: the cylinder $r < a$ and the regions between the irises for $b > r > a$. The latter can be considered to be a series of radial transmission lines and, as we have seen, these can produce the correct radial impedance E_z/H_θ at the boundary of the cylinder $r \leq a$ for the propagation of the cylindrical mode of Equations 8-73, 8-74, and 8-75. However, the modes of the radial transmission lines do not provide the boundary conditions required by the cylindrical mode of Equations 8-73, 8-74, and 8-75 exactly. In the former indeed, the radial component of the electric field is zero and furthermore there is no z dependence of the fields. In the first place, however, as we have seen in Equation 8-77, the radial component of the electric field given by Equation 8-74 can be made small with respect to the axial component at $r = a$ if ka is sufficiently small, and second, if the distance d between two irises is sufficiently small compared with the wavelength λ_g, the axial component of the electric field, given by Equation 8-73, is approximately a constant with z, at $r = a$, over a distance d. Therefore the wave which propagates in an iris-loaded waveguide consists *approximately* of a cylindrical mode (of the kind described by Equations 8-73, 8-74, and 8-75) in the region $r < a$ and of radial transmission line modes (Equations 8-84 and 8-85) for $b > r > a$. In the spirit of this approximation we can match the two kinds of solution together at $r = a$ by requiring that the *average* values of E_z and H_θ given by the two solutions coincide at $r = a$. Thus, if we use the subscripts 1 and 2 to indicate the solutions in the regions $r \leq a$ and $r \geq a$, respectively, we obtain the following two equations:

$$\frac{1}{d}\int_0^d E_{z1}(a, z)\, dz = \frac{1}{d}\int_0^d E_{z2}(a)\, dz = E_{z2}(a), \tag{8-87}$$

$$\frac{1}{d}\int_0^d H_{\theta1}(a, z)\, dz = \frac{1}{d}\int_0^d H_{\theta2}(a)\, dz = H_{\theta2}(a). \tag{8-88}$$

If we equate the ratios of the left-hand sides and of the right-hand sides of Equations 8-87 and 8-88, respectively, and use the expressions 8-73 and

8-75 for E_{z1} and $H_{\theta 1}$ and the expressions 8-84 and 8-85 for E_{z2} and $H_{\theta 2}$, we obtain

$$k_c' \frac{I_0(k_c'a)}{I_1(k_c'a)} = k \frac{N_0(kb)J_0(ka) - J_0(kb)N_0(ka)}{N_0(kb)J_1(ka) - J_0(kb)N_1(ka)} . \qquad (8\text{-}89)$$

As we have mentioned, we are interested in the form of this expression when $v_p \simeq c$ because in a linear accelerator the electrons rapidly become ultra-relativistic. If $v_p = c$, then $k = k_g$ and, from Equations 8-45 and 8-71, $k_c = k_c' = 0$; therefore we shall consider the limit of Equation 8-89 for $k_c' \to 0$. Thus, using the same asymptotic forms as for Equation 8-77, we find that in the limit $k_c' \to 0$ (that is, $v_p \simeq c$), Equation 8-89 becomes

$$\frac{2}{ka} = \frac{N_0(kb)J_0(ka) - J_0(kb)N_0(ka)}{N_0(kb)J_1(ka) - J_0(kb)N_1(ka)} , \qquad (8\text{-}90)$$

where, of course, $k = \omega/c$. This is the *frequency equation* for the waveguide, which connects the frequency of a wave (propagating with $v_p = c$) with the geometrical parameters of the waveguide. In the derivation of Equation 8-90 we have neglected the thickness s of the irises: this would enter in a factor $(1 - s/d)$ on the right-hand side of the equation (see, for example, Smith, 1959, p. 341).

Equation 8-90 has been derived under the assumption that there are many irises in a wavelength. However, as the energy losses in the waveguide increase with the number of irises per wavelength, this number cannot be made too large. An optimization procedure taking into account all the effects (including losses) gives an optimum value of 3.5 for the ratio λ_g/d; the value commonly used for such a ratio is 4. However, even with four irises per wavelength the difference between measured quantities and quantities derived from the frequency equation is only a few percent. Therefore the frequency equation is of great practical importance also in this case.

8-9 ELECTRON ENERGY AND BEAM LOADING IN THE LINAC

Up to this point in the treatment of the propagation of electromagnetic waves in a linac, we have neglected the energy dissipated in the walls of the waveguide due to their finite resistivity and also the energy transferred from the wave to the accelerated electrons. Both of these effects produce an attenuation of the fields propagating in the linac, with the result that for a given electromagnetic power input there is a limit to the particle energy that can be obtained.

Let us first consider the former effect. We suppose for the moment that the beam intensity is so low that it absorbs a negligible fraction of the wave energy. We call $P(z)$ the power flowing along the waveguide and so

$$-dP = -\frac{dP}{dz}\,dz \tag{8-91}$$

is the power lost in Joule heating at the wall over a distance dz. If $\mathscr{E}(z)$ is the electromagnetic energy of the wave contained per unit length of the waveguide, and v_g the group velocity of the wave, then

$$P = \mathscr{E}v_g. \tag{8-92}$$

As is commonly done for oscillating systems, we define the "quality factor" Q as the ratio of the energy stored (per unit length) and the power dissipated (per unit length) multiplied by the angular frequency ω, that is,

$$Q = \frac{\omega\mathscr{E}}{(-dP/dz)}. \tag{8-93}$$

The power dissipation dP/dz and, consequently, Q depend on the precise shape of the conducting walls and on the way the current is distributed on them; the quantity Q can be of the order of 10^4. If we eliminate $\mathscr{E}$ from Equations 8-92 and 8-93, we obtain

$$\frac{dP}{dz} = -\frac{\omega}{Qv_g}\,P \tag{8-94}$$

and, by integrating this equation, we get

$$P(z) = P_0 \exp(-\omega z/Qv_g), \tag{8-95}$$

where P_0 is the power sent into the waveguide at $z = 0$. The power flow can be computed for a given wave by calculating the net flux of the Poynting vector across the waveguide cross section. It is found that it is proportional to the square of the electric field on the axis of the waveguide, that is,

$$\frac{P(z)}{P_0} = \frac{E_z^2(z)}{E_{z0}^2}, \tag{8-96}$$

where we now denote by $E_z(z)$ the amplitude of the electric field (which in the presence of attenuation depends on z) and by E_{z0} its value at $z = 0$. Thus, if we define the attenuation length l_0 by

$$l_0 = \frac{2Qv_g}{\omega}, \tag{8-97}$$

from Equations 8-94 and 8-95 we obtain

$$E_z(z) = E_{z0} \exp(-z/l_0). \tag{8-98}$$

An important parameter in the design of a waveguide is the "shunt impedance per unit length," Z, defined as

$$Z = \frac{E_z^2}{(-dP/dz)} = \frac{l_0 E_z^2}{2P}, \qquad (8\text{-}99)$$

where the identity follows from Equations 8-94 and 8-97. The shunt impedance is a measure of the power required to maintain a given electric field in the waveguide and it is usually of the order of 50 MΩ/m. As we have seen (Section 8-4), the electric field cannot be too low and it is often of the order of 10 MV/m: hence Equation 8-99 shows that an enormous amount of power is necessary to excite the waveguide; with the above-mentioned values, it is of the order of 1 MW/m.

We can now calculate the energy, W, gained by an electron over a length l, when the attenuation of the wave is taken into account. From Equation 8-98 we obtain for a synchronous particle traveling on the crest of the wave (see Equation 8-13)

$$W = e \int_0^l E_z(z)\, dz = eE_{z0}l_0[1 - \exp(-l/l_0)] = eE_{z0}lA, \qquad (8\text{-}100)$$

where the constant A is given by

$$A = \frac{1 - \exp(-l/l_0)}{l/l_0}. \qquad (8\text{-}101)$$

If the value of the input power P_0 is given, we can derive E_{z0} from Equations 8-99 and 8-96, and by substituting its expression into Equation 8-100 we obtain

$$W = e(2ZP_0 l_0)^{1/2}[1 - \exp(-l/l_0)]. \qquad (8\text{-}102)$$

If we consider also the value of l as fixed (for instance, l can represent the distance between two successive feed points in the guide), we can see that expression 8-102 has a maximum when

$$l_0 \simeq 0.8l. \qquad (8\text{-}103)$$

This relation is used in choosing the dimensions of the waveguide.

Let us now consider the influence of the transfer of energy to the beam on the damping of the wave. If $I = q\nu$ is the average beam current (where q is the charge in each bunch and ν the repetition rate), the power transferred from the wave to the particles over a distance dz is

$$dP = -IE_z\, dz, \qquad (8\text{-}104)$$

where the minus sign indicates that this is a loss of power for the wave. Thus if we also take into account the power loss due to dissipation in the wall (given by Equation 8-94) we find that the net power loss over a distance dz is given by

$$dP = -\frac{2P}{l_0}\, dz - IE_z\, dz. \qquad (8\text{-}105)$$

where Equation 8-97 has been used. If we substitute for E_z in this equation the expression obtained from Equation 8-99, we obtain the following differential equation for P:

$$-\frac{dP}{dz} = \frac{2}{l_0} P + I \left(\frac{2Z}{l_0}\right)^{1/2} P^{1/2}. \tag{8-106}$$

This equation can be integrated[10] and, if P_0 again denotes the value of P at $z = 0$, we obtain

$$P^{1/2} = \left[P_0^{1/2} + I \left(\frac{l_0 Z}{2}\right)^{1/2} \right] \exp(-z/l_0) - I \left(\frac{l_0 Z}{2}\right)^{1/2}. \tag{8-107}$$

If we call

$$m = I \left(\frac{l_0 Z}{2 P_0}\right)^{1/2} \tag{8-108}$$

the beam loading coefficient, Equation 8-107 can also be written in the form

$$\left(\frac{P}{P_0}\right)^{1/2} = (1 + m) \exp(-z/l_0) - m. \tag{8-109}$$

Therefore, from Equation 8-96 it follows that

$$E_z(z) = E_{z0}[(1 + m) \exp(-z/l_0) - m]. \tag{8-110}$$

With this expression for the electric field we can again calculate the energy gained by a synchronous particle over a distance l:

$$\begin{aligned} W = e \int_0^l E_z(z)\, dz &= e E_{z0} l [A - m(1 - A)] \\ &= e[E_{z0} l A - l Z I (1 - A)], \end{aligned} \tag{8-111}$$

where we have used the definition of m and Equation 8-99, and the coefficient A is given by Equation 8-101. From Equation 8-111 it can be seen that, as the beam current is increased, the energy gained by the particles decreases and there is a limit to the current which can be obtained at a given particle energy. The expression 8-111 is similar to that for the voltage produced by a generator whose open-circuit voltage is $E_{z0} l A$ and whose internal impedance is resistive and given by $l Z(1 - A)$.[11] Values of I so high that V given by Equation 8-111 is negative would correspond to cases where energy is actually transferred from the injected beam to the electromagnetic wave propagating in the waveguide; however, the approximations made (see below) to derive Equation 8-111 cease to be valid for large currents.

[10] With the substitution $P^{1/2} = \xi$, the integration is straightforward.

[11] It must be noted that the presence of the beam loading term causes an increase of the numerical coefficient in the optimization condition 8-103.

In the above treatment we have neglected the effects due to the fact that the particles are bunched so that the beam current is pulsed, that the particles carry out phase oscillations, and that some particles are lost against the walls. It can be shown that these effects introduce a spread in the particle energy, and furthermore a reactive load term must be added to Equation 8-111. However, this equation still describes qualitatively the relationship between the energy and the beam current.

It can be seen from Equation 8-102 (or 8-111) that for a given linac the energy gained by the electrons depends on the power P_0 (proportional to E_{z0}^2) sent into the waveguide, and a change of this power does not alter the synchronism between the electrons and the wave because the particle velocity always approaches c very rapidly. Therefore electron linacs are variable-energy machines. As we shall see (Section 8-13) proton linacs instead are fixed-energy machines.

8-10   THE CONSTRUCTION OF ELECTRON LINACS

In the previous sections we have discussed the operation of an electron linac; let us now consider its construction. We shall describe separately the structure and the operation of the different systems which constitute the machine, namely,

1. the injection system;
2. the rf system;
3. the auxiliary systems (beam focusing and control, vacuum, cooling, and so on).

Before we describe the single parts we should note that, with present technology, all electron linacs are designed for pulsed operation: the rf power is switched on and after about 1 μsec it fills the waveguide and the required field distribution is produced; the electron gun is then pulsed on and the beam is accelerated for about 1 μsec; then the electron gun and finally the rf power are switched off. After the rf pulse the guide is completely deexcited because the residual energy is transferred to a dissipative load; then the system is ready for the next cycle. The repetition rates normally used go from a minimum of a few pulses per second up to about 1500–2000 pulses per second. Pulsed operation must be used because of the enormous power required. As we have seen in Section 8-9 this is of the order of 1 MW/m, so that a linac some 100 m long may require a peak power of hundreds of megawatts. The rf systems operating at the frequencies used in these machines (from about 3000 to 10,000 Mc/sec) can only supply such a power in pulsed operation with a low duty cycle.

Let us now discuss the different parts separately.

a. The Injection System. The electron beam produced by the injection system must be well collimated (because of the small acceptance of the loaded waveguide, due to the transverse instability; see Section 8-5) and it must be homogeneous in energy in order to avoid too large a momentum spread in the accelerated beam. Indeed in practical cases of linacs of medium or high power the solid angle of injection must not be greater than some thousandths of a steradian. The injection system for a linac is therefore a rather complicated accelerator itself, and usually consists of an electron source, an electrostatic accelerator (Van de Graaff or Cockcroft-Walton), and a system for transferring the beam from the latter to the waveguide. This system is a tube under vacuum with magnetic focusing devices (coils, quadrupole lenses, and so on). Pulsed operation is obtained by modulating the voltage on the control grid of the actual source. As we have seen in Section 8-4 (Equation 8-24) the value of the injection energy is usually chosen in relation to the value of the accelerating electric field, in such a way that the injected electrons are captured without requiring modulation of the waveguide phase velocity. As the electric fields usually produced in the loaded waveguides are from 50 to 150 kV/cm, the injection voltage falls in the range from 100 to 200 kV (see Equation 8-24). The entire injector (with the exception only of the transfer tube; see above) is enclosed in a container filled with gas at high pressure to avoid the danger of high-voltage breakdown (see Section 2-2).

b. The rf System. As we have mentioned, the microwaves used to accelerate the particles have a wavelength of some centimeters (frequencies between 3×10^3 and 10^4 Mc/sec). This value is so chosen as to optimize the conditions imposed by the dimensions of the loaded waveguide, by the phase and group velocities of the waves propagating in the guide, and by the parameters of the available microwave generators. In the construction of this system many identical elements of loaded waveguide are placed in series and each element is fed by a separate amplifier.[12] All the amplifiers of the linac receive the rf signal from a single generator. Figure 8-8 shows the block diagram of the part of the system in common with all the waveguide elements and also the part which feeds a particular element of loaded waveguide. As the system works under pulsed operation it has many points in common with conventional high-power radar systems. The rf signal is produced by an oscillator G (which usually has continuous operation), it is amplified by the amplifier A (with pulsed operation), and is then fed into a normal (low-power) waveguide WW, terminated with a matched load in order to avoid reflections. Along this waveguide as many T junctions are inserted as there are sections of loaded waveguide in the linac. From each junction the driving signal passes through a phase shifter (adjustable with continuity) and an attenuator, and reaches the input of a power amplifier (usually a klystron capable of giving 5 to 10 MW

[12] With present technology it is not possible to feed a high-power linac from one point only because prohibitively high electric fields would have to be used.

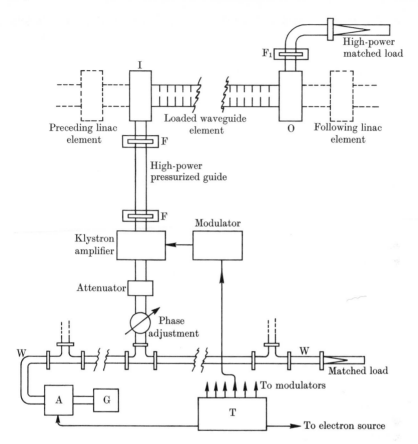

FIGURE 8-8. *Block diagram of the rf system for a linac showing the part (bottom of diagram) in common with all waveguide elements and the part which supplies a particular element. F and F_1 are coupling windows; I and O, input and output sections; WW, the low-power normal waveguide; G, the rf oscillator; A, the amplifier; T, the synchronizing unit.*

of pulsed output power).[13] The phase shifters are used in order to adjust the phase of the rf oscillation so that the synchronous electron does not see any change of phase of the accelerating electric field as it passes from one section of waveguide to the next. The attenuators serve to adjust the input power level and also to decouple, to some extent, the normal waveguide from the amplifiers.

Each klystron receives the power (to be transformed into rf power and to be supplied to the linac) from a modulator, in the form of a high-voltage pulse supplied at the proper instant of time. The correct timing of all the modulators

[13] Other kinds of power amplifiers can be used at this stage. For a general review of this problem, see Slater (1950) and Arguimbau and Adler (1956).

with respect to the timing of the oscillator amplifier, A, is controlled by a central synchronizing unit T (see Figure 8-8). The main technical difficulties associated with the modulator are due to the fact that the pulses it produces have a high voltage (100–300 kV), a high current (about 100 A), and short duration (about 1 μsec), and the requirements on the regularity and reproducibility of the pulses are very stringent (of the order of 1%), if one considers the high power involved.

The microwave power produced in the klystron is transmitted to the corresponding section of loaded waveguide through a pressurized uniform waveguide, terminating at both ends with a coupling window F (see Figure 8-8). High-pressure gas is used in this connecting waveguide in order to avoid breakdown discharges (for this purpose an evacuated waveguide could also be used; see Section 2-2); the gas is also useful for carrying away the heat produced by the dissipation of the power of the electromagnetic wave in the window coupling. These windows are made of very high quality ceramic material; they must maintain a good vacuum and they must not produce appreciable reflection or attenuation of the electromagnetic wave transmitted.

Thus the rf power is sent into the loaded waveguide through a connecting element I, called the input section. The structure of the input section is rather complex and it will not be discussed here. The input section, indeed, must send rf power into the guide in such a way as to excite the required mode; it must not obstruct or perturb the trajectory of the electrons arriving from the previous element of waveguide; and it should allow connection of the vacuum system to the loaded waveguide (a different solution for this connection can be used, as discussed further on).

The accelerating electromagnetic wave then propagates from the input section to the end of the waveguide element where there is an output section (indicated by O in Figure 8-8), whose structure and operation are similar to those of the input section. As the rf power reaching the output section is still large, it is usual to send it out of the guide through the window F_1 and to dissipate it on a matched load so that there is no reflection. The possibility of using the output power again by sending it back to the input (Shersby-Harvie and Mullet, 1949) has been studied and tested, but this is very difficult to carry out in practice and the solution of dissipating the output power is usually preferred.

The rf system is completed by many other devices, such as those for the measurement of the power going into each waveguide element; we have already mentioned the synchronizing unit, which controls the prescribed time sequence of the trigger circuits for the amplifier A, the modulators, and the electron source (see Figure 8-8). The choice of the time sequence and of the duration of the different pulses affects the energy homogeneity of the accelerated beam.

    c. *The Auxiliary Systems.* The focusing devices are used in order to correct

for the transverse instability along the entire trajectory and especially along
the first sections of the accelerator, where the particle velocity is low and the
defocusing forces are the strongest (see Section 8-1). Pairs of Helmholtz coils
coaxial with the waveguide are placed along the machine and often they are
wound directly on the accelerating sections; they produce a focusing axial
magnetic field. Magnetic quadrupole lenses (see Appendix 1) also are placed
in the sections connecting two successive waveguide elements. The focusing
magnetic fields thus produced can be modified locally, if required, by means of
correcting coils.

The vacuum system does not offer particular difficulties because the volume
to be evacuated is usually less than in other kinds of machine. Adsorption
pumps are used for the preliminary vacuum and ion pumps for the high vacuum.
Oil pumps (rotary or diffusion) should be avoided because even only a molecular
layer of oil on the walls of the guide enhances a parasitic phenomenon (the
multipacting discharge) which deteriorates the level of operation of the
machine (see Section 8-11). The vacuum system is often connected to the
input and output sections of each waveguide element. Another solution is to
enclose each waveguide element in a metal cylinder of larger diameter (a
vacuum jacket) and to attach the vacuum system to this; a series of small
holes drilled through the wall of the waveguide allows its evacuation.

As in the other machines (see, for example, Section 7-4) the cooling system
is very important. This carries away the large power dissipated and it contributes to the thermostating required by the waveguide elements (to within
1°C or some tenths of a degree Celsius according to the length of the sections),
in order to ensure that the geometrical dimensions and hence the phase
velocity remain constant (see Section 8-11). Because of the large powers
involved all the elements of the rf system (modulators and klystrons) must
also be cooled.

Finally we mention the complex problems of shielding and protection which
are characteristic of this machine. Indeed, as the accelerated beam is very
intense, if for any reason it hits any part of the internal structure of the
machine it produces a very intense and dangerous source of radiation. For
this reason, effective shielding must be placed along the entire length of the
machine and not only around the end section. The shielding must be especially
heavy in accelerators for electrons and positrons in the vicinity of the intermediate target where the conversion occurs.

8-11   SOME TECHNICAL PROBLEMS OF ELECTRON LINACS

In this section we discuss some of the technical problems which arise in
the design and in the operation of an electron linac. As the construction of
this machine must satisfy very strict tolerance requirements, for practical

and economical reasons the trend has been to study in detail a limited number of kinds of loaded waveguide and to use these in all the machines, and furthermore to make all the sections of the waveguide identical. However, because of the power losses along the guide (see Section 8-9), the accelerating electric field is not constant but it decreases along the guide (as Equation 8-98 shows). A way of correcting for this effect and thus of obtaining a more uniform acceleration is to reduce the diameter of the irises gradually: if indeed the same rf power were to propagate through a section of waveguide the electric field would be stronger where the area of the section is smaller. Thus it is possible to build a waveguide where the accelerating electric field is roughly constant along the length even in the presence of the beam: this is called a "constant-field waveguide."

However, this solution greatly complicates the construction, because it also involves the variation of other waveguide parameters along the tube (in particular, the wall diameter must also decrease in order to keep the phase velocity constant), and the tolerances in the construction become even more stringent. Furthermore such a waveguide can only operate at the beam intensity for which it has been designed. For these reasons a compromise is made and waveguides are used which are simpler to build but in which the condition of constant field is satisfied approximately. This is obtained by dividing each waveguide element (from one rf input section to the next output section) into two or three sections, each of which consists of a normal loaded waveguide, with the following conditions: (1) the phase velocity is constant and equal for all the sections; (2) in each section the iris diameter is a constant, but this diameter changes from one section to the next and it decreases from the section nearest the rf input down to the one nearest the output; (3) the connection between successive sections is designed so that the phase of the electric field seen by the beam does not jump in crossing it. This method has given good results and it has been used in many cases. It also has the advantages that it results in shorter elements than those of the corresponding variable-field waveguide, and that it does not give rise to the phenomenon called "pulse shortening" which we shall briefly discuss later.

As we have mentioned, the tolerances in the waveguide construction are rather stringent; we now give a more quantitative evaluation of them. Fluctuations of the energy of the accelerated beam are produced by fluctuations in the rf power or in the frequency, or by variations in the waveguide dimensions which may be due to temperature variations or to errors in the actual construction. All these effects produce variations in the phase ($\varphi = \omega t - k_g z$) of the wave at the particle location. As the energy gained by the electrons (see Equations 8-100 and 8-13) is given by[14]

$$W = e \int_0^L E_{z0}(z) \sin \varphi(z)\, dz, \qquad (8\text{-}112)$$

[14] Here we denote again by E_{z0} the amplitude of the electric field at the point z.

any variations in φ will result in variations in W. The loaded waveguide can be considered as a succession of coupled resonant cavities each consisting of the cell defined by two successive irises. From this point of view it is useful to consider any errors in the dimensions of the cells as errors in the resonant frequencies of the cells. Thus most of the effects leading to fluctuations in the phase can be reduced to an error $d\omega$ in the frequency, with a corresponding error dk_g in k_g. Thus the synchronous particle that theoretically encounters a field

$$E_z = E_{z0} \sin(\omega t - k_g z) = E_{z0} \sin \varphi \qquad (8\text{-}113)$$

with a constant phase will encounter in a particular cell a field

$$E_z = E_{z0} \sin[(\omega + d\omega)t - (k_g + dk_g)z] = E_{z0} \sin(\varphi + d\varphi), \quad (8\text{-}114)$$

and its phase changes by an amount $d\varphi$ which is a function of z and t. Let us calculate the variation of the phase between the particle and the wave over one cell, that is, over a distance $\Delta z = d$ (the distance between irises) and a time $\Delta t = d/v_p$ (as v_p is the velocity of the s.p. coinciding with the phase velocity in the undisturbed waveguide). Using the definitions of the phase velocity v_p and of the group velocity v_g (see Equations 8-2 and 8-7), we have

$$d\varphi = \Delta t\, d\omega - \Delta z\, dk_g = \Delta z \left(\frac{d\omega}{v_p} - dk_g\right)$$

$$= -k_g \Delta z \left(\frac{v_p}{v_g} - 1\right)\frac{d\omega}{\omega}. \qquad (8\text{-}115)$$

In general each cell contributes a change in the phase of the kind given by Equation 8-115, and the calculation of the net energy change in the accelerated beam involves the summation of the phase changes over all the cells. In order to obtain an idea of the energy fluctuations involved, let us suppose that the frequency change $d\omega$ is the same over the entire waveguide (such as could be produced by an overall temperature fluctuation). Then Equation 8-115 gives the change in phase as a function of the distance z, that is,

$$d\varphi(z) = -k_g \left(\frac{v_p}{v_g} - 1\right)\frac{d\omega}{\omega} z. \qquad (8\text{-}116)$$

As we shall consider only small changes of the phase about its undisturbed value, which usually is approximately $\pi/2$,[15] we can write

$$\sin \varphi(z) = 1 - \tfrac{1}{2}[d\varphi(z)]^2. \qquad (8\text{-}117)$$

If we now substitute Equation 8-116 into Equation 8-117 and this into Equation 8-112, we can calculate the relative energy change dW/W corresponding

[15] In practice, in electron linacs the particles are accelerated on the crest of the wave. This can be obtained without loss of intensity by means of an auxiliary device called a "buncher" (see later).

to the frequency change $d\omega/\omega$. If for simplicity we neglect the attenuation of the wave and suppose $E_{z0}(z)$ to be a constant, we obtain

$$\frac{dW}{W} = -\frac{(2\pi)^2}{6}\left(\frac{v_p}{v_g} - 1\right)^2\left(\frac{L}{\lambda_g}\right)^2\left(\frac{d\omega}{\omega}\right)^2. \qquad (8\text{-}118)$$

As we have mentioned (see Section 8-7), v_p/v_g is of the order of 100 and in general L/λ_g is also about 100; thus it can be seen from Equation 8-118 that if we wish to have $|\,dW/W\,| < 10^{-2}$ we must have $|\,d\omega/\omega\,| < 10^{-5}$. Usually the frequency change is related to the change of a linear dimension l and to the temperature change ΔT that produces it by the expression

$$-\frac{d\omega}{\omega} = \frac{dl}{l} = g\Delta T, \qquad (8\text{-}119)$$

where the expansion coefficient g for copper is $1.6 \times 10^{-5}\,°\text{C}^{-1}$. This expression gives an idea of the temperature stabilization required.

The energy spread of the accelerated beam must be reduced as far as possible because, although the beam current may be sufficient to permit energy selection at the output end, the undesired electrons produce a background that is difficult to eliminate.

In general the tolerance in the construction of the waveguide must be kept to about 10^{-3} cm in order to limit the errors in the final energy to about 1%. Of course, final adjustments (small mechanical deformations obtained with calibrated hammers, the insertion of screws, the opening of small holes in the walls) must be made directly on the waveguide sections ready for assembly. These adjustments are usually controlled by measurements of the resonant frequency.

We now come to the auxiliary devices which are used to increase the intensity of the accelerated beam. As we have seen in Section 1-9, the accelerator only accepts the particles that are injected in the interval of stable phases: if the injector supplies a continuous pulse of current, many of the injected particles are lost. In order to obtain a better injection efficiency, the current pulse supplied by the injector must be transformed into a series of very short pulses (with a frequency equal to that of the accelerating rf field) which enter the machine when the accelerating field has a phase in the stable range. The device which produces this transformation, called the *buncher*, consists essentially of a resonant cavity placed between the injector and the beginning of the waveguide. It is excited by the rf system and the voltage across the gap oscillates in such a way that particles injected successively gain different velocities; some are slightly accelerated, others decelerated, so that finally the particles bunch up around the s.p. (whose motion is not affected by the buncher). The phase φ_0 around which the particles are bunched up is determined from Equation 8-23, with $\cos \varphi \simeq 0$. In such a way, the "asymptotic" phase, reached by the particles as $\beta \approx 1$, and maintained for a large part of the trajectory, is practically $\pi/2$; thus the electrons travel on the crest of the wave, and reach the final energy through a shorter path.

Sometimes the buncher is followed by a second cavity, called the "chopper," whose purpose is to eliminate the particles which would enter the waveguide with an incorrect phase and so contribute to the loading without contributing to the accelerated beam. The chopper produces an oscillating magnetic field which does not change the energy of the particles crossing it: the magnetic field is zero for particles having the correct phase, and it increases and deflects the particles with incorrect phase. However, not only do these devices increase the beam intensity; they also enhance the energy spread of the accelerated beam.

Let us now consider two important parasitic effects, *"pulse shortening"* and *"multipacting,"* which strongly perturb the operation of a linac. Pulse shortening occurs when the injected beam intensity is greater than a certain value (which depends on the machine parameters). Below this value the pulse length of the accelerated particles is the same as the pulse length of the injected particles (although the intensity is lower); above this value the pulse length of the accelerated particles becomes shorter. There is therefore a further reduction of intensity, which for high currents can be very large. When pulse shortening occurs, at the output of the waveguide electromagnetic fields are observed whose frequencies are not harmonics of the applied frequency. The phenomenon is therefore explained by supposing that, when the current is large, the beam in the waveguide can excite undesired modes for which the phase velocity has the opposite direction to the group velocity. These modes absorb energy from the beam and introduce the defocusing forces which produce the shortening of the current pulse. It can be seen from the Brillouin diagram (Figure 8-6) that the undesired modes can belong to the higher passbands of the Brillouin diagram, and especially to the second one (see Section 8-7), and their frequencies are rather near those of the first passband (used for particle acceleration). As the rf power sent into the waveguide has a fairly wide frequency spectrum, the conditions for the excitation of these undesired oscillations are easily satisfied; however, if the beam intensity is not too high and the guide is not too long, these oscillations do not grow to large amplitudes before the beam has left the guide. As we have mentioned previously, pulse shortening occurs with more difficulty in constant-field guides. This is due to the fact that, as the Brillouin diagram changes from one section to the next, conditions which are favorable for the excitation of undesired modes in one section can be in general no longer favorable in the others. Greater details on the pulse shortening can be found in Bell *et al.* (1963).

The phenomenon called "multipacting" occurs in all the machines where intense high-frequency electric fields exist between opposite surfaces separated by a high vacuum, and in particular in the cyclotron and the synchrotron. However, we discuss it in detail here because this phenomenon has a particular importance in the linac. Multipacting is an electron discharge which occurs in high vacuum between two metal surfaces between which an oscillating voltage is applied. An electron produced in any way between the surfaces can be accelerated in such a way as to hit one of them and extract one or more secondary electrons. These can then be accelerated back to the other surface, where they again multiply by extracting other secondary electrons, and so on. Thus under the proper conditions an electron avalanche is formed which grows until the space-charge fields arrest the electron multiplication and the electron cloud between the surfaces reaches a stationary density. However, this very large charge density gives rise to a considerable amount of energy dissipation at each cycle. Moreover, this moving charge density introduces a strong reactive effect that in turn may appreciably change the impedance of the guide.

Obviously for multipacting to occur some particular conditions must be satisfied: The half-period of the voltage oscillation must be equal to the transit time of an electron between the two surfaces, and furthermore the amplitude of the applied voltage and the state of the metal walls must be such that the extraction efficiency for secondary electrons is larger than unity. For a complicated structure such as that of a loaded waveguide the conditions for the occurrence of the multipacting discharge depend on the parameters of the structure in a complicated way; in practice these conditions are often satisfied. It is also obvious that multipacting occurs with greater ease in high vacuum: indeed the collisions with the residual gas molecules disturb the multiplication process.

Multipacting is particularly dangerous in a linac because the discharge perturbs all the electrical properties of the waveguide. As the operation of the guide depends rather critically on its parameters (see the previous sections), the presence of these discharges endangers the entire acceleration process. Fortunately the multipacting discharge can develop rapidly only for certain values of the peak voltage which are characteristic of the resonant structure. If these values of the field amplitude are traversed very quickly, (and this requires that the voltage pulses driving the klystrons have a rise time which is short compared with the multiplication time and that the klystrons themselves be strongly coupled to the waveguide), then the multipacting discharge does not occur. Thus with a careful design of the rf system the discharge can be avoided. Furthermore the state of all the metal walls must be examined with care, and impurities which can give rise to a strong emission of secondary electrons must be avoided. Among these, thin layers of organic substances are particularly dangerous: for this reason (see Section 8-11) oil pumps should not be used in linacs.

Sometimes the multipacting discharge is produced on purpose, in order to improve the outgassing of the metal surfaces of the resonators or of the waveguide.

8-12 THE LINEAR ACCELERATORS FOR PROTONS

As we have mentioned in Section 1-5, linear accelerators for protons (and, in general, for heavy particles) cannot use the same kind of structure as the electron linacs, which we have described in the previous sections. Indeed, because of the much greater mass of these particles with respect to the electron, their velocity is very far from the ultrarelativistic limit (a 145-MeV proton has $\beta = 0.5$) and it changes strongly with energy. The use of a loaded waveguide for the acceleration of heavy particles would involve a structure where the phase velocity changes over a wide range and has a low value: such a structure would have to be so heavily loaded that the energy dissipation would be prohibitive. It is therefore necessary to turn to machines with discontinuous acceleration based on the use of drift tubes, as we have briefly described in Section 1-5.

The method of feeding energy into the accelerating structure illustrated in Figure 1-2, with an external generator as in the first linear accelerator of Wideröe (1928), is not practical because the system radiates a large amount of energy. Indeed if we consider the end faces of two adjacent drift tubes as the plates of a capacitor, the displacement current I_d flowing through it is given by

$$I_d = \omega C V = 2\pi \nu C V, \qquad (8\text{-}120)$$

where C is the capacitance between the tubes, V the accelerating voltage, and ν the frequency used. With the values used in practice, I_d is always very large. It is therefore convenient to enclose the gap existing between two successive drift tubes in a cavity which holds the electromagnetic energy (in the form of a magnetic field: "inductive load") and to make the resonant frequency of this cavity equal to that of the accelerating field. We thus obtain the structure shown in Figure 8-9, which is similar to the cavity we have illustrated in Section 5-8 (see Figures 5-8 and 5-9). Of course the length l of the cavity is of the same order of magnitude as the length of the drift tubes. The equivalent inductance L of such a coaxial system (with the notation of the figure) is approximately given by

$$L = \frac{\mu}{2\pi} l \log \frac{D_2}{D_1}, \qquad (8\text{-}121)$$

where μ is the magnetic permeability of the medium inside the cavity. (In vacuum $\mu = 4\pi \times 10^{-7}$ henry/m.) The condition for resonance requires that

$$4\pi^2 \nu^2 L C = 1. \qquad (8\text{-}122)$$

These two expressions are used in the design of the machine in order to determine the dimensions of the cavity. If many structures like that shown in Figure 8-9 are placed in series, the linac design shown in Figure 8-10 is obtained. Each cavity is fed from an amplifier and all these are driven (through phase shifters) by a single generator. In practice (see Figure 8-11) it is simpler for the cavities to be adjacent, with common side walls (fitting on the center of the drift tubes) and a constant external diameter. In this case the length of the cavities increases with the length of the tubes, and hence (see Equation 8-121) also L increases. In order for the resonant frequency to remain constant (equal to ν), the capacitance C must correspondingly decrease. This can be achieved by progressively reducing the diameter of the tubes (C is roughly proportional to $D_1{}^2$), as Figure 8-11 indicates schematically.

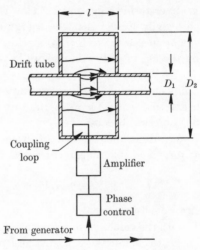

FIGURE 8-9. *Diagram of the basic cavity used in the proton linac. The lines of force of the electric field are indicated.*

This kind of structure can be excited in different ways. It is possible to give the electric field an opposite phase at successive gaps, similarly to the situation shown in Figure 1-2. In this case the lines of force of the electric field at a given time have the shape shown in Figure 8-12a, where the direction of the currents in the metal walls is also indicated. The length of the tubes must be designed so that the synchronous particle traverses each of them in one half-period of the field oscillation; that is, if λ is the vacuum wavelength of the accelerating voltage ($\lambda = c/\nu$), L_n is the length of the nth tube, and β_n is the normalized velocity of the particles traversing it, the following relation

$$L_n = \frac{\beta_n \lambda}{2} \tag{8-123}$$

must hold, and the machine is sometimes called a "half beta lambda" linac.

In another solution, at a given time, the field has the same phase at all the

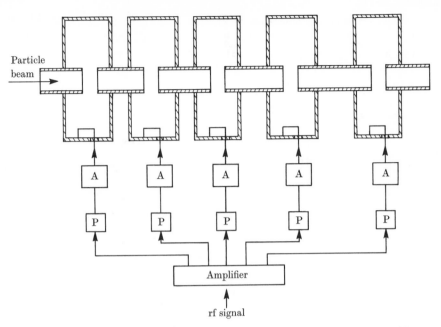

FIGURE 8-10. *A possible linac structure with drift tubes and separate resonant cavities. Amplifiers are indicated by* A *and phase shifters by* P.

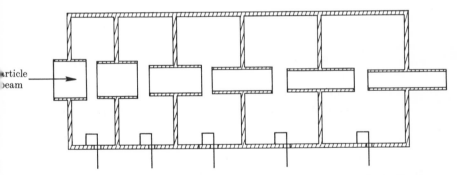

FIGURE 8-11. *A linac structure with a cavity for each accelerating gap, where adjacent cavities have a wall in common.*

gaps. The directions of the electric field and of the wall currents are shown in Figure 8-12b. As the particle must now traverse a tube in a full period of the field oscillation, instead of Equation 8-123 we now have

$$L_n = \beta_n \lambda, \tag{8-124}$$

and the machine is called a "beta lambda" linac.

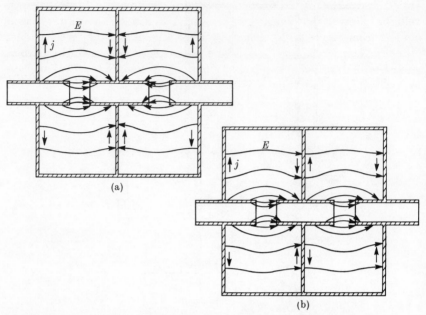

FIGURE 8-12. *Diagram showing the lines of force of the electric field, E, and the direction of the wall currents, j, for two adjacent cavities:* (a) *for a* βλ/2 *linac;* (b) *for a* βλ *linac.*

The latter case is of special interest because it leads to a proton linac which in practice consists of a single resonant cavity excited by one or a few synchronized generators. Indeed, from the diagram of Figure 8-12b, it can be seen that there is no net charge on the wall between two adjacent cavities (as many electric lines of force leave the wall on one side as there arrive on the other side), and no net current flows along the wall; thus the latter can be eliminated without any substantial change of the electromagnetic field in the system. Hence the design shown in Figure 8-11 can be replaced by the one shown in Figure 8-13, which is equivalent to the former as regards the acceleration of the particles, but has smaller wall losses because, the other conditions being the same, the wall currents have shorter paths. In this case the drift tubes are supported by (insulating or conducting) rods, indicated in the figure by a. These are connected to the center of the tubes and sometimes they are also used to carry the current required for the excitation of magnetic focusing devices (see later) inside the drift tube. A linac using this kind of structure is called an "Alvarez linac" (Alvarez, 1946) or an "infinite phase velocity" linac. Indeed the entire cavity containing the drift tubes can be considered as a section of cylindrical waveguide short-circuited at the ends and excited at the cutoff frequency. If the drift-tube diameter is small with respect to the cavity diameter, the drift tubes only introduce a small perturbation. Instead in the "half beta lambda" linacs (also called "matched phase velocity" linacs) the dividing walls cannot be eliminated because, as is obvious from Figure 8-12a, they carry a net current and they receive a net charge different from zero. However, the principle of using a single resonant system can be applied to this case too, by making holes in the dividing walls (and possibly adding some coupling loops), designed in such a way that successive cells are coupled 180° out of phase. In this way it is much simpler to excite the accelerating structure, which in some respects becomes similar to the loaded waveguide described in Section 8-7. Theoretical design studies indicate that above about 100 MeV the "half beta lambda" linac is more convenient.

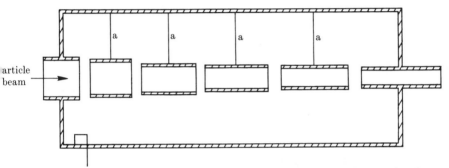

FIGURE 8-13. *Diagram of the structure of an Alvarez linac. The rods supporting the drift tubes are indicated by* a.

Finally it must be noted that in the previous treatment we have neglected the effect of the finite gap width on the particle motion. The effect is to reduce the energy actually gained in a gap, with respect to the energy ($qU \sin \varphi$, in an obvious notation) gained in crossing an infinitesimal gap. It can be computed (see, for example, Livingood, 1961, Section 14-2) that the energy W_n actually gained by a particle crossing the nth gap is given by

$$W_n = qU \sin \varphi \, \frac{\sin(\pi g_n / \alpha L_n)}{(\pi g_n / \alpha L_n)} , \qquad (8\text{-}125)$$

where g_n is the gap width, L_n is the length of the tube following the gap, and α is a parameter which is equal to 1 in beta lambda linacs and 2 in half beta lambda linacs. Thus in the latter the net energy reduction is smaller, the other conditions being equal. It is therefore convenient to make the gaps as small as possible, but not so small that electric breakdown occurs across the gap. It should be noted that in general the gap width changes along the linac, as the symbol g_n in Equation 8-125 shows. From Equations 8-123 and 8-124, it follows that, if the kinetic energy in the nth tube is T_n, we have

$$L_n \propto \beta_n = \frac{1}{c} \left(\frac{2T_n}{m} \right)^{1/2}, \qquad (8\text{-}126)$$

because the particles are always far from being relativistic. If one neglects the injection energy, then $T_n = n\,\Delta T$, where ΔT is the energy gained at each gap. Thus it can be seen that the length of the tubes increases as $n^{1/2}$. However, the injection energy should not be too low; otherwise the first tubes become prohibitively short (and the transit time factor of Equation 8-125 becomes smaller), and the transverse focusing is more critical. Therefore at injection a value of $\beta \gtrsim 0.03$ is used (that is, an injection energy of 500 keV for protons). Cockcroft-Walton generators are often used as injectors, and the injection energy T_0 is usually chosen so that $T_0 = n'\,\Delta T$, where n' is an integer somewhat greater than unity.

From Equations 8-123 and 8-124 it also follows that, with β_n of the order of 0.1 and L_n of the order of 10 cm, λ must be of the order of 1 m. Thus heavy-particle linacs must operate at frequencies of a few hundred megacycles per second and the linear dimensions of the resonant cavities are large (of the order of λ).

8-13   TECHNICAL PROBLEMS IN PROTON LINACS. LINEAR ACCELERATORS FOR HEAVY IONS

The construction of a proton linac is very complicated technically: theoretical calculations are not sufficient to determine the machine parameters with the required accuracy and hence these must be adjusted empirically on scale models or on the machine itself. Some problems are similar to those of the electron linacs, such as those concerning the power supplies, although the frequencies used are quite different (about 100–200 Mc/sec in proton linacs) and are thus produced by generators using conventional vacuum tubes. The multipacting discharge, which has been discussed in Section 8-11, can occur in these machines too. The rf power is again pulsed, with pulse lengths of a few hundred microseconds, at a repetition rate of several tens of pulses per second. For example, the 68-MeV proton linac at the University of Minnesota (Day *et al.*, 1958) uses about 6 MW of rf power and produces an average beam current of 0.02 μA.

It should be noted that in linacs with discontinuous acceleration the precise value of the accelerating electric field is more critical than in machines with continuous acceleration. Indeed, for a good operation of the machine the synchronous particle should cross a drift tube exactly in the correct time, and this time depends on the energy gained at each gap. For this reason the value of this energy is rigorously fixed (for a given kind of particle). In this sense linacs with discontinuous acceleration are "fixed-energy" machines.

It is of particular importance that the resonant cavity containing the drift tubes should oscillate only on the required mode and that other modes should not be excited, because these subtract energy from the system and change the value of the field in the gaps. This can occur easily in the structures described above, where the length of the cavity is usually much greater than its cutoff wavelength. This difficulty increases with the length of the cavity and it is the main limitation to the length of the machine. The only way to avoid this problem is to design and build the cavity with great accuracy.

In a proton linac the problem of the transverse stability is of great importance because of the low particle velocity (see Section 8-1). As we have seen, the net effect of the electrostatic lens at the gap is always defocusing when the electric field encountered is increasing in time (region of phase stability). This effect can be corrected by putting at the entrance of the drift tubes a thin metal grid (see Figure 8-14) which reduces the curvature of the lines of force. However, a part of the beam (from 25 to 50%) is lost by collision against the grids. Especially at the final sections of the machine where the beam intensity is lower, magnetic focusing devices are preferred (such as Helmholtz coils inside the drift tubes or quadrupole lenses).

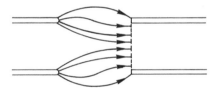

FIGURE 8-14.   *Diagram of the electric lines of force in the gap between two drift tubes when a focusing grid is used.*

Finally, we mention the linear accelerators for heavy ions (also called "hilacs"). It is obvious that a linear accelerator can accelerate particles with a different charge-to-mass ratio (q/m: specific charge) if the electric field or the synchronous phase, or both, is modified in such a way that the energy gained per nucleon remains the same. However, as the electric field cannot be increased over certain limits and φ_s cannot be too close to $\pi/2$ for reasons of intensity,[16] the heavier ions must have a greater charge. At present, sources of multiply ionized ions with a high specific charge are not intense enough; therefore ions with a low specific charge are brought to several hundred kiloelectron volts by a Cockcroft-Walton accelerator and injected into a first

[16] Usually the synchronous phase in a proton linac is chosen around 60–70°.

section of the linac, where they are given an energy of about 1 MeV per nucleon. Then the ions thus accelerated pass through a "stripper" (a thin metal foil or a jet of mercury vapor) where two or more electrons may be removed from each ion. Their specific charge thus increased, the ions are then accelerated in the second section of the linac up to a final energy of about 10 MeV per nucleon. Accelerators of this kind have been built at Berkeley, California, and at Yale University (Hubbard *et al.*, 1961): the rf power is about 3 MW, delivered in 3-msec pulses with a repetition rate of 10 per second. Ions of helium, carbon, nitrogen, and oxygen can be accelerated with currents of several microamperes.

CHAPTER 9

RECENT DEVELOPMENTS IN
PARTICLE ACCELERATORS

9-1 INTRODUCTION

With the progress of nuclear research, which has developed with the help of particle accelerators particularly, physicists have continuously called for machines capable of giving ever higher energies, or greater intensities for the energies already obtained. It is true that by further developing the possibilities of the existing kinds of accelerators (which are well understood) and consequently increasing their cost, both the energy and the intensity can be increased. However, new principles have been proposed on which to obtain the same improvement in particle accelerators without a large increase in the cost. A great number of studies have been carried out in different directions and a vast literature is available. However, because the new ideas lead to severe technical difficulties most of them have remained at the stage of a proposal or an experiment. Only a few of the new ideas seem to offer the possibility of immediate application even though the theory of the phenomena connected with the practical construction of such machines is not yet so well understood as the theory of conventional accelerators.

In this chapter we discuss the developments of the two new principles for which machines have been built or are in a phase of advanced construction, namely,

1. fixed-field alternating-gradient (FFAG) accelerators;
2. storage rings for experiments with colliding beams.

For reasons of space and simplicity we shall not even mention other projects under study. The interested reader can refer to the specialized literature. [See, for example, the proceedings of the international conferences held at CERN (1956 and 1959), Brookhaven (1961), Dubna (1963), and Frascati (1965), cited in the General Bibliography, and the review article by Judd (1958).]

9-2   THE PRINCIPLE OF OPERATION OF FFAG ACCELERATORS

The circular machines known under the name of FFAG are essentially high-intensity and rather high-energy machines; these features are obtained by using continuous operation (as in the cyclotron) or in any case by increasing the frequency of the duty cycle with respect to a similar machine of conventional type. For this purpose the magnetic field is constant in time (fixed field) but it is strongly inhomogeneous, in two senses. First of all, the magnetic field *increases* strongly with radius (thus the field index is negative and very large), so that an increase of energy gives rise to a much smaller increase of the radius of curvature than in a constant (or small n value) field. As a result, the increase of the orbit radius with energy is not too large. The vertical instability resulting from a negative field index (see Section 4-3) is then corrected by means of a variation of the magnetic field in the azimuthal direction, whose effect, in a sense, is similar to the alternating-gradient principle (hence the name FFAG). These machines are also called azimuthally varying field (AVF) accelerators.

Before describing in greater detail the structure of this kind of accelerator we list the types of machine that can be built on this principle:

Class 1: cyclotrons (also called "isochronous cyclotrons"). In these machines the radial variation of the magnetic field, required by the FFAG principle, leads to a compensation of the relativistic increase of mass, so that the particles remain in synchronism with the frequency of the electric field between the dees without any need of modulation. Thus one obtains a machine which can reach the energy of a synchrocyclotron with the intensity of a cyclotron.

Class 2: synchrotrons. These are ring-shaped fixed-field accelerators in which the particles are injected near the inner wall of the doughnut and accelerated by an rf cavity; the frequency of the cavity is modulated following the energy variation of the particles. These follow a spiral path outward which is very tight as a consequence of the radial increase of the magnetic field. There is a great improvement of the intensity with respect to an ordinary synchrotron because the repetition rate is given by the rf modulation cycle rather than by the (necessarily much slower) time variation of the magnetic field.

Class 3: betatrons. In these machines, also ring-shaped, the guiding field is kept constant in time and the acceleration is produced by the induction of an alternating magnetic field linking the orbit. (In this case, of course, it is not necessary that the betatron condition, Equation 1-27, be satisfied.) Also, for these machines there is a great improvement in the intensity.

It must be noted that, contrary to the ordinary case, the structure of the magnet in an FFAG synchrotron and in an FFAG betatron is, in principle, the same, and the only difference is in the method of acceleration.[1]

9-3 FFAG CYCLOTRONS. THOMAS FOCUSING

In order to illustrate the problem of vertical stability in an FFAG machine, we first consider the case of a cyclotron. We suppose that the surface of the magnet poles is shaped in such a way as to produce a periodic azimuthal variation of the magnetic field. This can be obtained, for example, by giving the surface of the magnet pole tips a contour of sinusoidal shape (see Figure 9-1a) or square-wave shape (see Figure 9-1b), so that the height of the pole

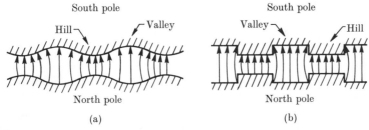

FIGURE 9-1. *Side view of the pole tips of an FFAG cyclotron, unrolled for clarity of illustration:* (a) *sinusoidal contour;* (b) *square-wave contour.*

gap becomes alternately larger and smaller as we go around the center of the machine. The regions where the pole gap is smaller are called "hills," and where it is larger, "valleys." An element of periodicity in the pole contour (including one hill and one valley) constitutes a "sector." The situation is illustrated in Figure 9-2a, which shows the plan of a three-sector machine (where the loci of hill maxima and valley minima are radial). By means of a proper choice of the shape and of the value of the magnetic field, it is possible to obtain a closed trajectory for a particle of given momentum. An example of such a trajectory is shown schematically in Figure 9-2a, by assuming for simplicity that the pole contour is of the kind shown in Figure 9-1b (constant radius of curvature

---

[1] It must be noted that the terminology introduced in this section is not of general use. Many authors prefer to avoid the expression "FFAG cyclotron" (because a cyclotron is always a fixed-field machine), and they use the term AVF or isochronous cyclotron. Others prefer the generic term "ring accelerators," rather than the specific terms, for the machines of Classes 2 and 3.

in a hill or in a valley). Thus we obtain a curve which is more or less distorted with respect to the circular trajectory which the particle would follow in the absence of an azimuthal variation.

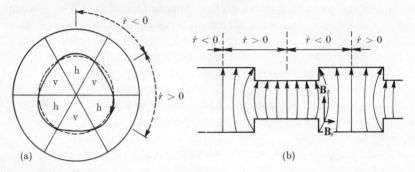

FIGURE 9-2. *Diagram of a radial-sector FFAG cyclotron showing the regions where $\dot{r} > 0$ and those where $\dot{r} < 0$. (a) Top view showing a typical orbit and the hills (h) and valleys (v); (b) unrolled side view.*

We now show that this azimuthal magnetic field variation produces a vertical focusing effect along the entire trajectory. Let us again consider the contour of Figure 9-1b (repeated in Figure 9-2b) and suppose that we are looking from the inside outward; we suppose the accelerated particles to be positive so that they move clockwise in the machine (see Figure 9-2a). As the lines of force are curved when we pass from a hill to a valley, there is an azimuthal component $\mathbf{B}_\theta$ of the field; this component reverses its direction when one crosses the median plane or when one goes through a maximum or a minimum of the magnetic field ("top" of a hill or "bottom" of a valley). In these transition regions, of course, the component $\mathbf{B}_\theta$ is zero. This characteristic behavior of the azimuthal component of the field does not occur only for the particular contour shown in Figure 9-2b but also for any other contour having the same kind of periodicity and symmetry. This component $\mathbf{B}_\theta$, with the radial velocity $\dot{r}$ of the particle, produces a vertical component $\mathbf{F}_v$ of the Lorentz force, according to the formula

$$\mathbf{F}_v = q\,\dot{\mathbf{r}} \times \mathbf{B}_\theta. \tag{9-1}$$

As the particle follows a trajectory of the kind shown in Figure 9-2a, it can be seen that in the transition zones from a hill to a valley r decreases and $\dot{r} < 0$ ($\dot{r}$ is directed inward); the opposite occurs in the transition from a valley to a hill. The regions where $\dot{r} < 0$ and where $\dot{r} > 0$ are indicated in Figures 9-2a and 9-2b. If one finds the direction of the Lorentz force from Equation 9-1, it can be seen that it is always directed toward the median plane and hence it has a focusing effect. The same conclusions are reached for the motion of a negative charge.

This focusing effect is known as "Thomas focusing" because it was first proposed by L. H. Thomas (1938). It is clear that the effect is the greater, the stronger the curvature of the lines of force, that is, the greater the relative variation of the magnetic field between the hills and the valleys. The detailed shape of the profile instead has little influence on the magnitude of the effect.

Thus, with the proper design of the magnetic field contour, it is possible to compensate the defocusing action introduced by the radial increase of the field. A quantitative discussion will be given later.

The focusing effect in an FFAG cyclotron can be enhanced if the hills and valleys do not occur at the same azimuth for different radii but are distributed in a spiral form from the center outward (see Figure 9-3). In this case, in

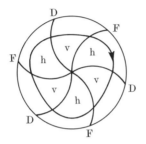

FIGURE 9-3. *Plan of a spiral-sector FFAG cyclotron showing a typical orbit and the relative positions of the focusing* (F) *and defocusing* (D) *edges with respect to hills* (h) *and valleys* (v).

addition to the Thomas focusing (along the entire trajectory) there are two new focusing effects. The first one is essentially an "edge effect" of the same kind as the one described in Section 6-11 for the zero-gradient synchrotron. In the structure shown in Figure 9-1b it is obvious that a particle entering or leaving a hill encounters similar conditions to a particle entering or leaving a magnetic sector of a racetrack synchrotron. If the machine has the structure shown in Figure 9-3, the entrance and exit of a hill appear to the particle similar to the edges of a slant magnet and there will therefore be a corresponding vertical focusing or defocusing (see Section 6-11); one has focusing at the entrance of the hills and defocusing at the exit[2] (see Figure 9-3). The net result will be a focusing effect as a consequence of the alternating-gradient

[2] It must be noted that in these machines it is not possible to obtain a vertical focusing effect at all the edges as in the ZGS. As we have seen in Section 6-11, in a ZGS the average magnetic field decreases from the center outward, whereas in an FFAG machine it must increase.

principle discussed in Chapter 6, and it will be the stronger, the larger the inclination of the tangent to the spiral with respect to the radial direction. A further focusing effect can be seen by considering the actual particle trajectory: this does not encounter all the spiral branches with the same angle of incidence. As a consequence of the smaller curvature of the trajectory in the valleys, the incidence on the edges which give a focusing effect (indicated by F in Figure 9-3) is more oblique than that on the defocusing edges (indicated by D): thus the particle is subject to the focusing action for a longer time than to the defocusing one, and this leads to an enhancement of the vertical stability.

9-4   BETATRON OSCILLATIONS IN AN FFAG CYCLOTRON. THE AVERAGE FIELD INDEX

The treatment of betatron oscillations in an FFAG machine is much more complicated than for a conventional machine. This depends on the fact that the unperturbed orbit is no longer circular and hence we must now distinguish between the radial distance r and the radius of curvature ρ of the unperturbed trajectory; at each instant of time, the latter satisfies a relation of the kind of Equation 1-17[3]:

$$P = |q| B_z \rho. \tag{9-2}$$

Furthermore, it is useful to introduce another quantity, the "equivalent radius" R of a closed trajectory of length S (of the type shown in Figure 9-2a or 9-3), by the definition

$$R = S/2\pi. \tag{9-3}$$

The use of R is convenient because, for a closed trajectory followed with constant momentum, R satisfies a relation similar to Equation 9-2 and containing the average value $\bar{B}_z$ of the field along the trajectory, defined by

$$\bar{B}_z = \frac{1}{S} \oint B_z \, ds \tag{9-4}$$

(s indicates the distance along the trajectory). If indeed we derive B_z from Equation 9-2, we have

$$\bar{B}_z = \frac{|q| P}{S} \oint \frac{ds}{\rho} = \frac{|q| P}{S} \oint d\theta = \frac{2\pi |q| P}{S} = \frac{|q| P}{R}, \tag{9-5}$$

and so it follows that

$$P = |q| \bar{B}_z R. \tag{9-6}$$

This expression is useful because with it we can study the effect of the radial increase of the magnetic field independently of the azimuthal fluctuations over one turn.

---

[3] In this chapter B_z will always be considered as positive, unless otherwise specified.

In the first place we consider the simpler situation where we suppose the value of R to be sufficiently large so that we may neglect the scalloping of the actual trajectory (that is, we neglect the difference between r and R). This approximation is certainly not valid near the center of an FFAG cyclotron, but it does lead to a simpler description of the phenomena. The magnetic field in the median plane can always be written in the form

$$B_z(r, \theta, 0) = B_0\left(\frac{r}{r_0}\right)^k \Phi(r, \theta), \qquad (9\text{-}7)$$

where B_0 and r_0 are constants, k can be a slowly varying function of r, and $\Phi(r, \theta)$ is chosen in such a way that its average value over one turn is equal to 1:

$$\overline{\Phi} = \frac{1}{2\pi} \int_0^{2\pi} \Phi\,(r, \theta)\,d\theta = 1. \qquad (9\text{-}8)$$

(In the approximation we have discussed, averages over one turn with respect to s and with respect to θ are equivalent.) Thus $\overline{B}_z$ is given by

$$\overline{B}_z = B_0\left(\frac{r}{r_0}\right)^k \qquad (9\text{-}9)$$

and it has the same behavior as the field in a conventional circular machine. The quantity k, which corresponds to the quantity $-n$ in a conventional accelerator (see Equation 5-1) is called the "average field index" and it can be defined in a similar way to the field index n,

$$k = \frac{d \log \overline{B}_z}{d \log r} = \frac{r}{\overline{B}_z} \frac{d\overline{B}_z}{dr}. \qquad (9\text{-}10)$$

The change of sign with respect to the definition of n (Equation 4-2) derives from the fact that in practical cases positive values of k are used (field increasing with radius).

If we substitute r for R in Equation 9-6, according to the approximation considered, it can be shown in the same way as for conventional accelerators (see Section 5-3) that the momentum compaction α is given by

$$\alpha = 1 + k. \qquad (9\text{-}11)$$

It is clear that for a given magnet size the larger k, the higher is the energy which the particles can reach.

In FFAG machines the frequencies of the horizontal and vertical betatron oscillations do not depend only on k but also on the azimuthal configuration of the magnetic field. This dependence is particularly important for the vertical oscillations because it produces the focusing effect discussed earlier. The dependence of the frequency ratios $\omega_r/\omega = \nu_r$ and $\omega_z/\omega = \nu_z$ on the structure of the magnetic field is very complex and a rigorous calculation of the orbits in an FFAG machine can only be done numerically with an electronic computer. However, it can be shown (but for simplicity we give only the results here) that the leading terms in the expressions for ν_r and ν_z depend only on two quantities characteristic of the magnetic field structure, besides the dependence on k of course. These quantities are the following:

1. the *flutter function* $F(r)$, which is the mean square fluctuation, along the circle of radius r, of the function Φ defined by Equation 9-7, that is, using Equation 9-8,

$$F(r) = \frac{1}{2\pi} \int_0^{2\pi} (\Phi - \overline{\Phi})^2 \, d\theta = \frac{1}{2\pi} \int_0^{2\pi} (\Phi - 1)^2 \, d\theta \; ; \qquad (9\text{-}12)$$

2. the angle $\zeta(r)$ between the tangent to the spiral and the radial direction (see Figure 9-4). In terms of these two quantities and of the index k the following two approximate expansions can be found for the quantities $\nu_r{}^2$ and $\nu_z{}^2$:

$$\nu_r{}^2 = 1 + k + \ldots , \qquad (9\text{-}13)$$

$$\nu_z{}^2 = -k + F(R) \, (1 + 2 \tan^2 \zeta) + \ldots . \qquad (9\text{-}14)$$

The neglected terms are of the order of 10% or less. It can be seen that for the radial oscillations the dependence is practically the same as for conventional machines: for the vertical oscillations instead the azimuthal field variation (described by F) and the inclination of the spiral sectors (described by ζ) play an essential role in compensating the instability due to the radial increase of the magnetic field. The vertical focusing increases with F and with ζ, in agreement with the qualitative discussion of Section 9-3.

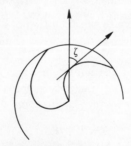

FIGURE 9-4. *Diagram showing the spiral angle.*

In order to understand better the meaning of the flutter function $F(r)$, let us consider its explicit expression in some simple cases. For the case of a sinusoidal contour (see Figure 9-1a) and purely radial sectors (see Figure 9-2a) we can take

$$\Phi \, (r, \, \theta) = 1 - f \sin N\theta, \qquad (9\text{-}15)$$

where N is the number of sectors and f is a constant called the flutter amplitude, which gives the maximum relative change of the field over one turn. In this case the flutter function (from Equation 9-12) is a constant and $F = f^2/2$. For the case of a sinusoidal contour and spiral sectors, Φ can be chosen of the form

$$\Phi(r, \theta) = 1 - f \sin N \, [\theta - g(r)], \qquad (9\text{-}16)$$

where the function $g(r)$ determines the shape of the spiral: again we find $F = f^2/2$. Two kinds of spiral are often used in the design of FFAG machines: the logarithmic spiral for which $\zeta = \text{const}$, and the Archimedean spiral where the radius increases linearly with the polar angle. One finds that the forms of $g(r)$ for the two kinds of spiral are, for the logarithmic spiral ($\zeta = \text{const}$),

$$g(r) = \tan \zeta \log \mu r, \qquad (9\text{-}17)$$

and for the Archimedean spiral,

$$g(r) = \mu r = \tan \zeta, \qquad (9\text{-}18)$$

where μ is a constant having the dimensions of an inverse length.

9-5 CONSTRUCTION AND OPERATION OF AN FFAG CYCLOTRON

The advantages of FFAG cyclotrons consist in the fact that with these machines it is possible to reach much higher energies than in conventional cyclotrons (of the order of magnitude of the energies reached with synchrocyclotrons), and that, as the operation is continuous, the intensity obtained is high. Furthermore there are advantages from the technical point of view: indeed, a fixed-frequency accelerating voltage is again used, but the very high peak voltages required in ordinary cyclotrons (see Section 7-3) are no longer necessary, and the problems of the rf circuit are simplified (in particular it is possible to use only one dee, as in the synchrocyclotron). However, for reasons to be specified later, the accelerating voltage should not be too low; values of the order of 20 kV are used, intermediate between the voltages used in cyclotrons (100–200 kV) and in synchrocyclotrons (5–10 kV).

The main difficulties in the construction of these machines are associated with the design of the magnetic field. In general the theoretical calculations of the trajectories, however accurate, are not sufficient for the design of the machine; a test on a scale model, where the parameters can be adjusted empirically, is necessary. The machines presently (1966) in operation (some of which were obtained by modifying existing cyclotrons) have the kind of structure shown in Figure 9-3, with three or four spiral sectors and a square-wave pole contour, which is easier to construct. The radial increase of B_z (described by the index k) can be obtained by decreasing the gap width between the poles, but this is limited by the minimum space required for the dees and for the auxiliary equipment. However, a structure is preferred where the required radial increase of the magnetic field is obtained by means of circular coils, excited by separate currents, coaxial among themselves and with the machine axis: they are called "trimming coils" or "k-coils." Additional coils, called "flutter coils," are also used in the regions of the valleys in order to obtain variations of the flutter function F. The use of independent currents to obtain the required magnetic field distribution gives the machine greater flexibility; different kinds of particles can be accelerated or different energies can be obtained (variable-energy multiple-projectile isochronous cyclotrons) with only a rather small change of the accelerating voltage frequency (for example, a factor of 1.5 : 1) which can readily be obtained.

The condition for isochronism of the particle motion and the accelerating voltage requires that the average field index k be a function of radius. The law of variation of the field can easily be obtained from Equation 9-6 (with $R \approx r$) if we express P in terms of γ and of r by means of Equations 1-9 and 1-7:

$$P = \frac{E_0}{c}(\gamma^2 - 1)^{1/2} = |q| r\bar{B}_z. \qquad (9\text{-}19)$$

If we differentiate the logarithm of this equation, we obtain

$$\frac{\gamma \, d\gamma}{\gamma^2 - 1} = \frac{dr}{r} + \frac{d\bar{B}_z}{\bar{B}_z}. \qquad (9\text{-}20)$$

If we now write Equation 9-6 again in terms of the frequency of rotation ω $(P/r = m_v\omega)$ and if we require that the latter be always equal to the (constant) frequency of the accelerating electric field ω_e, we obtain a synchronism condition which (with $\bar{B}_z$ in place of B) is the same as Equation 7-6 derived for the cyclotron: we can write it, with the substitution $E = \gamma E_0$ (see Equation 1-7) as

$$\omega = \frac{|q| c^2}{E_0} \frac{\bar{B}_z}{\gamma}. \qquad (9\text{-}21)$$

If we differentiate the logarithm of this expression and recall that we want $\omega = \omega_e = \text{const}$, we obtain

$$\frac{d\bar{B}_z}{\bar{B}_z} - \frac{d\gamma}{\gamma} = 0. \qquad (9\text{-}22)$$

This equation tells us that, in order to preserve isochronism, the average magnetic field must increase proportionally to γ in the radial direction.

In order to find the dependence of k on r, let us divide Equation 9-20 by dr/r; using the definition 9-10 of k, we have

$$1 + k = \frac{\gamma^2}{\gamma^2 - 1} \frac{d\gamma/\gamma}{dr/r}. \tag{9-23}$$

On the other hand, from Equations 9-10 and 9-22 we get

$$k = \frac{d\gamma/\gamma}{dr/r}. \tag{9-24}$$

From these two equations we finally obtain

$$k = \gamma^2 - 1 = \left(\frac{E}{E_0}\right)^2 - 1. \tag{9-25}$$

Thus the condition for isochronism requires that the field index should *increase* radially according to Equation 9-25 up to a value determined by the final energy of the particles.[4]

As a consequence of the variation of the field index, also the frequency ratios ν_r and ν_z change during the acceleration. From Equation 9-14 it can be seen that the increase of k must be compensated by an increase of the positive term, in order to maintain an adequate vertical focusing, In general, as it is difficult to produce an increase of the field flutter together with an increase of the average field intensity, it is preferable to increase the angle ζ and use the Archimedean spiral (ζ increasing linearly with radius, $g(r)$ given by Equation 9-18) for the shape of the spiral sectors. Some control can be exercised on F by means of the flutter coils. For the radial oscillations it follows from Equations 9-13 and 9-25 that

$$\nu_r = \gamma + \ldots . \tag{9-26}$$

Thus, as ν_r changes appreciably with energy, in an FFAG cyclotron great attention must be given to the problem of resonances between radial oscillations and orbital motion. In particular, the integral resonance $\nu_r = 2$ limits the use of an FFAG cyclotron to energies less than that for which $\gamma \simeq 2$ ($T \simeq E_0$; for protons it is about 940 MeV). Nonintegral resonances (such as the one for which $\nu_r = 3/2$) can be crossed without destroying the beam, if the peak accelerating voltage is sufficiently high so that the resonance is crossed rapidly. A further limitation (which for simplicity we shall not describe) is

---

[4] It must be noted that from Equations 9-25 and 9-11 it follows that the momentum compaction in this case is $\alpha = \gamma^2$. Therefore, from the discussion in Sections 1-10 and 6-9 it can be seen that in an FFAG cyclotron the particles are always at the transition energy and hence there is no phase stability.

placed by the radial oscillations and is associated with the "alternating-gradient" nature of the magnetic field; it is required that

$$\nu_r < N/2. \tag{9-27}$$

As $\nu_r \simeq \gamma > 1$, it follows that the number of sectors in an FFAG cyclotron must be at least 3.

It must be noted that at the beginning of the acceleration the simplified theory given above is no longer valid because, for orbits near the center of the machine, R is appreciably different from r. However, in this region the effect both of the flutter and of the focusing associated with the angle ζ is very small because of the radial convergence ($r \to 0$). Thus in order to avoid the vertical instability, the magnetic field near the center of the machine is made to decrease slightly from the center outward without any azimuthal modulation, up to a certain value of r. Therefore, at the beginning of the acceleration the machine operates as a conventional cyclotron: later the particles encounter the azimuthal variation and the radial increase of the magnetic field and then the operation becomes of the type described in this chapter. Most of the FFAG cyclotrons presently (1966) in operation produce particles of different energies below 100 MeV; machines of even greater energy (of the order of some hundred million electron volts) have been considered. However, in this case the so-called "separated orbit cyclotron" (see the next section) seems to be the most convenient.

FFAG cyclotrons are nowadays built commercially for energies of about 10 MeV and currents of about 100 μA. These machines are used for medical and industrial purposes and they are much less expensive than comparable conventional cyclotrons.

9-6 THE SEPARATED ORBIT CYCLOTRON

The separated orbit cyclotron (SOC) is one of the most recent developments in the field of FFAG machines. It looks very promising as a high-energy, superhigh-intensity proton and ion accelerator.

The first idea of the SOC can be found in the work of F. M. Russell (1963),[5] but it has been somewhat modified in later studies. The version of SOC considered at present (see Livingston *et al.*, 1965) works along the following lines:

The accelerated particles circulate in a spiral-shaped vacuum chamber, which follows their equilibrium path. They traverse alternately a succession of fixed-frequency rf cavities and constant-field magnet sectors, located radially and symmetrically around the center of the machine (Figure 9-5a). Each of these units is traversed by the vacuum chamber several times. The rf

---

[5] An analogous idea had been proposed by J. W. Gallop (1953, 1957). However, strong focusing was not used and the particles were accelerated in a spiral waveguide.

cavities accelerate the particles, if their phases are suitably correlated; the magnetic field of the sectors keeps the particles on the equilibrium path. In order for acceleration to be achieved at each transit of the particles through the cavities, the time needed to pass from one cavity to the next must be the same along the entire trajectory (as in the cyclotron). Therefore, in order to compensate the relativistic increase of mass, the average magnetic field $\bar{B}_z$ must increase proportionally to γ from the inside outward, as in isochronous cyclotrons (see Equation 9-22). In order to secure stability of the beam, the

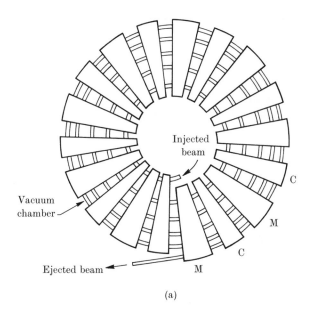

(a)

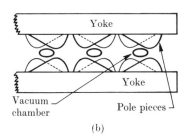

(b)

FIGURE 9-5. *Schematic diagram of a separated-orbit cyclotron.* (a) *Plan of the machine, showing the succession of alternating sector magnets (indicated by* M) *and rf cavities (indicated by* C). (b) *Side view of a sector magnet, showing the succession of pole pieces with opposite gradients at each orbit crossing.*

magnetic pole pieces are locally modified at each of the crossings with the vacuum chamber, so as to produce an AG structure. An example of a possible design for the magnets (Livingston *et al.*, 1965) is shown in Figure 9-5b. The radial magnet yokes embrace all the turns of the spiral, and pole pieces are attached to the yoke at the points where it is crossed by the trajectory. The pole pieces are designed so as to produce the succession of a strong positive field gradient and a negative one at a certain crossing of a magnet sector, and the opposite succession at the next crossing on the following magnet sector. With an odd number of magnet sectors, the two types of pole pieces alternate also along the radial direction, as shown in Figure 9-5b.

The AG structure thus obtained produces a strong focusing action, both radially and vertically. However, because of the unavoidable drift spaces between magnet sectors, the radius of the machine is larger than that of an FFAG cyclotron of the same energy.

It is expected that this machine will provide proton or ion beams of very high intensity; for present projects (Livingston *et al.*, 1965) average intensities up to 75 mA for proton energies up to 1 BeV are predicted. Indeed, such a machine allows continuous operation, like the isochronous cyclotron; with respect to the latter, it has the advantages of a much larger energy gain per turn (because of the large number of cavities traversed), of high-energy injection, which avoids the large beam losses occurring at low velocities, and of the elimination of the resonances between orbital motion and betatron oscillations, because the same region of magnetic field is never crossed twice. Moreover, such a machine can operate as a multiple-projectile, variable-energy accelerator. In order to obtain particles of different energies, one can think of extracting the beam at one of the intermediate turns of the spiral path.

The principle of operation of an SOC is very close to that of a linear accelerator. With respect to the latter, the SOC has the advantages of compact design, greater economy of rf power (because of the smaller number of cavities), continuous operation, and better definition of the beam, due to the strong transverse stability.

9-7 SPIRAL-SECTOR ANNULAR FFAG ACCELERATORS

Annular FFAG accelerators (synchrotrons and betatrons) are characterized by a ring-shaped magnet where the field is constant in time and has a distribution of the kind described in the previous sections; that is, it has a periodic azimuthal variation and it increases on the average from the inside outward. These accelerators can be divided into two classes:

1. spiral-sector accelerators;
2. radial-sector accelerators.

Although historically the latter were proposed earlier, we describe the spiral-sector accelerators (with special reference to the synchrotrons) first because these seem to be more convenient from a practical point of view.

The magnetic field structure of a spiral-sector annular accelerator, apart from some features which will be discussed later, is similar to that of the AVF cyclotrons described in the previous sections; the ring-shaped magnet of the machine can be considered as the outer part of the magnet of a large FFAG cyclotron with many sectors (see Figure 9-6). In such a machine we can again

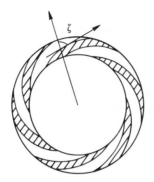

FIGURE 9-6.   *Diagram of the ridges on the pole face of a spiral-sector annular FFAG accelerator.*

speak of hills and valleys, which appear as a succession of ridges and troughs on the magnet poles. The considerations concerning particle stability remain the same as for the FFAG cyclotron. Again the magnetic field is given by the expression 9-7 and Equations 9-13 and 9-14 are still valid, giving the frequency ratios ν_r and ν_z in terms of the index k, the flutter function F (again defined by Equation 9-12) and the angle ζ between the spiral ridges and the radial direction. However, as the FFAG synchrotron is designed as a high-energy machine, k must be as large as possible in order to limit the width of the magnet and of the vacuum chamber. It can be seen from Equation 9-27 that, if k is large, the number of ridges N also must be large. Furthermore, in order to avoid resonances, we must abandon isochronism and keep k, F, and ζ constant so that also ν_r and ν_z are constant. A constant value of ζ entails the use of the logarithmic spiral for the shape of the ridges; that is, the function $g(r)$ appearing in Equation 9-16 must be chosen of the kind given by Equation 9-17. In order to compensate for the vertical instability associated with the very strong radial increase of the field, as F cannot be made too large (because of saturation where B_z is very high), the angle ζ is made large (even near to 90°) so that the shape of the spirals is of the kind shown in Figure 9-6.

As there is no isochronism, the frequency of the accelerating system must be modulated so as to follow the variation of the rotation frequency of the particles. Consequently in the FFAG synchrotron there is a synchronous particle (s.p.) and the problem of phase stability arises in a way similar to that in conventional AG synchrotrons. Thus the machine has a pulsed operation, with a period equal to the modulation period of the radio frequency; however, a much greater beam intensity is obtained than in conventional AG synchrotrons, because in the latter the repetition rate is determined by the variation of the magnetic field. A further increase of the intensity is due to the fact that particles which go out of phase are not generally lost but remain "stacked" in an orbit (within that of the s.p.), where they are no longer accelerated because they encounter an electric field which on the average is zero (for example, see the discussion of Section 1-9). During modulation of the frequency, one of the circulating bunches of this type may happen to be in synchronism with a harmonic of the fundamental frequency, and so it is again accelerated and proceeds further toward the outside until it again stops on an orbit of higher energy. Through this mechanism, repeated many times, also some of the particles initially out of the range of stable phases reach the end of the acceleration process.

The law of frequency modulation is essentially given by Equation 1-42, which can be written in the form

$$\frac{d\omega}{\omega} = -\frac{d\tau}{\tau} = -\left(\frac{1}{\alpha} - \frac{1}{\gamma^2}\right)\frac{dP}{P}.$$ (9-28)

As the momentum compaction α, given by Equation 9-11, is very large, it can be seen that $d\omega/\omega$ changes sign at the energy for which $\alpha = \gamma^2$ (the transition energy)[6] and it passes from positive to negative values. The frequency of the accelerating system must therefore first increase and then decrease after attaining a maximum at the transition energy. This fact usually reduces the required range of frequency modulation with respect to a conventional machine; furthermore the requirements of the rf system are simplified because the frequency modulation is no longer tied to the variation of the magnetic field and it can follow any assigned law.

Other technical advantages with respect to a conventional synchrotron are absence of eddy currents in the magnet and greater mechanical stability due to the fact that the magnet is not subject to the intense impulsive forces caused by the variation in time of the exciting currents.

The disadvantages of these machines are the complicated structure of the magnetic field and, above all, the much greater cost of the magnet with respect to a conventional AG machine of the same energy: for a 10-BeV proton synchrotron the circumference of the magnet is about 2 times greater and the

_____

[6] At this energy, the phase of the accelerating electric field must suddenly jump as in conventional AG synchrotrons, in order to preserve phase stability.

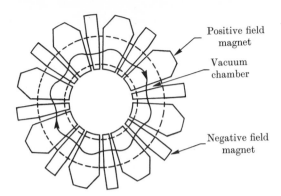

Positive field
magnet

Vacuum
chamber

Negative field
magnet

FIGURE 9-7.   *Plan of a radial-sector annular FFAG accelerator showing a typical orbit.*

weight about 10 times larger. This is the reason why machines of this kind have not yet (1966) been built. There exists only a 120-keV spiral-sector FFAG betatron (52-cm radius, 21-cm magnet width) built by MURA[7] with the aim of studying the orbits, in view of the possible construction of a larger machine (whose parameters are given in Table 9-1). It should be noted that in this project the doughnut is very wide (4 m). Usually straight sections are avoided in these machines because they would greatly complicate the design of the magnet.

9-8   RADIAL-SECTOR ANNULAR FFAG ACCELERATORS

In these machines the magnet consists of radial sectors where the magnetic field has alternate direction and increases in modulus from the center outward, according to the law

$$B_z = \pm B_0 \left(\frac{r}{r_0}\right)^k, \qquad (9\text{-}29)$$

with k constant and large (of the order of 100). Thus the trajectory bends alternately inward and outward (see Figure 9-7). If the sectors with negative field are shorter than the ones with positive field, the trajectory can be closed. It has been shown by T. Ohkawa (1958) that it is possible to obtain a closed trajectory even with "positive" and "negative" magnets of equal length. The magnets with negative field are required to ensure vertical stability. Indeed the magnetic field gradient, with respect to the machine center, is the same in all

---

[7] MURA (Midwestern Universities Research Association) is a pool of scientists of different universities of the United States who work mainly on the study of new techniques in the field of particle accelerators, and in particular of FFAG machines.

sectors, but with respect to the local center of curvature (which is alternately inside and outside the orbit) the gradient alternates and one can obtain an overall focusing effect both in the vertical and in the radial directions. Here again the calculation of the stability condition is very complex: we can again state that the frequency ratios ν_r and ν_z are approximately given by Equations 9-13 and 9-14 (with $\zeta = 0$) but the terms neglected [which are of the order of $(k/N)^2$] are more important than for the spiral-sector machines. The flutter function F can again be defined by means of Equation 9-12, where Φ is assumed to be a square-wave function of the angle θ only: this function is shown in Figure 9-8 for a particular case.[8]

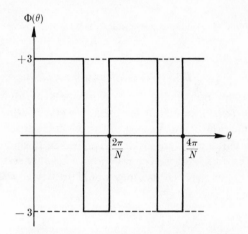

FIGURE 9-8. *The modulation function $\Phi(\theta)$ of the magnetic field in a radial-sector synchrotron where positive field magnets are twice as long as negative field magnets. Φ is normalized to 1 (see Equation 9-8 in the text). The flutter function F is equal to 8 in this case.*

The advantages of a radial-sector machine over a spiral-sector one are the much greater simplicity in the construction of the magnet and the possibility of inserting straight sections. However, as the trajectory continuously changes its curvature, the equivalent radius R is much larger than the radius of

[8] It must be noted that, when "positive" and "negative" magnet sectors have the same length, $\bar{B}_z = \bar{\Phi} = 0$, and, since Φ cannot be normalized to 1, the definition of F is uncertain by an arbitrary factor. This factor turns out to be infinite, if F is calculated as a function of the positive-to-negative sector length ratio, and this parameter is made to go to 1. In any case, it is true that a machine of this type has the greatest vertical stability.

TABLE 9-1.	*Parameters for a* 10-*BeV FFAG Proton Synchrotron*

	Radial-sector	Spiral-sector
Number of sectors, N	64	30
Field index, k	192.5	53
Injection energy	5 MeV	50 MeV
Injection radius	95 m	46 m
Final radius	97.3 m	50 m
Gap height at full energy	6 cm	15 cm
Frequency ratios ν_r, ν_z	21.7; 3.9	8.4; 7.2
Positive-to-negative sector length ratio	1.6	—
Spiral angle ζ	0	84.3°

curvature in each sector and the size and weight of the magnet required are prohibitive. It has been estimated that the magnet for a radial-sector proton synchrotron should have about 6 times the circumference and 15–20 times the weight of the magnet for a conventional AG synchrotron of the same energy (without straight sections). No machine of this kind has yet been built. A model has been put into operation at MURA: it is a 400-keV FFAG betatron and it is used for the study of orbits and of resonance effects, which are very severe in this machine too. In order to give an idea of the characteristics of a high-energy FFAG synchrotron, Table 9-1 gives a possible choice of the parameters for 10-BeV high-intensity proton machines of the radial-sector and spiral-sector types. These data are quoted in Livingston and Blewett (1962, pp. 632, 634), and have been taken from early studies performed at MURA. Such values have undergone some changes in more recent developments of the projects (see, for example, Cole, 1959; The MURA Staff, 1961a).

9-9   EXPERIMENTS WITH COLLIDING BEAMS

Up to the present point we have always referred to the "energy" of the accelerated particles without specifying the frame of reference in which this quantity is measured. Indeed we have always intended it to be the so-called "laboratory coordinate system" (LS), that is, the reference frame attached to the particle accelerator and to the building containing it. In this frame the target, with which the particles collide to produce nuclear reactions, is at rest. However, the energy available for the products of the nuclear reaction (that is the quantity we are essentially interested in) is more easily measured in a different reference frame, the so-called "center-of-mass coordinate system" (CMS), defined to be the reference frame where the net momentum of the two interacting particles (projectile and target particle) is zero.[9] All the energy measured in this frame is "available" for the products of the nuclear reaction and it makes up their mass and their relative motion. In the laboratory frame, instead, a large part of the energy is "wasted" in the motion of the center of mass (the net momentum), which, by the general principles of dynamics, is not modified by the occurrence of a nuclear reaction.

Therefore it is of interest to compute the total energy W in the CMS, that is, the "available" energy for a nuclear reaction occurring in a conventional accelerator (where a particle with rest energy E_{01} and kinetic energy T_1 collides with a particle of rest energy E_{02} at rest). A simple calculation of relativistic mechanics shows that

$$W = [2E_{02}\,T_1 + (E_{01} + E_{02})^2]^{1/2}. \qquad (9\text{-}30)$$

This quantity is always *less* than the total energy of the particles in the LS, given by $(T_1 + E_{01} + E_{02})$, and the difference increases with increasing T_1: at very high energies W is approximately equal to $(2E_{02}T_1)^{1/2}$. For example, with a proton as a target particle ($E_{02} = 938.2$ MeV), we find for incident protons of 3 BeV (Brookhaven Cosmotron) that $W = 3.025$ BeV, while for protons of 28 BeV (CERN proton synchrotron), $W = 7.486$ BeV.

A much larger energy in the CMS can be obtained if, instead of sending a beam against a target at rest, we make a beam collide against another beam moving in the opposite direction ("colliding beams" or "intersecting beams" experiments). In this case the energy in the CMS is of the order of magnitude of the beam energies. In particular, if the two beams consist of the same kind of particle at the same energy, the CMS coincides with the LS and the total energy in the CMS, W, is given directly by the sum of the total energies of the two particles. With reference to this case let us consider two colliding beams of particles of rest energy E_0 and kinetic energy T and let us find what energy T_1 is required in a conventional machine in order to produce the same energy in the CMS. As we have mentioned, in the case of colliding beams we have

$$W = 2(E_0 + T). \qquad (9\text{-}31)$$

If we equate this expression to the relation 9-30 (with $E_{01} = E_{02} = E_0$) and solve with respect to T_1, we obtain

$$T_1 = 2T\left(\frac{T}{E_0} + 2\right). \qquad (9\text{-}32)$$

Thus T_1 is a quadratic function of T and for ultrarelativistic energies is approximately equal to $2T^2/E_0$. This quantity can reach enormous values:

[9] In nonrelativistic mechanics this frame can be defined as a coordinate system attached to the center of mass of the bodies (and of constant orientation); hence the name also used in relativistic mechanics, where the interpretation is less direct.

for example, two colliding beams of 3-BeV protons correspond to $T_1 = 31.2$ BeV and beams of 28-BeV protons to $T_1 = 1780$ BeV. Even higher values of T_1 are obtained for electrons. In conclusion, with the use of colliding beams, the experiments on nuclear reactions can be extended to energies which are inaccessible to present conventional accelerator techniques.

However, the use of colliding beams presents an important practical drawback because the density of particles in a beam is always extremely small with respect to that existing in any solid or liquid target; thus the number of collisions per unit time is also extremely smaller. In the case of ordinary machines, the rate $\dot{\mathcal{N}}$ of a nuclear reaction whose cross section[10] is σ (for a machine with continuous operation) is given by

$$\dot{\mathcal{N}} = \sigma n N V v, \qquad (9\text{-}33)$$

where n is the density of the beam (number of particles per unit volume), N is the density of target particles, V is the useful target volume (product of the thickness of the target by the area of the beam cross section), and v is the velocity of the beam particles. In the case of two colliding beams, whose respective densities are n_1 and n_2 and particle velocities v_1 and v_2, we have (again for continuous operation)

$$\dot{\mathcal{N}} = \sigma n_1 n_2 V'(v_1 + v_2), \qquad (9\text{-}34)$$

where V', the "target volume," is the volume of the interaction zone where the two beams intersect, and is given by the product of the transverse section common to the beams and the length of the interaction region. With the proper choice of V', Equation 9-34 holds even if the beams intersect obliquely, as long as the collision angle is sufficiently small.

By comparing Equations 9-33 and 9-34, it can be seen that the reaction rate in a conventional machine is enormously larger than in a colliding-beam machine. The ratio of the two rates is of the order of N/n, that is, 10^{15} to 10^{17}, because the density of solid bodies is about 10^{24} particles/cm³ and the beam densities obtained in existing accelerators are about 10^7 particles/cm³ (this refers to high-energy machines; in general, larger densities can be obtained only at low energies, $\lesssim 100$ MeV). With the intensities at present available, an experiment with high-energy colliding beams would not give an observable reaction rate: higher intensities are required.

In principle, among the high-energy machines, the FFAG synchrotron seems the most promising for development in this direction. Indeed preliminary projects carried out at MURA show that reasonable reaction rates could be obtained with the beams of two 15-BeV spiral-ridge FFAG synchrotrons (with a common straight section) or with a radial-sector machine where

---

[10] For the definition of the cross section of a nuclear reaction, see for example Segrè (1964, p. 10).

positive and negative sectors have the same length (two-way accelerator; see Ohkawa, 1958). In the latter project (see Figure 9-9) it is possible to accelerate the same kind of particle in both directions, because of the complete symmetry of the machine, and there are as many intersection regions as there are straight sections between the magnets.[11] However, because of the enormous cost of the FFAG machines, these projects have been set aside, at least for the immediate future. Much consideration instead has been given to another possible way of obtaining high-intensity colliding beams: it involves the use of *storage rings* and it will be discussed in the following sections.

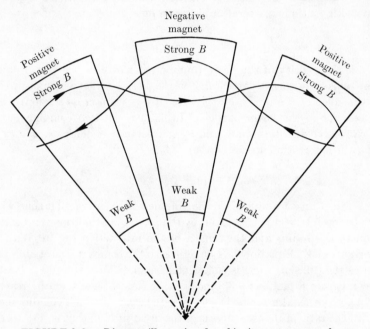

FIGURE 9-9. *Diagram illustrating the orbits in a two-way accelerator.*

9-10 THE PRINCIPLE OF OPERATION OF A STORAGE RING

A "storage ring" consists essentially of a doughnut-shaped vacuum chamber between the poles of an annular magnet, giving a magnetic field constant in time. As we shall see, a very good vacuum is required. A beam of particles that has been extracted from a conventional machine after acceleration to the required energy can be injected into this ring. If the particle momentum P,

---

[11] A model of this machine has been built at MURA for 40-MeV electrons (The MURA Staff, 1961b).

the radius of the doughnut R, and the magnetic field B satisfy the relation 1-17, the particles remain on an orbit of constant radius inside the doughnut without any further acceleration. Thus by "storing" the particles one can progressively increase the number of particles rotating in the ring, and so the beam density increases until values sufficient for colliding-beam experiments are reached. Such an experiment can be carried out essentially in two ways. In the first, two beams of the same kind of particle are stored in two separate rings and made to collide at some common point of the orbit, tangentially for example (see Figure 9-10). Both rings can be loaded from the same conventional machine, whose extracted beam is sent alternately into one and the other of the two rings by a deflecting system. This principle has been considered for electron-electron and for proton-proton collisions. For the first case, the most powerful machine operating at the present time (1966) is at Stanford, California, and involves the use of storage rings for 500-MeV electrons (see Section 9-12). In the USSR there is an operating machine for 130-MeV electrons at Novosibirsk (Bayer *et al.*, 1963; Budker, 1965, 1966), and another one for 100-MeV electrons is under construction at Kharkov (Walter *et al.*, 1963). For the second case, the only example of a machine under construction is the intersecting storage rings being built at CERN, Geneva, which have been planned for 28-BeV protons, supplied by the CERN proton synchrotron (see Section 9-12).

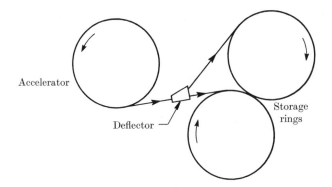

FIGURE 9-10. *Schematic diagram illustrating the use of tangential storage rings for colliding-beam experiments.*

The other way to obtain the collision of intersecting beams is to use a beam of particles and another of the corresponding antiparticles. These, in the same storage ring, follow the same orbits in opposite directions. Therefore only one storage ring is required, and into this the two beams are injected in opposite directions. Interactions can occur along the entire orbit. The only case in which this technique has been used so far is for electron-positron collisions. Preliminary experiments on proton-antiproton storage have been carried out at Novosibirsk, and a 25-BeV machine[12] is under construction (Bayer *et al.*, 1963; Budker, 1966). Electron-positron collisions were first studied at the Frascati National Laboratory (Rome) where a storage ring for 250-MeV electrons and positrons (called Ada) was built and put into operation. It has been used as a model for the design of a 1.5-BeV machine of the same kind (called Adone)[13] (see Section 9-12). Other machines based on the same principle are a 500-MeV storage ring operating at the Orsay Laboratory, France (The Orsay Storage Ring Group, 1963, 1965, 1966; Gendreau, 1964); a 700-MeV storage ring operating at Novosibirsk, USSR (Bayer *et al.*, 1963; Budker, 1965, 1966); and a 200-MeV AG storage ring, intended mainly for accelerator research, under construction at MURA (Rowe *et al.*, 1965, 1966). Three-billion-electron-volt machines also have been proposed in the USA (see, for example, Collins *et al.*, 1963; SLAC, 1963, 1964; Rees, 1966) and in Germany (Steffen, 1966). An interesting project being undertaken consists of the use of the 6-BeV Cambridge Electron Accelerator (CEA; see Table 1-3) as a 3-BeV electron-positron storage ring, without impairing the possibility of its working also as a conventional machine. This will be achieved by using a 130-MeV linac as injector (equipped with a positron source) and by observing the beam-beam collisions in an additional bypass section, which the beams will be made to traverse after the process of storage and acceleration up to the required energy has been completed. (See, for example, Robinson and Voss, 1966.)

Storage rings should not be considered as substitutes for a conventional machine yielding the same CM energy. In fact, the colliding-beams experiments are restricted to a few types of nuclear reactions, whereas a conventional machine, through the production of secondary beams (see Appendix 2), is a much more powerful and flexible tool of investigation. Storage rings are, in a sense, complementary to ordinary machines, insofar as they allow the observation of some basic elementary reactions to be pushed to regions of energy that, at present, seem otherwise technically inaccessible.

It should be noted that a storage ring is not necessarily used only for colliding-beam experiments. It can be used in parallel with the accelerator for reactions on a target at rest and this leads to a greater experimental flexibility. Changing the magnetic field enables particles of energy less than the maximum to be stored.

Before describing the machines mentioned above in greater detail, in the next section we shall introduce some general considerations on the operation of a storage ring (with one or two beams).

---

[12] A part of this machine will also be used for 3.5-BeV electron-positron collisions.

[13] The name Ada derives from the initials of the Italian expression "anello di accumulazione" (i.e., storage ring), while Adone means "large Ada" (i.e., large storage ring).

9-11 THE STRUCTURE AND TECHNICAL PROBLEMS OF STORAGE RINGS

If the beam circulating in a storage ring is to be used with profit its lifetime inside the ring must be sufficiently long (of the order of a few hours). The lifetime of a beam in a storage ring is limited primarily by collisions of the beam particles with molecules of the residual gas. The lifetime due to this cause is inversely proportional to the pressure in the doughnut; its value can easily be calculated from Equation 9-34, which is also valid for beam-gas collisions; in this case n_2 (the density of the residual gas) is proportional to the pressure (and $v_2 \simeq 0$). In order to obtain lifetimes of a few hours a vacuum of 10^{-9} mm Hg is necessary. In the "experimental" regions, this limit is further reduced, down to about 10^{-10} mm Hg, because the background of the beam-gas reactions must not swamp the beam-beam reactions to be observed. Such an ultra-high vacuum can be obtained by the use of better ion pumps and by a careful construction and baking of the doughnut in order to avoid gas emission from the walls. For an even better vacuum, which might be needed in certain experiments, liquid helium cryopumps have been proposed (Calder and Fischer, 1965).

It must be noted that the particles, as they move in the magnetic field, again carry out vertical and horizontal betatron oscillations, which follow the same law as in the other circular machines (see Section 4-5). The ring magnet must therefore be shaped in such a way as to ensure stability of the beam. As in conventional synchrotrons a weak-focusing structure or a strong-focusing one can be used. The latter has the advantage that it gives a high momentum compaction, that is, particles with a wide momentum spread can be stored in a small volume of space: as we shall see, this is important in the process of accumulation of the particles. An AG ring structure can be built either with high-field-index magnet sectors (as in AG synchrotrons) or by alternating focusing devices (such as quadrupole lenses; see Appendix 1) with magnetic sectors with uniform (or nearly uniform) field, which give the trajectory the required curvature. Of course, also in a storage ring care must be taken to avoid the resonances (see Section 5-7), and, in AG structures, to construct and align the magnets with the highest accuracy (see Section 6-8).

As they circulate in the storage ring, the particles lose energy by radiation (see Section 3-4). These losses are especially important for electrons and were they not compensated, the beam would rapidly spiral inward and be lost. Thus it is necessary to insert one or more rf cavities around the orbit; these at each turn supply the particles with the energy lost by radiation. For protons, at the present energies, the effect of radiation is negligible; however, in this case also, rf cavities are inserted in the machines, in order to facilitate the storage process (see later). As a consequence of the presence of the rf fields, the particles carry out phase oscillations and radial synchrotron oscillations (see Sections 5-2 to 5-5) and they bunch up into k bunches surrounding the respective synchronous particles (where the harmonic number k is the ratio between the cavity frequency and the rotation frequency; see Equation 5-6).

In conclusion, a storage ring can be defined as a (strong- or weak-focusing) synchrotron in which the magnetic field and the frequency do not change in time.[14] The quantity u (see Equation 5-18), which together with the value of the peak voltage U fixes the value of the synchronous phase φ_s through Equation 5-19, is determined essentially by the radiation losses. It is therefore large for electrons and very small for protons. Thus for protons $\sin \varphi_s$ is very near to 0. However, in electron machines, $\sin \varphi_s$ is also made rather small, that is, U is made sensibly larger than u. In this way the region of phase stability is wide, and particles are not lost owing to statistical fluctuations in the emission of radiation (that is, because of the emission of quanta of energy greater than the average value).

The bunching of particles produced by the radio frequencies is useful because it helps to increase the density of the colliding beams and hence also the reaction rate $\mathcal{N}$ (see Equation 9-34) for a given interaction volume. The length of the latter cannot exceed certain limits, mainly because of the problems of detection of the reaction products.

As new particles are successively injected into a storage ring, because of the condition of synchronism with the radio frequency, they join the particle bunches already circulating and hence the density of the latter increases. However, the density of the stored beam cannot increase above certain limits. An important limit is set by Liouville's theorem (see, for instance, Kennard, 1938, p. 343). According to this thorem, if we consider a bunch of particles whose equations of motion follow a Hamiltonian law, the volume of "phase space" occupied by the representative points of the particles is a constant during the motion. The volume of phase space $\Delta\Omega$ occupied by a particle bunch is given approximately (in Cartesian coordinates) by

$$\Delta\Omega = \Delta x \, \Delta y \, \Delta z \, \Delta P_x \, \Delta P_y \, \Delta P_z, \tag{9-35}$$

where $\Delta x, \Delta y, \Delta z$ represent the dimensions of the bunch and $\Delta P_x, \Delta P_y, \Delta P_z$ the spread of momenta in the three directions, x, y, z. New particles arriving in the ring cannot occupy a region of phase space already occupied by particles injected previously, and they must be stacked in another region of phase space available in the storage ring. Thus the number of pulses (that is, particle bunches) arriving from the accelerator which can be stored in the ring is limited to the ratio of the phase-space volume of the entire ring (determined by the physical volume of the vacuum chamber and by the range of momenta for which a particle is not lost) and the phase-space volume of one of the

[14] In some cases, as we shall see, it can be convenient to modulate the cavity frequency slightly (by a few percent).

pulses of the injected beam (determined by the amplitude of the longitudinal and transverse oscillations and by the range of momenta of the bunch at injection).

The actual density in phase space should be such as to produce the largest possible density in ordinary space. Generally, the beam size and momentum spread in the transverse directions are determined by particle oscillations: thus in the process of stacking successive pulses, an increase of space density can be obtained by allowing the longitudinal momentum spread to increase (compatibly with the conditions of acceptance of the rf cavity). It is, however, necessary that the accepted spread δP in longitudinal momentum cause a widening δR of the radial dimension of the beam, which is small compared to the amplitude of particle oscillations. Therefore, the ring should have a high momentum compaction (see Equation 1-39). For this reason it is convenient to use an AG structure. In the storage ring project at CERN for 28-BeV protons, the maximum number of pulses from the CERN proton synchrotron that can be accommodated in one of the rings is of the order of some hundreds.

The phase-space limitations set by Liouville's theorem are only important for protons. Indeed, for electrons, as a consequence of the strong dissipative forces associated with emission of the radiation, the equations of motion do not follow a Hamiltonian law and Liouville's theorem no longer holds. Because of the strong radiation the electron oscillations are rapidly damped, and the dimensions and the momentum spread of the beam decrease. The contraction of the beam is much greater in the vertical direction: in the radial direction indeed, owing to the recoil of the electron at the emission of each quantum of radiation, the width of the beam never becomes very small. The "natural" dimensions of a 250-MeV electron beam (that is, those determined only by the emission of radiation) are 1 or 2 mm in the radial direction and a few microns in the vertical direction. Thus the beam has the shape of a very flat ribbon. For protons instead, as the emission of radiation is very weak (and there is no relativistic increase of mass), the oscillations have practically no damping.

However, for electrons the density of the bunches is limited by other effects, which for protons are generally less important. They are essentially space-charge effects both between the two colliding beams and between particles of the same beam. The best known of these effects was first discovered in the Ada machine and it is known as the "Touschek effect," or the "Ada effect" (see Bernardini et al., 1963). Within a beam of electrons phenomena of electromagnetic scattering (Möller scattering) can occur between two particles traveling in the same direction (whose relative velocity is low, being essentially due to the radial motion). For small-angle scattering of the two particles in the CMS, the momenta in the laboratory system may be appreciably changed after the scattering and they may fall outside the acceptance region of the radio frequency. In this way, both particles are lost. Clearly this effect increases with the density n of the beam: it has been shown (Bernardini *et al.*, 1963) that the lifetime τ of the beam is influenced by this effect according to the law

$$\frac{1}{\tau} = \frac{1}{\tau_0} + n\alpha(E), \qquad (9\text{-}36)$$

where τ_0 is the lifetime due to other causes (such as gas scattering) and $\alpha(E)$ is a function strongly dependent on energy, which has a maximum at a rather low energy (70 MeV in Ada) and decreases rapidly with increasing energy. It is clear that, for a given energy, Equation 9-36 places a limitation on the value of n compatible with a desired lifetime. However, at high energies this limitation is not very severe. The Touschek effect is not important for protons as they have a much smaller cross section for electromagnetic scattering.

Besides the effect just described, other effects of electromagnetic nature can limit the density of the stored electron beams. Generally, such effects have been discovered first experimentally in the existing machines, and then interpreted theoretically; some of these phenomena are not yet well understood. A recent discussion about beam instabilities of electromagnetic nature can be found in Sessler (1965). We shall outline two of the most characteristic types of instability, namely, the so-called "resistive wall instability" and "negative mass instability."

The resistive wall instability is associated with a collective oscillation of the beam in the vertical direction. Such an oscillation, under proper conditions, may be enhanced by the forces due to the action of the charges induced on the metallic vacuum-chamber wall (Laslett *et al.*, 1965).

The negative mass instability, instead, is longitudinal, and happens only above the transition energy (that is, when $\gamma^2 > \alpha$; see Section 6-9). In this case, if a particle is accelerated, its revolution frequency decreases. The repulsive forces exerted by one particle of the beam on the neighboring ones of the same charge will accelerate those which are ahead, and decelerate those which lag behind; in both cases, the particles will show the tendency to accumulate together. Therefore, if the longitudinal charge distribution of the beam is inhomogeneous, this effect will tend to enhance the inhomogeneity, by clustering all the particles around the maxima of the charge distribution. For a discussion of the phenomenon and of the stability conditions, see Nielsen *et al.* (1959).

A further instability, which may occur at high beam intensity, is associated with the coupling between the charge of the bunches traversing the rf cavity and the cavity itself. Indeed, longitudinal charge oscillations induce in the cavity spurious electromagnetic oscillations, which may strongly perturb the motion of the beam. Such charge oscillations can be caused by coherent beam oscillations or by the process of injection into the storage ring.

It must be pointed out that all these effects are better known for electron beams than for proton beams, as far as the operation of storage rings is concerned, because experimental investigation has helped very much in the study of these phenomena. For protons, one can rely only on the indications of theory, which are sometimes of uncertain application. It is believed that the most serious instability for intersecting proton beams is caused by the direct electromagnetic interaction of the two beams.

Finally, we discuss the injection process and the use of the stored particles. As we have mentioned, the particle bunches are transferred from the accelerating machine to the storage ring through a fast ejection system and a deflecting system; the latter sends the particles onto a special orbit in the doughnut, the injection orbit, which is displaced from the orbit of the stored particles, the storage orbit. In correspondence with the injection orbit there is a magnetic inflector, which gives the particles a "kick" toward the central orbit of the doughnut. Then the bunches in a few turns reach the storage orbit; the slight change of radius required for this transfer is obtained by means of the accelerations or decelerations undergone by the bunches as they cross the rf cavity with a phase different from the synchronous phase. As the magnetic field is constant, an increase (decrease) of the particle energy leads to an increase (decrease) of the orbit radius. For electrons, inward spiraling is used by exploiting the radiation losses, not completely balanced by the rf cavity. Finally, the particles reach the storage orbit with the required synchronous phase, and their energy no longer changes.

In some cases, during the transition from the injection to the storage orbit, a slight frequency modulation (a few percent) of the cavity may be necessary. The inflector device must not disturb the motion of the bunches already injected; therefore it must have a structure that is open toward the center of the doughnut (see Figure 9-11) and it must be rapidly pulsed so that it operates only during the injection time.

In order to observe the reactions produced in the collision of the beams it is necessary to place the detectors very near the machine. We recall indeed that in a colliding-beam experiment the center-of-mass system essentially coincides with the laboratory system and therefore particles are emitted in all directions (whereas in conventional machines, because of the motion of the center of mass, all the reaction products are emitted, in the laboratory system, in the forward direction, within a very narrow cone). Usually the experimental region is placed in a straight section which must be sufficiently long (2 m or more at high energies) and free of auxiliary apparatus. As it has been observed that at high energies the reaction products in the center-of-mass system tend to follow the direction of the colliding beams, some of them will penetrate in the magnetic elements adjacent to the experimental zone. It may be convenient therefore, even if high-gradient elements are gener-·ally used in the machine, to use uniform (or nearly uniform) field magnets near the experimental zone so that these may also serve as analyzing magnets for small-angle reaction products. The focusing near these magnets is produced by means of quadrupole lenses (see Appendix 1).

A further problem concerns the measurement of absolute cross sections in a storage ring device. If the densities of the beams are known, the reaction cross sections can be deduced by a formula of the type 9-34 (where account must be taken of the discontinuous operation). However, the interaction volume V' is generally ill-defined experimentally. Therefore it is preferred to count simultaneously also the events from a reaction whose cross section is known to a certain accuracy (from other experiments, or from a reliable theory). The measurement of the rate of occurrence of such a reaction (monitor reaction) is equivalent to a measurement of the quantity V'; hence absolute cross sections can be derived. In electron machines, bremsstrahlung processes are generally chosen as monitor reactions, by counting the γ rays emitted in the direction of the two beams.

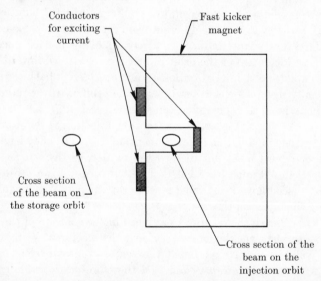

FIGURE 9-11. *Schematic cross section of the fast inflector showing the position of the beam at injection and on the storage orbit. For clarity, the doughnut wall is not shown.*

9-12   EXAMPLES OF STORAGE RINGS

In this section we describe some of the machines mentioned previously. Let us first consider the storage rings for electrons. For electron-electron collisions we shall refer to the tangential storage rings for 500-MeV electrons built at Stanford (O'Neill, 1959, 1961). Figure 9-12 shows the plan of the machine and

TABLE 9-2.   *Data Referring to Each of the Stanford Storage Rings for 500-MeV Electrons*

Beam current (1965)	50 mA	Peak voltage U	20 kV
No. of magnet sectors	4	Radiation loss per turn	4 keV
Sector radius	1.40 m	Synchronous phase	168°
Equivalent ring radius	1.88 m	Field index	0 and 1.1[a]
Magnetic field	1.2 Wb/m²	ν_r	0.77
Cavity frequency	25.4 Mc/sec	ν_z	0.88
Harmonic number, k	1		

[a]According to a pattern 0, 1.1, 0, respectively, in 1/4, 1/2, 1/4 of the length of the sector.

Table 9-2 some of the relevant data. In this machine the electrons are injected directly at the required energy and they are supplied by the "Mark III" 1-BeV linear accelerator. The rings are filled successively: the particles are injected at a radius larger than that of the central orbit, they lose energy by radiation, and they spiral inward until they reach the storage orbit. As can be seen from the table it is a weak-focusing device (ν_r, $\nu_z < 1$). In the experimental zone the collision of the beams occurs at a small angle (1° 45′); the particle detectors cannot measure reaction products at an angle less than 35°. In the experiments performed in 1965 (Barber *et al.*, 1965) the lifetime of the beam was ≈ 36 minutes, and the "luminosity" of the device (number of events observed per unit cross section and per unit time) was of the order of 10^{28} cm^{-2} sec^{-1}.

For the electron-positron storage rings, we shall describe the two projects of the Frascati laboratory, Ada (Bernardini *et al.*, 1960, 1961) and Adone (Amman *et al.*, 1963, 1965, 1966). As we have mentioned, Ada is the prototype

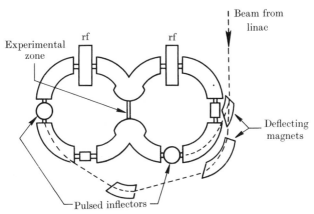

FIGURE 9-12.   *Schematic plan of the electron storage rings used with the Stanford Mark III linear accelerator.*

of machines of this kind. It has a circular structure, without straight sections, and a radius of 60 cm. It can store electrons or positrons at energies between 100 and 250 MeV. The weak-focusing ($n = 0.55$) ring magnet produces a maximum field of 1.4 Wb/m²; the harmonic number is $k = 2$. The stored beam density is low ($\lesssim 5 \times 10^7$ particles per beam when the ring is fed by the Orsay linac) owing to the low efficiency of the injection system. The electrons and positrons are produced by conversion when a target inside the storage ring is hit by γ rays produced by a conventional machine. Particles produced with the correct momentum are captured in the magnetic field and stored in the ring. In order to change from electrons to positrons it is necessary to displace and rotate the machine (see Figure 9-13). This operation, of course, must be carried out within the lifetime of the beam (which at 200 MeV and at a pressure of 10^{-9} mm Hg was measured to be about 6 hours). Because of the low intensity, Ada was not used to produce nuclear reactions, but rather as a model for the measurement of the behavior of the stored beams. Besides the discovery of the Touschek effect (see the previous section), Ada has also been used to develop methods of measuring the properties of the circulating beams. Research (Bernardini *et al.*, 1964) on the dimensions of the beam has shown that its height is much greater than the "natural" height (by a factor of 50: about 100μ instead of about 2μ). This effect is probably due to coupling between the radial and vertical oscillations and it may have great influence on the reaction rate.

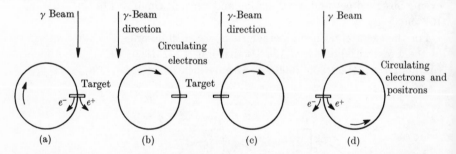

FIGURE 9-13. *Diagram illustrating the storage of particles in Ada:* (a) *storage of electrons;* (b) *displacement of the ring to the right by one diameter;* (c) *rotation of the ring about its axis by* 180°; (d) *storage of positrons.*

The project Adone (for 1.5-BeV electrons and positrons) involves a system of large dimensions (see Figure 9-14). Strong focusing with separate functions (weak-focusing bending magnets, plus quadrupole lenses) is used and the momentum compaction is large. Table 9-3 gives some data referring to this machine. Electrons and positrons are injected successively into the ring from a linear accelerator which can accelerate both kinds of particle (with a

TABLE 9-3. *Adone Storage Ring Project for 1.5-BeV Electrons and Positrons at the Frascati Laboratory*

No. of stored particles per beam	2.10^{11}	Magnetic field at injection	0.24 Wb/m²
Beam current	100 mA	Magnetic field at full energy	1.0 Wb/m²
No. of magnetic sectors	12	Cavity frequency	8.6 Mc/sec
Sector radius	5 m	Harmonic number k	3
Equivalent ring radius	16.7 m	Peak voltage U	4×50 kV
Injection energy	375 MeV (e⁻) / 360 MeV (e⁺)	Magnetic field index, n	0.5
		$\nu_r,\ \nu_z$ (variable)	≈ 3.2
Final energy	1500 MeV	Momentum compaction	16.3

much lower current for the positron beam of course; see Section 8-1). The injection energy is high (360 MeV) but lower than the final energy of the particles. Once the two beams have been stored in the ring with the required intensity they are further accelerated by slowly increasing the magnetic field. As the variation of the magnetic field is very slow compared with the rotation

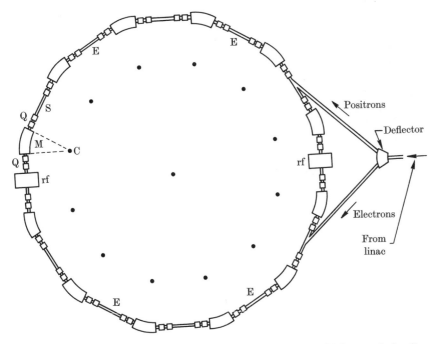

FIGURE 9-14. *Plan of the Adone electron-positron storage ring. M denotes the bending magnets; Q, the quadrupole lenses; S, the straight sections; E, the experimental regions; C, the centers of curvature of the bending magnets.*

frequency, at each turn the energy gained by the beams is a very small fraction of the energy supplied to compensate the radiation losses (and it is neglected in the design of the rf system). Thus the synchronous phase φ_s "slips" adiabatically and it decreases from values near π (at injection $U \gg u$; see Section 9-10) toward smaller values: the particle bunch follows the phase variation and the energy gradually increases.

The magnet does not need to be built up with thin laminations, because all eddy-current effects are negligible. Two double rf cavities are used simultaneously in order to provide against the chance of one of them having a short interruption of the operation. With only one cavity, even a very short break would lead to the loss of the beam (because of the large radiation loss which is normally compensated by the cavity), and the rather long time required for storing the particles would be wasted.[15]

In principle the beams can produce experimental results at all energies from the injection energy to the maximum. Thus experiments at different energies can be carried out in a single run: the rise of the magnetic field is arrested at the required intermediate energies for the time necessary to obtain a sufficient number of experimental data. With 100-mA beams circulating in both directions and a vacuum of 10^{-9} mm Hg the expected lifetime of the beam is between 5 and 10 hours, and the expected luminosity is of the order of 10^{33} cm^{-2} hr^{-1}.

Finally, we describe the CERN project of a storage ring for 28-BeV protons, as an example of a proton machine (De Raad, 1962; Johnsen et al., 1963; Johnsen, 1965b, 1966). In this case too, as in the Stanford machine for electrons, two rings are required, but in the CERN project these are nearly overlapping and cross at many points (see Figure 9-15) so that they can be contained in a single building, and furthermore there are many experimental zones. The structure of each ring is similar to that of the CERN proton synchrotron (PS), for which some data are given in Table 1-3; however, because of the large number of straight sections required, the radius is greater (by a factor 1.5). Alternating-gradient magnets are used, separated by straight sections of different lengths, and also auxiliary focusing devices, such as quadrupole lenses (Appendix 1), are used. Some data referring to this machine are given in Table 9-4. The technical problems for this machine are rather different from those occurring in electron storage rings. At the injection, which occurs directly at the storage energy, the phase-space of the ring must be filled to the largest possible extent (see Section 9-10) so as to reach the greatest density. It is therefore necessary that a bunch leaving the PS reach the rf cavity of the ring without spreading and be contained as tightly as possible within the zone of stable phases ("bucket") corresponding to the required syn-

---

[15] The storing time is about half an hour. This value is essentially due to the low positron current supplied by the linac, and it includes the time required for adjusting the linac from electron to positron acceleration.

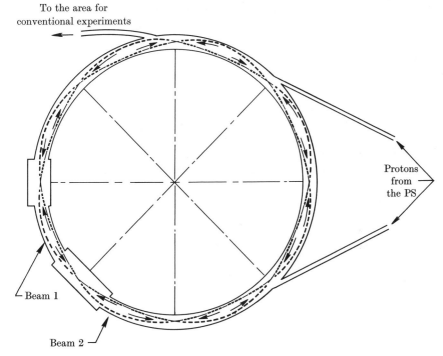

To the area for
conventional experiments

Protons
from
the PS

Beam 1

Beam 2

FIGURE 9-15. *Schematic plan of the storage rings for 28-BeV protons of the CERN
project. The dashes along the orbits indicate magnet sectors.*

TABLE 9-4. *CERN Storage Ring Project for 28-BeV Protons.
Data Refer to Each Storage Ring*

No. of stored particles	4×10^{13}	Equivalent ring radius	150 m
	4×10^{14} [a]	Maximum field	1.2 Wb/m²
Beam current	2–20 A [a]	Cavity frequency	9.55 Mc/sec
Equivalent number of		Harmonic number k	30
pairs of sectors	48 [b]	Peak voltage U	20 kV
Number of intersections	8	Field indices, n_1, n_2	238; −249
Intersecting angle of the		$\nu_r \ (= \nu_z)$	8.75
beams	15°	Momentum compaction	75
Sector radius	79.2 m	Transition energy E_t	8.5 BeV

[a] According to the tolerance allowed in the longitudinal momentum. The first value
refers to a tolerance of 0.2%, the second to a tolerance of 2% (for an energy of 28 BeV).

[b] As can be seen from the scheme of Figure 9-15, magnets of two different lengths
are used, one twice as long as the other. The number given in the table is obtained by
considering two "short" magnets equivalent to one "long" magnet, and gives the
number of pairs of such long magnets.

chronous phase.[16] For this purpose the rf circuits of the PS and of the rings must be locked together so as to ensure a precise synchronism. The difference in the period of rotation due to the different sizes is compensated by the fact that the harmonic number k is different and proportional to the radius. The parameters of the machine have been chosen so that the transition energy falls outside the useful energy range for storage (10–28 BeV).[17] Therefore the choice of ν_r, ν_z is limited to a rather narrow range. In this project with a vacuum of 10^{-9} mm Hg and beam intensities of a few amperes, a beam lifetime not less than about 12 hours is expected. The beam stored in one of the rings can also be used for conventional experiments (against a fixed target) and for these a separate experimental zone is planned.

[16] The region of space limited by one of the curves of Figure 6-7 (considered to be in motion together with the corresponding synchronous particle) is called a "bucket." Of course these buckets can be considered to be circulating in the machine even when there are no particles, and a bunch entering the machine may fit one of them more or less tightly.

[17] Within this energy range, the energy of each of the beams can be varied independently.

APPENDIX 1

THE MAGNETIC QUADRUPOLE LENS

A magnetic lens is a device which, by means of a magnetic field, acts on a beam of charged particles similarly to the way an optical lens acts on a beam of light; that is, it changes the convergence of the beam but not its principal direction.

The simplest type of magnetic lens is the one which uses a magnetic field nearly parallel to the motion of the particles (such as the field produced by a solenoid). This kind of lens is always converging and its focal length is proportional to the square of the momentum of the particles. Although this kind of lens is sometimes used in accelerators (linacs, for instance), for high-energy beams and with the magnetic fields obtainable in practice the focal length becomes so large that such lenses cannot be used where focusing in a short distance is required.

A different kind of lens, proposed by E. D. Courant, M. S. Livingston, and H. S. Snyder (1952), has a magnetic field transverse to the beam and hence for a given intensity the focusing effect is much greater. These lenses can therefore also be used for high-energy particles. In fact, they are widely used both in accelerators (in the straight sections of the synchrotrons and in linacs) and in auxiliary systems for the transport of the secondary beams to the experimental areas (see Appendix 2).

The principle of operation of this lens is the same as is used in AG synchrotrons (indeed it was proposed in the same paper as the AG principle) and it can be briefly explained as follows: In one lens a transverse magnetic field produces a strong focusing effect in the horizontal direction, for instance, and hence defocusing in the vertical direction; this lens is followed by a second one which is strongly focusing in the vertical direction and defocusing in the horizontal. The net effect of the doublet, as we shall show, is focusing in both directions.

In order to treat the operation of a magnetic lens in greater detail, let us introduce a system of coordinates s, x, z, where the s axis is in the direction of the unperturbed trajectory (the axis of the beam), and the x and z axes are in the horizontal and the vertical directions, respectively. In regions of space where there are no currents (nor displacement currents) the magnetic field **B** can be derived as the gradient of a "magnetic potential" V. Indeed, in these regions it is

$$\text{curl } \mathbf{B} = 0, \qquad \text{div } \mathbf{B} = 0. \tag{A1-1}$$

From the first equation, it follows that we can write $\mathbf{B} = \text{grad } V$; from the second, we see that V must satisfy Laplace's equation

$$\nabla^2 V = 0. \tag{A1-2}$$

The simplest magnetic lens of the kind described is the *linear quadrupole lens* where the potential $V(s, x, z)$ is of the form

$$V(s, x, z) = G(s)xz, \tag{A1-3}$$

and only small displacements from the unperturbed trajectory are considered, so that second-order terms in x and z can be neglected. In this approximation the function A1-3 satisfies Equation A1-2 and the component $B_s = \partial V/\partial s \approx 0$. Furthermore we have

$$B_x = \frac{\partial V}{\partial x} = G(s)z, \qquad B_z = \frac{\partial V}{\partial z} = G(s)x. \tag{A1-4}$$

The equations of motion (under the action of the Lorentz force only) are the following:

$$m_v \ddot{s} = 0,$$
$$m_v \ddot{x} = qvB_z, \tag{A1-5}$$
$$m_v \ddot{z} = -qvB_x.$$

Here v indicates the s component of the particle velocity; v practically coincides with the entire velocity and it will be considered to be a constant ($\dot{x}, \dot{z} \ll v$ and the forces which tend to change $\dot{s}$ are of second order in x, z); the relativistic mass m_v is also a constant. If we substitute Equations A1-4 into Equations A1-5 we obtain

$$m_v \ddot{x} = qvG(s)x, \tag{A1-6}$$

$$m_v \ddot{z} = -qvG(s)z. \tag{A1-7}$$

Thus it can be seen that the particle is subject in one of the two directions x and z to a restoring force, and in the other direction to a repulsive force, and that both forces are linear in the displacement (hence the name "linear lens"). From Equation A1-3 it can be seen that in the planes $s = \text{const}$ the equipotential lines are equilateral hyperbolas. On the other hand (if we neglect the permeability of air or of a vacuum, in comparison with that of iron), the pole surfaces of the magnet producing the field must be equipotentials, so they must be hyperbolic cylinders. Then the shape of the magnet is as shown in Figure A1-1, where N, S indicate the north and south polarity of the poles corresponding to a choice of values of $V(s, x, z)$ equal and opposite, $\pm V_0$. It can be seen that the resulting lens has four poles (hence the name "quadrupole lens"); more complicated (nonlinear) lenses are obtained with a larger number of poles (six or eight, for instance). In practice the cross section of a quadrupole lens has the shape shown in Figure A1-2. The exciting coils

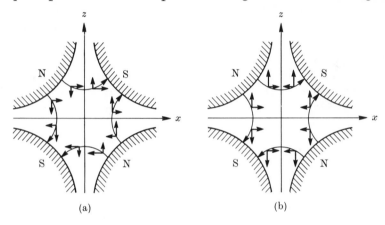

FIGURE A1-1. *Diagram of a quadrupole field showing* (a) *the components of the magnetic field;* (b) *the components of the Lorentz force produced by this field. There is focusing in the horizontal direction.*

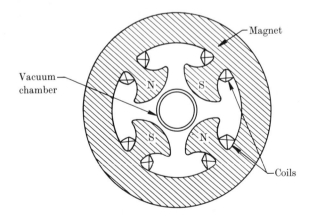

FIGURE A1-2. *Schematic diagram of the cross section of a magnetic quadrupole lens*

are usually connected in series but wound in opposite directions on poles N
and S. The hyperbolic profiles are usually approximated by circles.

The function

$$G(s) = \frac{\partial B_x}{\partial z} = \frac{\partial B_z}{\partial x} \tag{A1-8}$$

is called the "gradient" of the lens and it determines the properties of the lens
completely. The case usually considered is the one of an ideal lens (of length
L) where $G(s)$ is equal to a constant, G, inside the lens, for $(s_0 - L/2) < s$
$< (s_0 + L/2)$, and zero outside (see Figure A1-3a). In practice this cannot
be obtained exactly, because of the unavoidable edge effects, and the function
$G(s)$ has a shape of the kind shown in Figure A1-3b (the precise shape is determined by means of electrolytic tank measurements). In the calculations this
function is approximated by a function of the kind shown in Figure A1-3a,
and an effective length of the lens is defined by requiring that the approximating curve and the actual curve have the same peak value and that they
enclose the same area; the effective length is usually greater than the physical
length. Values of G of about 1–1.5 kG/cm over an aperture of about 10 cm
can be obtained in practice.

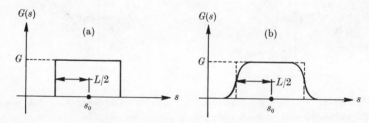

FIGURE A1-3.   *Diagram of the gradient $G(s)$ for* (a) *an ideal lens;* (b) *a real lens.*

In studying the effect of a quadrupole lens on particle motion it is very useful
to consider the analogy which exists (and can be rigorously proved) between
the trajectory of a charged particle across one of these lenses and the path of
a light ray across a thick optical lens. As for an optical lens, for a quadrupole
lens it is possible to define the principal planes and the focal length, separately
for the motion in the xs and zs planes. In general the focal lengths and
the positions of the principal planes differ in the two cases. Indeed, it can
be shown that, given a point P near the axis of the lens, there is always an
image point Q_x of P with respect to the lens for the xs plane such that after
the trajectories cross the lens, the directions of all of them passing through P
and lying in the xs plane converge in Q_x. Similarly there is an image point Q_z
of P for the zs plane and in general Q_x and Q_z do not coincide.

For simplicity, we here treat only the limiting case where the length L of the lens is small with respect to the focal length f (thin lens approximation). In this case, as in conventional optics, a trajectory parallel to the s axis and displaced (for instance) in the x direction (see Figure A1-4), after crossing the lens, will still be at the same distance x_0 from the axis (to first order in L), but its direction will be changed by an angle α (measured in the anticlockwise direction). We now show that in this approximation the direction of the trajectory after the lens always intersects the axis at the same point F (image of the point at infinity) whatever the value of x_0. The distance (with its sign) $OF = f_x$ is precisely the focal length of the lens (for the xs plane) which we shall now determine.[1]

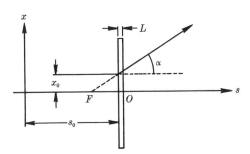

FIGURE A1-4. *Diagram of a trajectory in a thin (diverging) lens. OF is the focal distance.*

If we denote differentiation with respect to s by a prime, and observe that $x'' = \ddot{x}/v^2$ and $m_v v = P$, the constant momentum of the particle, we can write Equation A1-6 in the form

$$x'' = \frac{qG(s)}{P}\, x. \qquad (A1\text{-}9)$$

Assuming now for $G(s)$ the ideal shape of Figure A1-3a, and integrating this equation over the lens (from $s_1 = s_0 - L/2$ to $s_2 = s_0 + L/2$), we obtain

$$x'(s_2) - x'(s_1) = \tan\alpha = \int_{s_1}^{s_2} x''\, ds = \frac{qG}{P}\int_{s_1}^{s_2} x\, ds = \frac{qGx_0L}{P}, \quad (A1\text{-}10)$$

because in the lens $x \approx \text{const} = x_0$. From figure A1-4 it can be seen that $f_x = -x_0/\tan\alpha$ (in value and sign), and therefore from Equation A1-10 we have

$$f_x = -\frac{P}{qGL}, \qquad (A1\text{-}11)$$

[1] It can be shown that in the thin lens approximation the principal planes of the lens coincide with its median plane to first order in L/f_x.

which does not depend on x_0. For the z direction one finds in a similar way a focal length f_z which is equal and opposite to f_x:

$$f_z = \frac{P}{qGL}. \tag{A1-12}$$

If $qG > 0$, then $f_x < 0$ and we have precisely the case of an x-diverging lens illustrated in Figure A1-4. The same lens is, of course, a z-converging one.

It is now easy to show that a system of two coupled quadrupole lenses, one of which is converging in the xs plane and the other converging in the zs plane, is converging in both planes. Indeed, given two thin lenses of focal distances (in a given plane) f_1 and f_2, placed at a distance a, it is easily proved as in conventional optics that the focal distance F of the system (in the same plane) is given by

$$\frac{1}{F} = \frac{1}{f_1} + \frac{1}{f_2} - \frac{a}{f_1 f_2}. \tag{A1-13}$$

In the case of two equal quadrupole lenses rotated by 90°, for both directions we have $f_1 = -f_2 = f$ and then

$$F = \frac{f^2}{a} > 0, \tag{A1-14}$$

where f is given by the right-hand side of Equation A1-11 or A1-12. In practice the thin lens approximation can only be used to give a first evaluation of the effect. A satisfactory treatment can be obtained by considering also second-order terms in L. In general it can be shown that the thin lens approximation overestimates the focusing effect of the system. As for optical lenses, also for magnetic lenses it is possible to define different kinds of aberrations. For example, the dependence of the focal length upon particle momentum (see Equations A1-11 and A1-12) corresponds to the chromatic aberration; the distortion of the trajectories crossing the lens far from the axis corresponds to the spherical aberration.

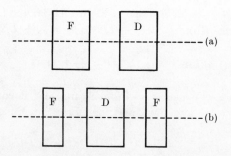

FIGURE A1-5. *Diagram of the succession of lenses used* (a) *in a doublet;* (b) *in a triplet. Lenses which are focusing (e.g. in the xs plane) are indicated by* F; *defocusing ones by* D. *For the zs plane the symbols* F *and* D *must be interchanged.*

Finally it must be noted that the use of a quadrupole doublet consisting of a focusing and a defocusing lens does not produce symmetrical effects in the x and z directions: the angular magnification and the total focal length are different in the two directions. This means that a doublet is astigmatic and it focuses a vertical line at one position and a horizontal line at another. In order to reduce these effects, which are usually undesired, a triplet is used (see Figure A1-5). The triplet can be thought of as derived from a doublet by dividing one of the elements into two parts and placing the other element between them. With a careful choice of the length and gradient in each element of a triplet it is possible to correct the astigmatism and some of the other aberrations of the lens.

APPENDIX 2

THE TRANSPORT OF
SECONDARY BEAMS

A2-1 INTRODUCTION TO SECONDARY-BEAM TRANSPORT

The nuclear reactions studied in experiments in high-energy accelerators are not produced directly with the primary beam accelerated by the machine, but with secondary beams which are obtained by collision of the primary beam with an internal target, and which are extracted from the machine and guided into the experimental zone. Modern accelerators can produce secondary beams of a satisfactory intensity, even if it is smaller by some orders of magnitude than the primary beam intensity. The intensity of a secondary beam, however, depends not only on the intensity of the primary beam, but also on the so-called *transport system* which guides the beam to the experimental area, sometimes rather far from the machine. Thus the study and improvement of the techniques of beam transport over long distances are very important in order to make good use of the possibilities of a high-energy accelerator.

The secondary beams produced by an accelerator can be divided into two distinct classes: those consisting of charged particles and those consisting of neutral particles. In the latter case it is difficult to control the beam; indeed the neutral particles cannot be selected, guided, or focused in any way. Thus a neutral beam travels in a straight line; its cross section and its angular spread are defined by slits and collimators. One or more sweeping magnets are placed along the trajectory in order to remove the charged particles. Usually a beam of neutral particles has a broad energy spectrum, an appreciable angular spread, and a strong contamination of undesired particles.[1] In order to reduce the latter, selective absorbers which remove a certain component of the background may be used (for example, lead shields to eliminate γ rays). However, a part of the background always reaches the experimental apparatus, so that the detectors must be able to discriminate between the "desired" and "undesired" events.

Beams of charged particles instead can be guided and controlled along the entire trajectory by means of electric and magnetic fields. Thus much more stringent requirements can be placed on charged-particle beams than on neutral-particle beams. The theory of beam transport refers precisely to charged-particle beams, and this is the case which will be considered in the following.

A secondary beam of charged particles is defined by assigning the characteristics it is required to have in the experimental zone. They refer to the following points:

1. the kind of particle required and the maximum tolerable contamination;
2. the beam energy and the maximum tolerable energy spread;
3. the maximum tolerable angular spread;
4. the particle flux (in particles per pulse) and the pulse length.

It must be noted that the selection of a given kind of particle (separated beam) is not always required; in many experiments, in order to have a greater intensity, the beam is only analyzed in momentum and the detector system is left to discriminate between "good" and "bad" events. In general the secondary-beam characteristics required can be very different according to the experiment. For bubble-chamber experiments a low flux is required (of the order of 10 particles per pulse) and one needs a good definition of the beam in energy and direction, a low contamination, and a short pulse length. For experiments using systems of counters as detectors the main requirement is a large intensity, that is, a high flux (up to 10^6 particles per pulse) and a long pulse length. For this purpose other requirements are made less stringent; for example, a larger energy spread may be accepted.

The transport system consists of a succession of many elements which have different purposes and which are placed at the correct positions along the trajectory to be followed by the beam from the internal target to the experimental zone. The elements constituting a transport system are the following:

1. slits and collimators which define the cross section and the direction of the beam and also eliminate a large part of the background;
2. bending magnets, which define the electric charge and the momentum of the particles;

---

[1] There is no contamination only in the case of γ-ray beams produced in electron machines by collision of the primary beam against a target.

3. focusing devices, in particular magnetic quadrupole lenses (see Appendix 1) or lenses of other kinds;

4. electrostatic separators, which are used to separate a certain kind of particle in a beam of given momentum.

The bending magnets are high-field magnet sectors which deflect particles of different momentum in different directions. They are usually followed (see Figure A2-1) by a collimator, which defines the accepted momentum range and excludes other particles. In general, in order to keep a good definition and purity of the beam, it is convenient to use more than one of these elements in order to remove spurious particles formed in the beam during the transit (decay products of unstable particles, particles scattered from the edges of the collimators, and so on). Further details on the construction of bending

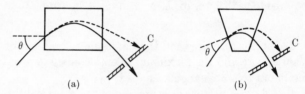

(a)   (b)

FIGURE A2-1. *Plan of a bending magnet of rectangular shape* (a) *and of sector shape* (b), *showing typical trajectories of particles of desired momentum (solid line) and undesired momentum (dotted line) selected through the collimator* C. *Usually the angle of incidence* θ ≠ 0, *and particles of required momentum are made to follow a symmetrical trajectory in the magnet.*

magnets are given in Section A2-3. Among the focusing devices, doublets or triplets of quadrupole lenses are used most commonly because they are linear systems (see Appendix 1 and the next section) and so it is simple to compute the beam trajectory. In some cases (to correct aberrations, for instance) non-linear lenses may be used. The separators select the particles of the beam on the basis of their velocities. If the beam has already crossed a momentum analyzer, this velocity selection is equivalent to selection of the mass and thus of the kind of particle. The electrostatic separators are usually parallel plate capacitors (some meters in length), and a strong electric field E normal to the particle motion is established between the plates. Particles having different velocities are deflected by different amounts in the direction of the electric field. Sometimes a magnetic field B is added, normal both to the motion and to the electric field, and its value is adjusted in such a way that particles having the required mass and momentum are not deflected, because the electric and magnetic forces are equal and opposite. These particles have a velocity given by

$$v = \frac{E}{B}.$$ (A2-1)

The resulting magnetic fields are usually very low (of the order of a few hundred gauss). For highly relativistic particles, where separators of great length and high voltages must be used, the presence of a magnetic field seems to encourage the onset of breakdown discharge. For this reason in recent designs only electric fields are used in the separator, and this is followed by a separate magnet which corrects the bending effect produced by the electric field.

In a beam transport system the "axis" of the system is the trajectory of a particle of the required kind emitted from the target with the correct momentum tangential to the axis itself. However, the beam also contains particles of the desired kind emitted from the target with small deviations from the axis and with a momentum slightly different from the correct one. It is necessary that these particles not be lost in crossing the system. Hence the concept of "beam stability" (entirely similar to the one introduced for the betatron and for the synchrotron) can be defined, and we see the necessity of computing the actual particle trajectories through the system, at least approximately.

A2-2   THE PARTICLE TRAJECTORIES IN THE BEAM TRANSPORT SYSTEM

The analysis of the particle trajectories in a beam transport system can be treated in a manner similar to the one used for the circular machines (see Chapters 4 to 6). We assume a system of coordinates s, x, z, where s is the distance measured along the axis of the system, and the x and z axes are contained in a plane normal to the unperturbed trajectory, and are oriented in the horizontal and vertical directions, respectively. We assume that the particles are not accelerated in the longitudinal direction, so that $\dot{s} = v =$ const, and furthermore we only consider small displacements from the axis of the system and small angles of the trajectories with this axis. Thus we neglect second-order terms in x, z, $(\dot{x}/v)$, and $(\dot{z}/v)$. The relativistic mass m_v of the particles is therefore considered as a constant because its variation is given by terms of the order of $(\dot{x}/v)^2$ and $(\dot{z}/v)^2$.

With this hypothesis it can be shown that, for all the elements of a transport system (with the exception of nonlinear magnetic lenses, which will not be considered here), the motion in the x direction is uncoupled from the motion in the z direction (to first order) in the same way as we have seen for the case of the synchrotron. As we have done for the AG synchrotron we can completely describe the motion in the zs plane, for example, by giving the distance z from the axis and the inclination $z' = dz/ds$ for each value of s. These two quantities can be represented by a two-component vector $\boldsymbol{u}(s)$, like the one we have introduced through Equation 6-51:

$$\boldsymbol{u}(s) = \begin{bmatrix} z \\ az' \end{bmatrix}. \qquad \text{(A2-2)}$$

The same convention will be used for the choice of the arbitrary constant a as in Chapter 6. For a given element of the system (including the sections without fields, between the actual elements, which are similar to the straight sections of a synchrotron), let us determine the relation between the values of u at the entrance and at the exit of the element. We shall indicate these values with the subscripts 1 and 2 and call s_1 and s_2 the corresponding abscissas. We are concerned with the *linear* case, for which this relation can be expressed by the following generalization of Equation 6-55 (or 6-59),

$$u_2 = \Gamma u_1 + p, \tag{A2-3}$$

where the matrix Γ (of order 2), and the vector p are independent of z, and only depend on s through the length l of the path through the element, $l = s_2 - s_1$. Of course, a relation of the kind of Equation A2-3 holds separately for the xs and zs planes with different expressions for Γ and p. If the transport system is designed so that particles having the required momentum and mass follow the axis of the system ($u \equiv 0$), for these particles we must have $p = 0$ for each element of the system. Values of p different from zero are possible only for particles of momentum (or mass) different from the one for which the selectors (bending magnets or electrostatic separators) are adjusted.[2]

We now verify that Equation A2-3 is satisfied by all the kinds of elements considered. For a (focusing) magnetic sector we have already found the expression for Γ: it is given by Equation 6-53.[3] The vector p is always equal to zero except in the xs plane for particles having a momentum differing by ΔP from the required value P_0. From the equation of motion it can be shown that, in this case,

$$p = \frac{\Delta P}{P_0 R k^2} \begin{bmatrix} 1 - \cos kl \\ ka \sin kl \end{bmatrix}, \tag{A2-4}$$

with the same notation as in Section 6-4 (see, for example, Banford, 1966, Section 5.1.8). If the direction of incidence of the trajectory is not normal to the edge of the magnet (see Figure A2-1), it is necessary to consider the effect of the focusing at the edges, which has been discussed in Section 6-11.

For a region without field, Γ is given by Equation 6-58, derived for the straight sections of a synchrotron, and $p = 0$.

For a thin quadrupole lens the parameters of Equation A2-3 can easily be

[2] For electrostatic separators alone, always $p \neq 0$ in the vertical direction (see later); however, it is possible to get $p = 0$ for the required particles by adding a transverse magnetic field, whose value is defined by Equation A2-1.

[3] In the common case of constant-field magnets (see the next section), for the motion in the vertical direction the magnet is similar to a region without field.

computed; indeed, from the treatment given in Appendix 1 it follows that (with the meaning given above for the indices 1 and 2)

$$z_2 = z_1,$$

$$z'_2 = z'_1 - z_1/f. \quad (A2\text{-}5)$$

Thus it can be seen that $p = 0$ and the expression for Γ is

$$\Gamma = \begin{bmatrix} 1 & 0 \\ -\dfrac{a}{f} & 1 \end{bmatrix}. \quad (A2\text{-}6)$$

The determinant of this matrix (and of the previous ones) is equal to 1 and Equation A2-6 holds for both the xs and zs planes with the proper value for f.[4]

Finally, we discuss the case of the electrostatic separators, where for simplicity we consider the magnetic field to be absent (its effect can be computed separately). If we suppose the electric field (of intensity E) in the separator to be parallel to the z axis, there will be no effect in the xs plane and in this plane the separator will be similar to a region without fields. In the zs plane, it can be shown from the equation of motion that the matrix Γ is again of the kind of Equation 6-58 (region without fields) and the vector p is given by

$$p = \frac{qEl^2}{2Pv} \begin{bmatrix} 1 \\ 2a/l \end{bmatrix}. \quad (A2\text{-}7)$$

By adding a horizontal magnetic field and thus introducing a further deflection in the vertical plane it is possible to make p equal to zero for particles with the required momentum and velocity.

As we have done for AG synchrotrons, it is possible to calculate the matrix Γ and the vector p for an arbitrary succession of elements, and so to relate the values of u at the entrance and at the exit of this group of elements. As in the case of the AG synchrotrons, it is possible to calculate the conditions for beam stability in the transport system, but this is not an important problem because of the strong focusing action produced by the quadrupole lenses. The calculation of the trajectories is mainly useful for other reasons, which will now be explained.

We have not yet considered the role played by the slits and collimators which define the beam, both in size and (when used with an analyzing element) in momentum or in velocity. In order to visualize the motion of the beam on the whole, it is useful to refer (as we have done in Section 9-10) to the points in phase space representing the particles of the beam. As the motion in the xs

[4] Equation A2-6 can also be used in the calculation of the characteristic matrix of the periodic element in an AG synchrotron (see Section 6-4), if it contains quadrupole lenses.

282   **Appendix 2**

plane (and also in the zs plane) is independent of the other degrees of freedom, for a description of this motion we can consider the evolution of the representative points in a phase plane (x, x') or (z, z'), that is, the motion of the projections of the points in phase space onto this phase plane.[5] In particular (considering, for example, the motion in the xs plane) in the phase plane (x, x') Liouville's theorem holds also, so that as long as the number of particles is conserved the area covered by the ensemble of representative points remains constant. A collimator of width h (in the x direction) and length l (in the s direction) placed at the abscissa s_0 limits the region of phase plane accessible for the particles to the zone indicated in Figure A2-2a. All the

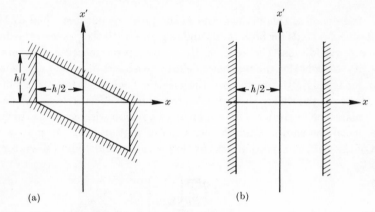

(a)   (b)

FIGURE A2-2. *Phase plane representation of the acceptance region for* (a) *a collimator of width h and length l;* (b) *a slit, $h/l = \infty$.*

particles whose representative points do not fall within this zone are lost when they cross the abscissa s_0. In practice if $l \ll h$ (vertical slit), the allowed zone becomes the strip limited by two vertical lines parallel to the x' axis see Figure A2-2b). Each point of the phase plane corresponds to a particular choice of the vector $u(s_0)$. Working backward through the matrices of the intermediate elements, from $u(s_0)$ to $u(0) = u_0$ (the value of u at the beginning of the path of the beam, that is, at the target), we can see that to each of the points of the phase plane of Figure A2-2 there corresponds a point of the *initial phase plane* (x_0, x'_0). By Liouville's theorem, corresponding ensembles of points in the two planes will cover equal areas. In particular the two lines of Figure A2-2b will be transformed in the initial plane into two parallel lines, which in general are inclined with respect to the axis (see Figure A2-3a). If

---

[5] For the present conditions (since the velocity and the relativistic mass are constant) the use of x' instead of P_x (and of z' instead of P_z) is equivalent to the introduction of a scale factor. The (x, x') [or (z, z')] plane is sometimes called the "displacement-divergence phase plane"; we call it simply the phase plane.

we repeat the same procedure independently for the various slits and collimators of the system, on the initial phase plane we will determine a zone
with a polygonal boundary (the acceptance region) which is symmetrical with
respect to the origin if all the elements of the system are symmetric with
respect to the axis (see Figure A2-3b). The points inside the acceptance region
determine all the values of $\boldsymbol{u_0}$ for which the particles can cross all the slits of
the system.

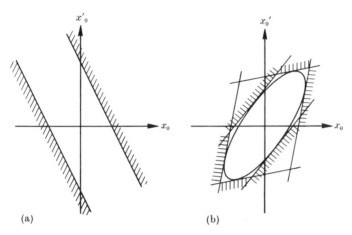

(a)   (b)

FIGURE A2-3. *The acceptance region (unshaded) on the initial phase plane for one
slit* (a), *and for three slits* (b). *The acceptance ellipse is also shown in* (b).

On the other hand, the beam coming from the accelerator will occupy a
certain region in the same initial phase plane. In the case of a beam extracted
from a circular accelerator, the transverse motion of the particles is governed
by the betatron oscillations; therefore, the trajectories of the particles in the
initial phase plane will be concentric ellipses, and the region occupied by the
beam will be enclosed by the largest of these ellipses, corresponding to the
maximum amplitude of the oscillations. Even when this is not exactly the
case, it is generally assumed that the beams to be propagated through the
transport system have an elliptical phase-space boundary ("emittance
ellipse")in both initial planes (x_0, x'_0) and (z_0, z'_0). In practice, we may consider
the smallest elliptical contours circumscribing the regions occupied by the
beam in the initial phase planes. The choice of an elliptical boundary is very
convenient, because it turns out (see, for instance, Banford 1966, Chapter 2)
that on the phase plane, under the action of the elements of the kind described
above, an ellipse is transformed into another ellipse, possibly of different
form and orientation, but of the same area by Liouville's theorem. In
this way, the evolution of the system can be described in terms of the variation
with s of a small number of parameters. Also the acceptance region in the

initial phase plane can be approximated by an ellipse ("acceptance ellipse",) as shown in Figure A2-3b. The design of the transport system must be such as to match the emittance ellipse (for the desired particles) and the acceptance ellipse in both initial phase planes (x_0, x'_0) and (z_0, z'_0).

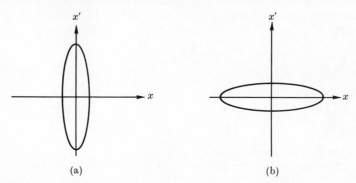

(a)   (b)

FIGURE A2-4. *The phase ellipse (in the xs plane) for* (a) *a beam focused at a point;* (b) *a beam parallel to the axis.*

It must be noted that a very narrow ellipse placed as in Figure A2-4a corresponds to a beam approximately focused at a point (in the xs plane): there is a wide angular spread, and a small beam width. An ellipse such as that in Figure A2-4b instead represents a practically parallel beam (in the xs plane). It is obvious that, starting from a given acceptance ellipse on the initial phase plane, the evolution with s is different for different values of particle momentum. Indeed, as we have seen, after the beam crosses a bending magnet, there are different values of p (relative to the motion in the xs plane) corresponding to different values of the momentum P. As a consequence, at the exit of the bending magnet, the ellipses on the (x, x') phase plane corresponding to the same ellipse at the entrance of the magnet but to different values of P will be distinct: with a proper choice of the scale factor of the ordinates (see Figure A2-5), the displacement of the center of the ellipse corresponding to the value $P_0 + \Delta P$ with respect to the one corresponding to the required value P_0 will be given precisely by the vector p of Equation A2-4. In the example of Figure A2-5 the ellipses relative to P_0 and to $P_0 \mp \Delta P$ are completely separated. This is the condition we seek in order to obtain an efficient analysis—where all the particles whose momentum differs from the required value P_0 by more than the accepted tolerance ΔP are removed. Indeed, if we place a slit after the magnet at a position where the accepted ellipse is oriented as in Figure A2-4a, the undesired ellipses will remain separated and they will fall on the absorbing zone of the collimator (see Figure A2-6). The required orientation of the ellipses shown in Figure A2-6 can be obtained by means of one or more quadrupole doublets which focus the beam onto the position of the slit.

In optical terms, the system is arranged so that, for the required value of momentum, the system produces an image of one slit on another one. Similar considerations hold for the (z, z') phase plane with respect to the velocity separators. It should be noted that, when the acceptance ellipse has a small size, the calculation of the parameters of the system, as far as the selection

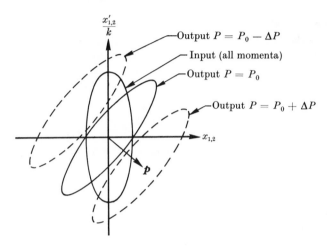

FIGURE A2-5. *Diagram illustrating the relation between the phase ellipse at the entrance (input) of a bending magnet and at the exit (output) for different momenta.*

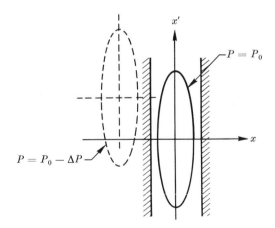

FIGURE A2-6. *Diagram illustrating the acceptance region of a collimator (unshaded) following a bending magnet, with phase-space ellipses corresponding to the desired momentum (solid line) and undesired momentum (dotted line).*

criteria are concerned, can be carried out very simply by considering only the trajectory of the center of the ellipse and using the optical analogy. If instead large acceptances are required, it is necessary to follow the evolution of the whole beam in phase space, as discussed above.

A2-3 TECHNICAL PROBLEMS OF BEAM TRANSPORT SYSTEMS

As we have mentioned in Section A2-1, the intensity of the secondary beams depends mainly on the yield from the target, which has been measured experimentally for different materials and for different kinds of secondary particles. This yield is strongly dependent on the angle of emission, especially at high energies: in order to obtain a high intensity the particles accepted must be those emitted at small angles ($\lesssim 10$ degrees) with respect to the direction of the primary beam. In the case of circular high-energy machines, the particles emitted under these conditions from the target are subject for a certain part of their trajectory to the action of the fringing field of the accelerator magnet, which produces a complicated distortion of the path and size of the beam. Usually the trajectory of the beam in the magnetic field of the accelerator is computed numerically. Sometimes it is possible to reduce the distortion by shielding the exit channel of the secondary beam from the magnetic field of the accelerator. The intensity of the beams obtained also depends on the length of the path in the transport system. This is especially true for unstable particles (π mesons, K mesons), due to their decay in flight. Also the scattering on the edges of the collimators and the collisions with gas molecules produce a loss of particles. Since it is found that scattering from air molecules is especially important, the beams are made to travel either in vacuum or in a helium atmosphere. Concerning the decay of unstable particles, it is necessary, besides using analyzing elements, to reduce the beam path as far as possible. In the case where one is particularly interested in the decay products (beams of μ mesons produced by the decay of π mesons), it is necessary instead for the beam path to be long.

The pulse length of particles in the secondary beam is determined by controlling the collision process of the primary beam against the target. Pulses of short length (from 30 μsec to 2 msec for bubble chamber experiments) are obtained by arresting the primary beam against the target all at once. Long pulses (for counter experiments) can be obtained only with circular machines: the process of collision of the primary beam against the target is slowed down and made to occur gradually over many successive turns. In this way the pulse length in the secondary beam can even be about 300 msec.

In general, the parameters of the transport system are determined by trial and error, after a first approximate evaluation obtained by using the methods described in the previous section. In the case of separated beams the greatest limitations to the acceptance of the system are placed by the electrostatic separators. At a high velocity the analyzing power of the separators is small and one requires strong electric fields (some tens of kilovolts per centimeter), great lengths (up to 10 m), and narrow slits, in order to select small deflections. In this case, in order to increase the efficiency, the beam must have a small vertical spread: the height of the target must be small, the vertical focusing very accurate, and the electric field in the separators uniform to within a few percent. Often for beams of high purity two successive stages of separation are necessary. Recently the use of rf separators has been proposed for high-velocity particles. A version of this device, proposed by Blewett (1959), consists essentially of a waveguide element where the phase velocity (in the direction of the beam) matches the velocity of the undesired particles (for example, the π^- mesons in a beam of K^- mesons) so that these are removed by the transverse electric field of the electromagnetic wave; the desired particles instead are subject to an action which is zero on the average and are not deflected. A brief description of rf separators can be found in Banford (1966, Section 7.1.2).

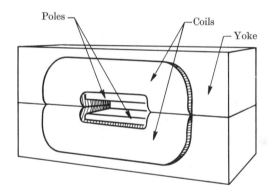

FIGURE A2-7.   *A typical uniform-field bending magnet.*

The bending magnets often have the shape indicated in Figure A2-7 and produce a uniform field. In this way very high fields are produced. The edge effect (see Figure A2-1) contributes to the vertical stability; however, as we have mentioned, the problem of stability is not important. The vertical aperture is made of the same order as that of the quadrupole lenses (about 10 cm). The aberrations of the lenses may disturb the optics of the beam. Chromatic aberrations are the most serious, but they can be corrected by means of nonlinear lenses (with six or eight poles). The spherical aberrations are not serious because usually the inclination of the beam with respect to the axis is very small (of the order of 10 milliradians, that is, about 30'). As we have mentioned, among the most serious aberrations are those produced by the magnetic field of the accelerator and these are corrected locally for each case.

Finally Figure A2-8 is a diagram of a typical beam layout for a two-stage separated beam geometry of the kind most frequently used with high-energy machines. We have indicated the internal target by T, the quadrupole doublets by Q, the magnets by M, the electrostatic separators by S, the detector by D. M_1 corrects for the effect of the accelerator fringing field; Q_1 matches the beam from the target onto the first separator S_1; Q_2 focuses the desired beam at the collimator V_1 (where velocity selection occurs); M_2 clears the background of scattered particles and decay products, and with the collimator H_1 produces momentum selection. A similar second stage follows.

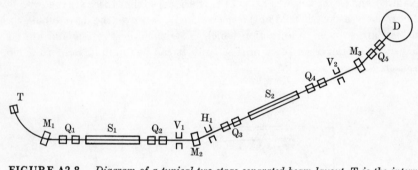

FIGURE A2-8.   *Diagram of a typical two-stage separated beam layout.* T *is the internal target and* D *the detector; bending magnets are indicated by* M, *quadrupole doublets by* Q, *electrostatic separators by* S, *(vertical) velocity collimators by* V, *and (horizontal) momentum collimators by* H.

REFERENCES

Alvarez, L. W. (1946). *Phys. Rev.* **70**, 799 (A).

Amman, F., Andreani, R., Bassetti, M., Corazza, G., Ferlenghi, E., Mango, L., Massarotti, A., Pellegrini, C., Placidi, M., Puglisi, M., Renzler, G., and Tazzioli, F. (1963). *Proc. Intern. Conf. on High Energy Accelerators, Dubna, 1963.* Atomizdat, Moscow, 1964, page 249.

Amman, F., Andreani, R., Bassetti, M., Bernardini, M., Cattani, A., Chimenti, V., Corazza, G., Fabiani, D., Ferlenghi, E., Massarotti, A., Pellegrini, C., Placidi, M., Puglisi, M., Soso, S., Tazzari, S., Tazzioli, F., and Tenore, A. (1965). *Proc. Intern. Conf. on High Energy Accelerators, Frascati, 1965.* CNEN, Roma, 1966, page 703.

Amman, F., Andreani, R., Bassetti, M., Bernardini, M., Cattani, A., Chimenti, V., Corazza, G., Fabiani, D., Ferlenghi, E., Massarotti, A., Pellegrini, C., Placidi, M., Puglisi, M., Soso, F., Tazzari, S., Tazzioli, F., and Tenore, A. (1966). *Proc. Intern. Symp. on Electron and Positron Storage Rings, Saclay, 1966.* Presses Universitaires de France, Paris, 1966, paper III-2.

Arguimbau, L. B., and Adler, R. B. (1956). *Vacuum Tube Circuits and Transitors.* Wiley, New York.

Banford, A. P. (1966). *The Transport of Charged Particle Beams.* Spon, London.

Barber, W. C., Gittelman, B., O'Neill, G. K., and Richter, B. (1965). *Proc. Intern. Conf. on High Energy Accelerators, Frascati, 1965.* CNEN, Roma, 1966, page 266.

Bayer, V. N., Blinov, G. A., Bondarenko, L. N., Budker, G. I., Erozolimsky, B. G., Korobeinikov, L. S., Mironov, E. S., Naumov, A. A., Onuchin, A. P., Panasyuk, V. S., Popov, S. G., Sidorov, V. A., Silvestrov, G. I., Skrinsky, A. N., and Khabakhpashev, A. G.; Ausländer, V. L., Bayer, V. N., Blinov, G. A., Budker, G. I., Kiselev, A. V., Kushnirenko, E. A., Livshitz, A. A., Mironov, E. S., Naumov, A. A., Panasyuk, V. S., Rodionov, S. N., Sidorov, V. A., Silvestrov, G. I., Skrinsky, A. N., Synakh, V. S., and Yudin, L. I.; Abramyan, E. A., Bayer, V. N., Budker, G. I., Wasserman, S. B., Vecheslavov, V. V., Dimov, G. I., Naumov, A. A., Panasyuk, V. S., Papadichev, V. A., and Protopopov, I. Ya. (1963). *Proc. Intern. Conf. on High Energy Accelerators, Dubna 1963.* Atomizdat, Moscow, 1964, page 274.

Beck, A. H. W. (1958). *Space Charge Waves and Slow Electromagnetic Waves.* Pergamon Press, London.

Bell, M., Bramham, P., and Montague, B. W. (1963). *Nature* **198**, 277.

Bellman, R. (1960). *Introduction to Matrix Analysis.* McGraw-Hill, New York.

Bernardini, C., Corazza, G. F., Ghigo, G., and Touschek, B. (1960). *Nvovo Cimento* **18**, 1293.

Bernardini, C., Bizzarri, U., Corazza, G. F., Ghigo, G., Querzoli, R., and Touschek, B. (1961). *Proc. Intern. Conf. on High Energy Accelerators, Brookhaven, 1961.* USAEC, Washington, 1961, page 256.

Bernardini, C., Corazza, G. F., Di Giugno, G., Ghigo, G., Haissinski, J., Marin, P., Querzoli, R., and Touschek, B. (1963). *Phys. Rev. Letters* **10**, 407.

Bernardini, C., Corazza, G. F., Di Giugno, G., Haissinski, J., Marin, P., Querzoli, R., and Touschek, B. (1964). *Nuovo Cimento* **34**, 1473.

Bizzarri, U., and Turrin, A. (1965). *Nuovo Cimento* **37**, 751.

Blewett, J. P. (1959). *Proc. Intern. Conf. on High Energy Accelerators, CERN, 1959.* CERN, Geneva, 1959, page 422.

Bohm, D., and Foldy, L. (1946). *Phys. Rev.* **70**, 249.

Bohm, D., and Foldy, L. (1947). *Phys. Rev.* **72**, 649.

Bouwers, A., and Kuntke, A. (1937). *Z. Tech. Physik* **18**, 209.

Brand, L. (1947). *Vector and Tensor Analysis.* Wiley, New York.

Budker, G. I. (1965). *Proc. Intern. Conf. on High Energy Accelerators, Frascati, 1965.* CNEN, Roma, 1966, page 389.

Budker, G. I. (1966). *Proc. Intern. Symposium on Electron and Positron Storage Rings, Saclay, 1966.* Presses Universitaires de France, Paris, 1966, paper II-1.

Burshtein, E. L., Veksler, V. I., and Kolomensky, A. A. (1955). *Some Questions of the Theory of Cyclic Accelerators.* Akad. Nauk S.S.S.R. Moscow.

Calder, R., and Fischer, E. (1965) *Proc. Intern. Conf. on High Energy Accelerators, Frascati, 1965.* CNEN, Roma, 1966. page 179.

Cockcroft, J. D., and Walton, E. T. S. (1932a). *Proc. Roy. Soc. (London)* **A136**, 619.

Cockcroft, J. D., and Walton, E. T. S. (1932b). *Proc. Roy. Soc. (London)* **A137**, 229.

Cockcroft, J. D., and Walton, E. T. S. (1934). *Proc. Roy. Soc. (London)* **A144**, 704.

Cohen, B. L. (1953), *Rev. Sci. Instr.* **24**, 589.

Cole, F. T. (1959). *Proc. Intern. Conf. on High Energy Accelerators, CERN, 1959.* CERN, Geneva, 1959, page 82.

Collins, T. L., Fischer, G. E., Livingston, M. S., Rees, J. R., Robinson, K. W., Pipkin, F. M., Ramsey, N. F., Street, J. C., Walker, J. K., Wilson, R., and Feld, B. T. (1963). A study of an electron-positron storage ring at the Cambridge Electron Accelerator. Report CEAL TM-107.

Courant, E. D., Livingston, M. S., and Snyder, H. S. (1952). *Phys. Rev.* **88**, 1190.

Crewe, A. V. (1959). *Proc. Intern. Conf. High Energy Accelerators, CERN, 1959.* CERN, Geneva, 1959, page 359.

Day, E. A., Featherstone, R. P., Johnston, L. H., Lampi, E. E., Tucker, E. B., and Williams, J. H. (1958). *Rev. Sci. Instr.* **29**, 457.

De Raad, B. (1962). Some aspects of concentric storage rings. CERN Report AR/Int SG/62-6.

Elder, F. R., Langmuir, R. V., and Pollock, H. C. (1948). *Phys. Rev.* **74**, 52.

Gallop, J. W. (1953). *Nature* **171**, 306.

Gallop, J. W. (1957). *Nature* **179**, 492.

Gendreau, G. (1964). Les anneaux de stockage à électrons. Orsay Report LAL-1110.

Greinacher, H. (1921). *Z. Physik* **4**, 195.

Henrich, L. R., Sewell, D. C., and Vale, J. (1949). *Rev. Sci. Instr.* **20**, 887.

Hubbard, E. L., Baker, W. L., Ehlers, K. W., Gordon, H. S., Main, R. M., Norris, N. J., Peters, R., Smith, L., Van Atta, C. M., Voelker, F., Anderson, C. E., Beringer, R., Gluckstern, R. L., Knox, W. J., Malkin, M. S., Quinton, A. R., Schwarcz, L., and Wheeler, G. W. (1961). *Rev. Sci. Instr.* **32**, 621.

Johnsen, K., Middelkoop, W. C., De Raad, B., Resegotti, L., Schoch, A., Symon, K. R., and Zilverschoon, C. J. (1963). *Proc. Intern. Conf. on High Energy Accelerators, Dubna, 1963.* Atomizdat, Moscow, 1964, page 312.

Johnsen, K., (1965a). *Proc. Intern. Conf. on High Energy Accelerators, Frascati, 1965.* CNEN, Roma, 1966, page 3.

Johnsen, K., (1965b). *Proc. Intern. Conf. on High Energy Accelerators, Frascati, 1965.* CNEN, Roma, 1966, page 168.

Johnsen, K. (1966). *Proc. Intern. Symp. on Electron and Positron Storage Rings, Saclay, 1966.* Presses Universitaires de France, Paris, 1966, paper VIII-2.

Judd, D. L. (1958). *Ann. Rev. Nucl. Sci.* 8, 181.

Kaiser, T. R. (1950). *Proc. Phys. Soc. (London)* 63, 52.

Kapitza, S. P. (1965). *Proc. Intern. Conf. on High Energy Accelerators, Frascati, 1965.* CNEN, Roma, 1966, page 665.

Keefe, D. (1965). *Proc. Intern. Conf. on High Energy Accelerators, Frascati, 1965.* CNEN, Roma, 1966, page 18.

Keller, R., Dick, L., and Fidecaro, M. (1959). *Compt. Rend.* 248, 3154.

Kennard, E. H. (1938). *Kinetic Theory of Gases.* McGraw-Hill, New York.

Kerst, D. W. (1940). *Phys. Rev.* 58, 841.

Kerst, D. W. (1941). *Phys. Rev.* 60, 47.

Kerst, D. W. (1948). *Phys. Rev.* 74, 503.

Kerst, D. W., and Serber, R. (1941). *Phys. Rev.* 60, 53.

Kerst, D. W., Adams, G. D., Koch, H. W., and Robinson, C. S. (1950a). *Rev. Sci. Instr.* 21, 462.

Kerst, D. W., Adams, G. D., Koch, H. W., and Robinson, C. S. (1950b). *Phys. Rev.* 78, 297.

Laslett, L. J. (1964). *Phys. Today* 17 [11], page 42.

Laslett, L. J., Neil, V. K., and Sessler, A. M. (1965). *Rev. Sci. Instr.* 36, 436.

Lawrence, E. O., and Edlefsen, N. E. (1930). *Science* 72, 376.

Lawrence, E. O., and Livingston, M. S. (1931a). *Phys. Rev.* 37, 1707.

Lawrence, E. O., and Livingston, M. S. (1931b). *Phys. Rev.* 38, 136.

Lawrence, E. O., and Livingston, M. S. (1932). *Phys. Rev.* 40, 19.

Livingood, J. J. (1961). *Principles of Cyclic Particle Accelerators.* Van Nostrand, Princeton, New Jersey.

Livingston, M. S. (1966). *Perspectives in Modern Physics* (R. E. Marshak, editor). Interscience, New York, page 245.

Livingston, M. S., and Blewett, J. P. (1962). *Particle Accelerators.* McGraw-Hill, New York.

Livingston, R. S., Martin, J. A., Worsham, R. E., Hudson, E. D., Lord, R. S., Mann, J. E., Mosko, S. W., Ziegler, N. F., Richardson, E. G., Jr., and Howell, L. N. (1965). *Proc. Intern. Conf. on High Energy Accelerators, Frascati, 1965.* CNEN, Roma, 1966, page 431.

McLachlan, N. W. (1961). *Bessel Functions for Engineers.* Clarendon Press, Oxford.

McMillan, E. M. (1945). *Phys. Rev.* 68, 143.

MURA Staff (The) (1961a). *Proc. Intern. Conf. on High Energy Accelerators, Brookhaven, 1961.* USAEC, Washington, 1961, page 57.

MURA Staff (The) (1961b). *Proc. Intern. Conf. on High Energy Accelerators, Brookhaven, 1961.* USAEC, Washington, 1961, page 344.

Nielsen, C. E., Sessler, A. M., and Symon, K. R. (1959). *Proc. Intern. Conf. on High Energy Accelerators, CERN, 1959.* CERN, Geneva, 1959, page 239.

Ohkawa, T. (1958). *Rev. Sci. Instr.* 29, 108.

Oliphant, M. L. E., and Rutherford, E. (1933). *Proc. Roy. Soc. (London)* A141, 259.

Oliphant, M. L. E., Gooden, J. S., and Hide, G. S. (1947). *Proc. Phys. Soc.* (*London*) **59**, 666.

O'Neill, G. K. (1959). *Proc. Intern. Conf. on High Energy Accelerators, CERN, 1959.* CERN, Geneva, 1959, page 125.

O'Neill, G. K. (1961). *Proc. Intern. Conf. on High Energy Accelerators, Brookhaven, 1961.* USAEC, Washington, 1961, page 247.

Orsay Storage Ring Group (The) (1963). *Proc. Intern. Conf. on High Energy Accelerators, Dubna, 1963.* Atomizdat, Moscow, 1964, page 288.

Orsay Storage Ring Group (The) (1965). *Proc. Intern. Conf. on High Energy Accelerators, Frascati, 1965.* CNEN, Roma, 1966, page 271.

Orsay Storage Ring Group (The) (1966). *Proc. Intern. Symp. on Electron and Positron Storage Rings, Saclay, 1966.* Presses Universitaires de France, Paris, 1966, papers II-3 and 4.

Panofsky, W. K. H., and Phillips, M. (1962). *Classical Electricity and Magnetism* (2nd edition). Addison-Wesley, Reading, Massachusetts.

Penning, F. M. (1937). *Physica* **4**, 71.

Persico, E. (1955). *Suppl. Nuovo Cimento* **2**, 459.

Piccioni, O., Clark, D., Cool, R., Friedlander, G., and Kassner, D. (1955). *Rev. Sci. Instr.* **26**, 232.

Pierce, J. R. (1954). *Theory and Design of Electron Beams.* Van Nostrand, Princeton, New Jersey.

Rees, J. R. (1966). *Proc. Intern. Symp. on Electron and Positron Storage Rings, Saclay, 1966.* Presses Universitaires de France, Paris, 1966, paper III-5.

Robinson, K., and Voss, G. A. (1966). *Proc. Intern. Symp. on Electron and Positron Storage Rings, Saclay, 1966.* Presses Universitaires de France, Paris, 1966, paper III-4.

Rose, M. E. (1938). *Phys. Rev.* **53**, 392.

Rose, P. H. (1961). *Nucl. Instr. and Methods* **11**, 49.

Rowe, E. M., Meier, H. K., and O'Meara, J. E. (1965). *Proc. Intern. Conf. on High-Energy Accelerators, Frascati, 1965.* CNEN, Roma, 1966, page 279.

Rowe, E. M., Hicks, J. W., Johnson, R. G., Lee, G. M., Meier, H. K., and O'Meara, J. E. (1966). *Proc. Intern. Symp. on Electron and Positron Storage Rings, Saclay, 1966.* Presses Universitaires de France, Paris, 1966, paper III-3.

Russell, F. M. (1963). *Nucl. Instr. and Methods* **23**, 229.

Sands, M. (1955). *Phys. Rev.* **97**, 470.

Sands, M. and Touschek, B. F. (1953). *Nuovo Cimento* **10**, 604.

Schwinger, J. (1949) *Phys. Rev.* **75**, 1912.

Segré, E. (1964). *Nuclei and Particles.* Benjamin, New York.

Sessler, A. M. (1965). *Proc. Intern. Conf. on High Energy Accelerators, Frascati, 1965.* CNEN, Roma, 1966, page 319.

Shersby-Harvie, R. B. R., and Mullet, L. B. (1949). *Proc. Phys. Soc.* (*London*) **62**, 270.

SLAC (1963). Reports on plans for a 3-BeV electron-positron storage ring for the SLAC accelerator. SLAC report (not numbered).

SLAC (1964). Proposal for a high-energy electron-positron storage ring at the Stanford Linear Accelerator Center. Stanford University report (not numbered).

Slater, J. C. (1950). *Microwave Electronics.* Van Nostrand, Princeton, New Jersey.

Sloan, D. H., and Lawrence, E. O. (1931). *Phys. Rev.* **38**, 2021.

Smith, L. (1959). Linear accelerators. *Handbuch der Physik.* Springer, Berlin, Vol. 44, page 341.

Smith, L. (1965). Proc. 1st National Particle Accelerator Conference. *IEEE Trans. Nucl. Sci.* NS-12, Vol. 3, page 1042.

Steffen, K. G. (1966). *Proc. Intern. Symp. on Electron and Positron Storage Rings, Saclay, 1966.* Presses Universitaires de France, Paris, 1966, paper VIII-7.

Symon, K. R., Steben, J. D., and Laslett, L. J. (1965). *Proc. Intern. Conf. on High Energy Accelerators, Frascati, 1965.* CNEN, Roma, 1966, page 296.

Teng, L. C. (1963). *Proc. Intern. Conf. on High Energy Accelerators, Dubna, 1963.* Atomizdat, Moscow, 1964, page 187.

Teng, L. C. (1965). *Proc. Intern. Conf. on High Energy Accelerators, Frascati, 1965.* CNEN, Roma, 1966, page 104.

Thomas, L. H. (1938). *Phys. Rev.* **54**, 580.

Tomboulian, D. H., and Hartman, P. L. (1956). *Phys. Rev.* **102**, 1423.

Turrin, A. (1958). *Nuovo Cimento* **8**, 511.

Tuve, M. A., Dahl, O., and Hafstadt, L. R. (1935). *Phys. Rev.* **48**, 315.

Van de Graaff, R. J. (1931). *Phys. Rev.* **38**, 1919 (A).

Veksler, V. I. (1944a). *Doklady Akad. Nauk S.S.S.R.* **43**, 346.

Veksler, V. I. (1944b). *Doklady Akad. Nauk S.S.S.R.* **44**, 393.

Veksler, V. I. (1945). *J. Physics (U.S.S.R)* **9**, 153.

Walter, A. K., Grigorev, Yu. N., Grishaev, I. A., Dudkina, I. N., Ivanov, V. F., Ilin, O. G., Koba, I. I., Kondratenko, V. V., Mocheshnikov, I. N., Tarasenko, A. S., Terekhov, B. A., Tolstoi, A. E., and Shenderovich, A. M. (1963). *Proc. Intern. Conf. on High Energy Accelerators, Dubna, 1963.* Atomizdat, Moscow, 1964, page 295.

Wideröe, R. (1928). *Arch. Elektrotechn.* **21**, 387.

GENERAL BIBLIOGRAPHY

SURVEY BOOKS

Livingood, J. J. (1961). *Principles of Cyclic Particle Accelerators.* Van Nostrand, Princeton, New Jersey.

Livingston, M. S., and Blewett, J. P. (1962). *Particle Accelerators.* McGraw-Hill, New York.

Kolomensky, A. A., and Lebedev, A. N. (1962). *Theory of Cyclic Accelerators.* North Holland Publishing Co., Amsterdam, 1966 (translated from Russian by M. Barbier).

Kollath, R. (editor) (1967). *Particle Accelerators.* Pitman and Sons, London (translated from the 2nd German edition by W. Summer).

Bruck, H. (1966). *Accélérateurs Circulaires de Particules.* Presses Universitaires de France, Paris (in French).

CONFERENCES ON PARTICLE ACCELERATORS: PROCEEDINGS

CERN Symposium on High Energy Accelerators and Pion Physics, CERN, 1956 (edited by E. Regenstreif), Vol. 1. CERN, Geneva, 1956.

International Conference on High Energy Accelerators and Instrumentation, CERN, 1959 (edited by L. Kowarski). CERN, Geneva, 1959.

International Conference on High Energy Accelerators, Brookhaven, 1961 (edited by M. H. Blewett). USAEC, Washington, 1961.

Proceedings of the International Conference on High Energy Accelerators, Dubna, 1963 (edited by A. A. Kolomensky), Atomizdat, Moscow, 1964.

Fifth International Conference on High Energy Accelerators, Frascati, 1965 (edited by M. Grilli). CNEN, Roma, 1966.

The First National Particle Accelerator Conference, 1965. *IEEE Trans. Nucl. Sci.* NS-12, Vol. 3 (1965).

BIBLIOGRAPHIC REVIEWS OF THE MOST IMPORTANT REFERENCES ON ACCELERATORS

Livingston, M. S. (editor) (1966). *The Development of Particle Accelerators.* Dover, New York.

Blewett, J. P. (1966). Resource Letter PA-1 on Particle Accelerators. *Am. J. Phys.* **34**, 742.

REFERENCES FOR PARTICULAR SUBJECTS

CHAPTER 1

Ion Sources
Livingston, M. S., and Blewett, J. P. (1962) (*op. cit.*), Chapter 4.
Kamke, D. (1956). Elektronen und Ionenquellen. *Handbuch der Physik.* Springer, Berlin, Vol. 33, page 1 (in German).

Heavy-Ion Accelerators
Hubbard, E. L. (1961). Heavy ion accelerators. *Ann. Rev. Nucl. Sci.* 11, 419.

List of Operating Machines
Gordon, H. S., and Behman, G. A. (1963). Particle accelerators. *American Institute of Physics Handbook* (2nd edition). McGraw-Hill, New York, Section 8i.

CHAPTER 2

Electron Optics
Pierce, J. R. (1954). *Theory and Design of Electron Beams.* Van Nostrand, Princeton, New Jersey.
Sturrock, P. A. (1955). *Static and Dynamic Electron Optics.* Cambridge University Press.

Van de Graaff Generators
Van de Graaff, R. J., Trump, J. G., and Buechner, W. W. (1948). Electrostatic generators for the acceleration of charged particles. *Rept. Progr. in Phys.* 11, 1.
Herb, R. G. (1959). Van de Graaff generators. *Handbuch der Physik.* Springer, Berlin, Vol. 44, page 64.

Cockcroft-Walton and Other Types of Generators
Fortescue, R. L. (1950). High voltage direct current generators. *Progr. Nucl. Phys.* 1, 21.

Tandem Accelerators
Van de Graaff, R. J. (1960). Tandem electrostatic accelerators. *Nuclear Instr. and Methods* 8, 195.
Burrill, E. A. (1965). Tandem accelerators of the future. Proc. National Particle Accelerator Conference. *IEEE Trans. Nucl. Sci.* NS-12, Vol. 3, page 235.

CHAPTER 4

Kerst, D. W. (1959). The betatron, *Handbuch der Physik.* Springer, Berlin, Vol. 44, page 193.
Kerst, D. W. (1946). Historical development of the betatron. *Nature* 157, 90.

CHAPTERS 5 AND 6

Electron Synchrotrons
Wilson, R. R. (1959). Electron synchrotrons. *Handbuch der Physik.* Springer, Berlin, Vol. 44, page 170.
Livingston, M. S. (1965). The future of electron synchrotrons. Proc. National Particle Accelerator Conference. *IEEE Trans. Nucl. Sci.* NS-12, Vol. 3, page 1027.

Proton Synchrotrons
Blewett, J. P. (1956). The proton synchrotron. *Rept. Progr. in Phys.* **19**, 37.
Green, G. K., and Courant, E. D. (1959). The proton synchrotron. *Handbuch der Physik.* Springer, Berlin, Vol. 44, page 218

Theory of the AG Synchrotron
Courant, E. D., and Snyder, H. S. (1958). Theory of the alternating gradient synchrotron. *Ann. Phys.* (*N.Y.*) **3**, 1.

CHAPTER 7

Cohen, B. L. (1959). Cyclotrons and synchrocyclotrons. *Handbuch der Physik.* Springer, Berlin, Vol. 44, page 105.

Cyclotrons
Livingston, M. S. (1944). The cyclotron. *J. Appl. Phys.* **15**, 2, 128.
Mann, W. B. (1953). *The Cyclotron* (4th edition). Methuen and Co., London.

Microtrons
Kapitza, S. P. (1965). Modern developments of the microtron. *Proc. Intern. Conf. on High Energy Accelerators, Frascati, 1965.* CNEN, Roma, 1966, page 665.

CHAPTER 8

Smith, L. (1959). Linear accelerators. *Handbuch der Physik.* Springer, Berlin, Vol. 44, page 341.

Theory of Loaded Waveguides
Chu, E. L., and Hansen, W. W. (1947). Theory of disk-loaded waveguides. *J. Appl. Phys.* **18**, 996.
Walkinshaw, W. (1948). Theoretical design of linear accelerator for electrons. *Proc. Phys. Soc.* (*London*) **61**, 246.

CHAPTER 9

Isochronous Cyclotrons and High-Intensity Machines
Blosser, H. G. (1965). Sectored cyclotrons. Proc. National Particle Accelerator Conference. *IEEE Trans. Nucl. Sci.* NS-12, Vol. 3, page 985.
Richardson, J. R. (1965). Meson factories. Proc. National Particle Accelerator Conference. *IEEE Trans. Nucl. Sci.* NS-12, Vol. 3, page 1012.

Theory of FFAG Machines
Symon, K. R., Kerst, D. W., Jones, L. W., Laslett, L. J., and Terwilliger, K.M. (1956). *Phys. Rev.* **103**, 1837.

Storage Rings and Colliding Beam Experiments
No comprehensive general reference is available. See, however: *Proceedings of the International Symposium on Electron and Positron Storage Rings, Saclay, 1966* (edited by H. Zyngier and E. Cremieu-Alcan), Presses Universitaires de France, Paris, 1966.

APPENDIXES

Chamberlain, O. (1960). Optics of high energy beams. *Ann. Rev. Nucl. Sci.* **10**, 161.
King, N. M. (1964). Theoretical techniques of high energy beam design. *Progr. Nucl. Phys.* **9**, 71.
Steffen, K. G. (1965). *High Energy Beam Optics.* Interscience Publishers, New York.
Banford, A. P. (1966). *The Transport of Charged Particle Beams.* Spon, London.
(N.B. Quadrupole lenses are exhaustively discussed in the last three items.)

INDEX